TRANSISTOR CIRCUIT
ANALYSIS AND DESIGN

Integrated Circuit prior to final enclosure. The semiconductor wafer contains the equivalent of 31 conventional components. In this circuit the diffused areas are interconnected by the deposited aluminum pattern to form a bistable multi-vibrator or flip–flop network. (Courtesy Texas Instruments, Inc.)

THE VAN NOSTRAND SERIES IN ELECTRONICS AND COMMUNICATIONS

Edited by HERBERT J. REICH, *Dunham Laboratory*

Yale School of Engineering

ABRAHAM SHEINGOLD *Fundamentals of Radio Communications*

H. J. REICH, P. F. ORDUNG, H. L. KRAUSS, J. G. SKALNIK

Microwave Theory and Techniques

H. J. REICH, J. G. SKALNIK, P. F. ORDUNG, H. L. KRAUSS *Microwave Principles*

GORDON J. MURPHY *Basic Automatic Control Theory, 2nd Ed.*

GORDON J. MURPHY *Control Engineering*

RUDOLF G. E. HUTTER *Beam and Wave Electronics in Microwave Tubes*

FRANKLIN C. FITCHEN *Transistor Circuit Analysis and Design, 2nd Ed.*

PARRY MOON & DOMINA E. SPENCER *Foundations of Electrodynamics*

PARRY MOON & DOMINA E. SPENCER *Field Theory for Engineers*

WOLFGANG W. GARTNER *Transistors: Principles, Design, and Applications*

H. J. REICH *Functional Circuits and Oscillators*

Y. H. KU *Transient Circuit Analysis*

EDWARD PESKIN *Transient and Steady-State Analysis of Electric Networks*

L. S. NERGAARD & M. GLICKSMAN *Microwave Solid-State Engineering*

JEROME L. ALTMAN *Microwave Circuits*

FREDERICK J. TISCHER *Basic Theory of Space Communications*

JOSEPH LINDMAYER & CHARLES Y. WRIGLEY

Fundamentals of Semiconductor Devices

H. J. REICH, H. L. KRAUSS, J. G. SKALNIK

Theory and Applications of Active Devices

A series of text and reference books in electronics and communications. Additional titles will be listed and announced as published.

TRANSISTOR CIRCUIT ANALYSIS AND DESIGN

by

FRANKLIN C. FITCHEN

Electrical Engineering Department
South Dakota State University

SECOND EDITION

D. VAN NOSTRAND CO., INC.

Princeton, New Jersey

Toronto

London

Van Nostrand Regional Offices: *New York, Chicago, San Francisco*

D. Van Nostrand Company, Ltd., *London*

D. Van Nostrand Company (Canada), Ltd., *Toronto*

First Edition, June 1960
Seven Reprintings

Second Edition, April 1966
Reprinted, March 1967

PRINTED IN THE UNITED STATES OF AMERICA

To

SALLY

PREFACE TO THE SECOND EDITION

The content of this textbook is intended for an electronics course for Electrical Engineering students at the junior or senior level. By selective screening of text material and assigned problems it may be well utilized in the advanced technical institute curriculum. The practicing engineer will find the analysis and design examples helpful as background for the solution of many specific problems.

It is assumed that the reader has a working knowledge of the fundamentals of electric circuit theory. Rearrangement and revision of a portion of the material now makes it unnecessary to precede use of this second edition by a course in vacuum-tube or conventional electronics. Although this edition is more suitable as an introductory text, it also contains additional advanced topics that will be of value to the serious reader.

Widespread acceptance of the first edition and vast changes in the characteristics of available devices have stimulated the revision of this text. During the six-year period between editions, the vacuum tube greatly diminished as a useful general-purpose active element. The field-effect transistor grew to manhood and currently threatens the superiority of conventional transistors. For power switching, controlled rectifiers became the predominant device while, in the realm of high-frequency applications, transistor operation exceeded the one gigacycle barrier.

This edition is larger than its predecessor. Several advanced design techniques are described. Ties between semiconductor physics and device characistics have been made stronger. More emphasis has been placed upon the hybrid-π and y representations for the transistor. The feedback story has been strengthened by the addition of a separate chapter on Gain Stability. Logic circuits are now covered in some detail, and the noise problem is treated more thoroughly.

The semiconductor field covers such a vast array of devices and circuits that it is impossible in a book of this length to completely cover the subject. Therefore it seemed desirable to concentrate on two areas germane to the learning process, efficiency and motivation. It is hoped that this book so efficiently covers the main stream of transistor material that time spent in study will most effectively contribute to the solution of real problems. Student motivation should be enhanced as he recognizes that studying the text and doing the problems are not simply "academic exercises." In this light, the response to assigned design problems and the noticeable increase in self-confidence manifested by many students as they progress through the material has been most encouraging.

This book is an outgrowth of work and associations with the General Electric Company, the General Dynamics Corporation, Electric Boat Division, the University of Rhode Island, as well as South Dakota State University. Portions represent work done by the author in cooperation with Yale University. My thanks are extended to these organizations and to the other assisting industrial concerns. Individual thanks are extended to Dr. Herbert Reich and Dr. Herbert Krauss for their assistance.

FRANKLIN C. FITCHEN

Brookings, South Dakota
April, 1966

CONTENTS

Chapter 1

INTRODUCTION TO TRANSISTORS

The birth of the transistor in 1948 signaled the start of a vast scientific revolution. Rapid expansions of the fields of computation, communications, and control initiated by the advent of semiconductor devices, particularly transistors, have enabled technology to make great strides in a relatively short period of time.

Prior to the invention of the transistor by Drs. W. H. Brattain and J. Bardeen[1] of the Bell Telephone Laboratories, the processes of electrical signal amplification, generation, wave shaping, and switching were performed by vacuum tubes, magnetic amplifiers, and relays. Because the transistor can perform these functions more efficiently, it has replaced the other active devices in most of our military, industrial, and consumer products. Some of the basic characteristics of the transistor that make it superior to the vacuum tube in many applications are the following:

1. Long operating lifetime
2. No heating (cathode) power required
3. Operation at low voltages
4. Small physical size
5. Extreme ruggedness

Because the transistor does not require a heating element to raise its temperature well above ambient, as is the case with the familiar vacuum tube where a hot cathode is mandatory, transistor circuits are relatively cool. Since heat is a main contributor to circuit-component breakdown, transistor circuits are exceedingly reliable. Coupling this advantage with the long operating life of the transistor itself (possibly interminable life compared to 2000 to 10,000 hours for tubes), and with the possible miniaturization and shock and vibration resistance also afforded, it is not difficult to comprehend the widespread application of the transistor wherever feasible.

*Superior numbers refer to references cited at the end of each chapter.

The advantages afforded by the small physical size and ruggedness of transistors are obvious. Low-voltage operation is generally a distinct advantage; in certain applications, however, operation at higher voltages is a requirement. The electronic engineer has been provided with a family of transistors that will operate at all practical voltage levels.

The transistor is not a perfect active device; we would be astonished if it were. It is more sensitive to ambient temperature than its predecessors, and generally exhibits large variations in characteristics among units of the same type because of rather wide production tolerances. For these reasons successful design of transistor circuits requires considerable study. It is hoped that this book will most efficiently guide the reader to a level of understanding that will enable him to cope with the challenges presented by the design of transistor circuits and will assist him in understanding and applying future semiconductor devices.

Early transistors were of the *point-contact* variety. They were limited in their power-handling capacity, difficult to fabricate, and electrically noisy. The introduction of the *junction transistor* in 1951 and its subsequent development was a major factor in the rapid growth of transistor electronics, for the junction device can handle large amounts of power, can be fabricated economically, generates little noise, and is operable to the kilomegacycle region. As a switch, junction units can operate in tenths of a nanosecond. Where the word *transistor* is employed in this text, the *junction transistor* is implied. This device is also referred to as the *diffusion transistor* or *bipolar transistor*.

Although known in theory as far back as 1926, and thoroughly analyzed by Shockley in 1952, the *field-effect transistor* (FET) was not successfully fabricated for commercial use until 1961.[2,4,11] The FET, or *unipolar transistor*, exhibits certain characteristics superior to those of the junction device. Its input impedance is nearly infinite at low frequencies. Therefore, cascaded FET stages are effectively isolated from one another, resulting in simplification of circuit design and improved circuit operation in many instances.

For certain applications, other members of the transistor family are of considerable value. The conventional semiconductor *diode*, the *Zener diode*, the *unijunction transistor*, the *silicon controlled rectifier*, *the tunnel diode*, and other devices will be discussed at appropriate places in the pages that follow.

1-1. Semiconductors. The transistor is a solid structure formed from *semiconductors*. Semiconductors are materials whose electrical resistivity is lower than that of insulators and higher than that of conductors. By way of comparison, the resistivities of conductors are of the order of 10^{-6} Ω cm; of insulators, 10^{6} Ω cm, and greater; and of semiconductors 10^{1} Ω cm. But electrical resistance is not the only defining characteristic of a semiconductor. The resistivity of a semiconductor generally decreases with temperature, rather than increasing, as is common with metallic conductors. Another characteristic is the type and degree of the binding force between atoms, and a fourth characteristic of a semiconductor is the extent to which electrical properties depend upon impurity content. Two members of the carbon family, the elements *germanium* and *silicon*, in their crystalline form are classified as semiconductors, and have widespread use in solid-state devices.

The addition of small amounts of impurities to the pure elements alter their conductional properties and the composite is termed either *n-type* material, which has an excess of free electrons compared to a crystal of the pure element, or *p-type* material, which has a deficiency of electrons in its crystalline structure when so compared. By sandwiching *n*-type and *p*-type materials together, various conduction characteristics may be achieved.

The physical principle of operation of the transistor, and also the semiconductor diode, bears little similarity to that of the familiar vacuum tube. Vacuum-tube operation relies upon the control of the movement of free electrons through a vacuum, or in certain tube types, through a gas. In semiconductor devices, charge movement occurs *within* solid materials, and a high temperature is not required for electrons to escape from a surface, because operation is not dependent upon surface emission. A more detailed treatment of semiconductor physics and a discussion of the interesting process by which amplification is achieved is reserved for Chapter 2.

The operational characteristics of a semiconductor device are dictated by the voltages applied to its terminals, or the currents supplied to its terminals. In a *linear device*, such as a wirewound resistor, we expect terminal voltage and current to be linearly related by Ohm's Law. Not so with semiconductor devices, for such devices exhibit saturation and cutoff properties (unchanging value of one quantity while another may vary), power-law relationships between quantities, and negative resistance properties as well as linear behavior. Certain semiconductor devices are capable of voltage, current, and power amplification. Which of the properties noted here are available depends upon the physical makeup of the particular device being considered, and upon external stimuli.

1–2. Diodes. Before proceeding with the discussion of the junction transistor, let us briefly consider the semiconductor diode, a two-element device useful for rectification and detection in electronic circuits. The *junction diode*, which consists of a single *p–n junction*, is said to be a unilateral circuit element because it allows current to pass easily in only one direction. Vacuum-tube nomenclature is applicable to all semiconductor diodes; they are said to pass current easily from anode (plate) to cathode.

In regard to circuits and construction, the semiconductor diode may be symbolized as shown in Fig. 1–1. The arrowhead, which is an integral part of the symbol, serves to indicate the direction of "forward" conventional current. If a positive potential is applied to the anode, the diode is said to be *forward-biased*, and will exhibit a fairly low value of forward resistance. On the other hand, a direct-voltage supply of the opposite polarity provides a *reverse bias*, very little current flows, and the diode exhibits a high reverse or back resistance. Should this reverse voltage exceed a certain value, called the rated *peak-inverse-voltage*

(P.I.V.) of the diode, normal operation ceases, and a large back current is possible. This reverse breakdown is apparent for reverse voltages greater than 30V in Fig. 1–1(b).

It may also be noted from Fig. 1–1(b) that the potential drop across the diode when forward-biased is but a few tenths of a volt. A reverse bias of 30 V is possible with this sample unit before a significant reverse current will flow. Types are available that exhibit a wide range of breakdown voltages and maximum forward current-carrying capacities.

In the conventional operation of a diode, reverse breakdown is an undesirable characteristic to be avoided. It is normally required that the diode present a high reverse resistance. However, it has been found that the region between points *a* to *b* in the figure is valuable for use in the process of *voltage regulation*. Special diodes referred to as *Zener* or *breakdown diodes* are designed for use in their breakdown mode. If the slope of the *a–b* line is high, the potential drop across the diode will be approximately constant regardless of the reverse current flowing in the diode (within limits). This characteristic can be of extreme value in maintaining a constant voltage level in a circuit even though other components or power supply voltages may be changing. Problem 1–2 may be used to investigate the use of a breakdown diode for voltage-regulation purposes.

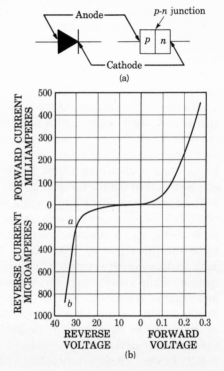

Fig. 1–1. Typical semiconductor diode: (a) circuit symbol and symbolic construction; (b) typical characteristic of germanium unit.

Diodes will be further discussed in Chapter 2 and in other passages throughout the text where their use is complementary to transistor circuitry. For a discussion of rectifying circuits, power supplies, and filtering, the reader is referred to other texts.[8]

1–3. The Transistor. The common transistor is a three-terminal device and is referred to as a *triode*. It is formed from layers of *p*- and *n*-type semiconductor materials as shown symbolically in Fig. 1–2. Both *n–p–n* and *p–n–p* structures are manufactured and are in common use. The sections are designated *emitter*, *base*, and *collector*, and the structure contains two *p–n* junctions. Although diode junctions exist in the device, *performance of a transistor is not that of two back-to-back diodes.*

Figure 1–2 does not differentiate between emitter and collector regions for each is a layer of the same type of material. While successful transistors may be made with identical emitter and collector regions, generally improved performance is possible if these regions differ in physical size and in conductivity of the material. In the circuit-diagram symbols also shown in Fig. 1–2, it may be noted that the distinction between *p–n–p* and *n–p–n* units is the direction of the arrowhead on the emitter lead. The arrowhead also serves to specify the direction of conventional biasing current as discussed later in Sec. 1–6.

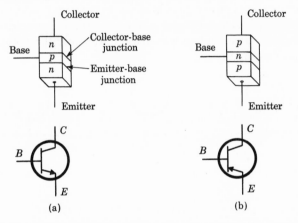

Fig. 1–2. Symbolic construction of the junction transistor and circuit diagram symbols: (a) *n–p–n*; (b) *p–n–p*.

When the transistor is connected in a circuit to perform a specific function, one terminal of the device may be designated as the input terminal, one as the output terminal, and the third as the common. Thus there are six possible configurations that could be utilized, only three of which have proved generally useful and will be seriously considered here: the *common-emitter* configuration (also called grounded-emitter), in which the input signal is applied between base and common; the *common-collector* configuration (also called grounded-collector), with the base again the input terminal; and the *common-base* configuration (also called grounded-base), in which the emitter terminal is supplied by the signal source. For power gain to be achieved, it has been found that the base terminal must always be one of the two input terminals and the collector must always be one of the two output terminals. The three useful amplifying configurations or orientations are shown in Fig. 1–3.*

*The reader familiar with vacuum-tube technology will recall the three practical configurations of that device, grounded-cathode, grounded-plate, and grounded-grid. The base, emitter, and collector of the transistor are analogous to the grid, cathode, and plate of a tube, respectively.

When operated in any one of the three connections noted in Fig. 1–3, and the input supplied from a signal voltage source, signal current is evident in the input lead of the transistor because its input impedance is finite and fairly low-valued. In some applications this loading effect upon the source is undesirable. To minimize it the common-collector (also called *emitter-follower*) connection may be used, for it presents the highest input impedance of the three noted connections, or the circuit designer may employ either of the other connections along with degenerative feedback to raise the impedance level.

Because the circuit load is supplied with an amplified version of the input signal voltage and current, the transistor is considered to be a *power amplifier*. Since the device provides power amplification, we need not expect voltage gain from all circuitry nor should we expect current gain from all usable connections, but in almost all practical circuits a transistor will raise the power level of a signal supplied to its input.

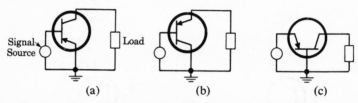

Fig. 1–3.   Configurations: (a) common-emitter; (b) common-collector; (c) common-base.

The existence of transistors of opposite conductivity types (p–n–p and n–p–n) permits *complementary–symmetry* circuits impossible with other amplifying devices. Circuits that employ both types of devices can be of importance; as applications for complementary circuits arise they will be treated.

1–4. Symbols.   A system of symbols to be used to designate circuit quantities in this book is both desirable and necessary, for a great many abbreviations will be encountered by the reader. In general, transistor circuit notation follows several general rules—they are listed here and will be used in the pages that follow. Symbols have been chosen to conform with current practice.[3]

1. DC values of quantities are indicated by capital letters with capital subscripts (I_B, V_{CE}). Direct supply voltages have repeated subscripts (V_{BB}, V_{EE}).
2. Rms values of quantities are indicated by capital letters with lower-case subscripts (I_c, V_{cb}).
3. The time-varying components of currents and voltages are designated by lower-case letters with lower-case subscripts (i_x, v_{cb}).
4. Instantaneous total values are represented by lower-case letters with upper-case subscripts (i_C, v_{BE}).
5. Maximum or peak values are designated like rms values but bear an additional final subscript m (V_{cm}, V_{bem}).

6. Circuit elements are given capital letters (R_1, C_P); transistor parameters have lower-case symbols (r_e, h_{11}).

Figure 1–4 may help in understanding this notation system. In the diagram i_B is the instantaneous total value of the wave, and i_b is the instantaneous value of the time-varying component of i_B. I_B designates the average or dc value, I_{bm} represents the peak, and I_b the effective value of the alternating component.

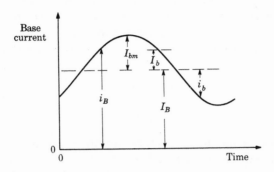

Fig. 1–4. Example of transistor notation.

To designate a constant-current source or generator on circuit diagrams, the symbol of Fig. 1–5(a) will be employed. No distinction is made in the symbol between dc and time-varying currents; should a confusing situation arise, the time function will be specified. The arrow indicates the instantaneous direction of the current supplied by the source.

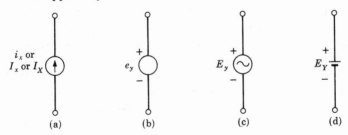

Fig. 1–5. Symbols for sources.

Constant-voltage sources are symbolized in (b), (c), and (d) of Fig. 1–5. The general symbol is in (b) with instantaneous polarity as shown. When the supply is specifically sinusoidal, a "cycle" may be employed as in (c). Direct-voltage supplies are characterized by the familiar battery symbol as in (d).

1–5. Graphical Characteristics. A graphical representation of the terminal properties of the transistor is desirable because it is a nonlinear active circuit element. It has been stated that the input impedance is finite; therefore, an input characteristics curve is required, as well as a curve to represent output-circuit properties. Indeed, *two sets of curves are necessary to completely specify transistor operation.*

For *each* of the three practical circuit configurations, both an input curve and an output curve are applicable. Consider first the common-emitter-oriented low-power transistor shown in Fig. 1–6(a), with supply potentials and appropriate indicating devices. Intentional variations in the supply potentials yield data for the curves of Figs. 1–6(b) and 1–6(c), commonly known, respectively, as the static *collector characteristics* and the static *base characteristics* for the common-emitter-connected transistor. A family of curves is necessary in each instance because

$$i_C = f(i_B, v_{CE}) \tag{1--1}$$

and

$$i_B = f(v_{BE}, v_{CE}). \tag{1--2}$$

The total values of important electrical quantities are equivalent to their dc values when dc measurements are made.

Negative signs preceding current and voltage values on the curves are the results of the conventions of general network theory; currents flowing *into* a device or circuit node are considered *positive*, and when potentials are designated by double subscripts, *the first subscript indicates the point imagined to be the more positive.* The use of negative signs preceding base-current and collector-current values in Fig. 1–6(b) suggests that for normal operation the static portions of these currents must be leaving their respective terminals (p–n–p). Emitter current, although not used in the curves, must enter the transistor and therefore would be considered positive. V_{CE} is shown as negative because the collector (first subscript) is *not* more positive than the emitter (second subscript). These polarities pertain to the p–n–p device. For an n–p–n transistor all quantities would normally be positive except emitter current.

The quantities selected for display in Figs. 1–6(b) and 1–6(c) are standard. The output or collector characteristics portray the behavior of I_C and V_{CE} with an input quantity, in this instance I_B, free to take on various values. While it can be recognized that V_{BE} could just as likely be used as the input quantity of interest, base current has been chosen because the common transistor tends to linearly amplify input current. This linear function is apparent when one plots *transfer characteristics*. A transfer-characteristics curve portrays the relation between an input and an output quantity; for example, I_B vs I_C or V_{BE} vs I_C; in either case V_{CE} could be held constant. Information for these presentations may be obtained from the plots of Fig. 1–6 (see Problem 1–3). An example of a transfer characteristic is given in Fig. 1–10.

Examination of Figs. 1–6(b) and 1–6(c) can tell us a great deal about the device. A current amplification is available because rather small values of I_B allow much larger values of I_C to flow. Collector current is nearly independent

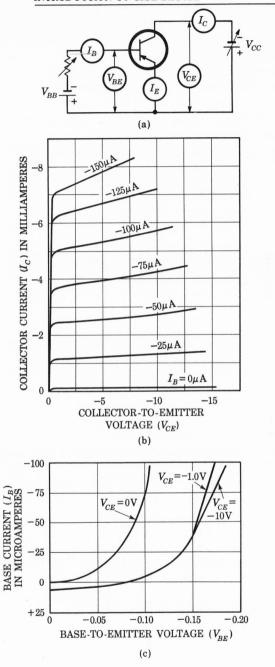

Fig. 1–6.　Common-emitter configuration: (a) circuit for determination of characteristics; (b) typical output family; (c) typical input family.

of V_{CE}; this fact suggests that the device has a high output resistance and thus it may be represented equivalently by a constant-current generator. Operation in other quadrants is not possible, unless one redefines collector and emitter regions.

From the input characteristics of Fig. 1–6(c), we learn that for base currents above 25 μA, the incremental or dynamic input resistance of the device, as represented by the slope of the lines of constant V_{CE}, is fairly low valued. It is also to be noted that the input characteristics are somewhat dependent upon the output-circuit quantity V_{CE}.

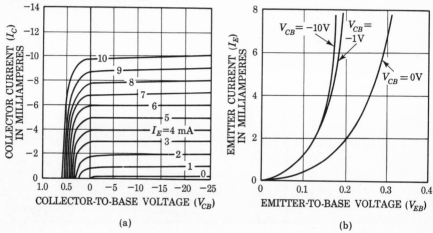

(a)   (b)

Fig. 1–7. Common-base connection: (a) typical output family; (b) typical input family.

A complete set of data taken of all currents and potentials in the circuit of Fig. 1–6(a) would enable us to plot not only the common-emitter curves, but the common-base and common-collector characteristics as well. For the common-base configuration, interest is centered about the collector-to-base voltage (V_{CB}) and collector current (I_C) as output quantities, and emitter-to-base voltage (V_{EB}) and emitter current (I_E) as input quantities. The static input and output characteristics for this configuration are displayed in Fig. 1–7.

The common-base collector curves are extremely flat, indicating a large output resistance, and the spacing between curves of constant input current is extremely uniform, denoting that an extremely linear relation exists between input and output current.

Common-collector circuits exhibit output characteristics similar to those of the common-emitter connection, for output quantities are nearly the same ($V_{EC} = -V_{CE}$ and $I_E \cong I_C$). Some of the problems at the end of the chapter may be used to investigate this connection further.

1–6. The Operating Point. Establishing a proper operating point for a transistor stage is necessary in order for the input signal to be transferred to the load faithfully and to be amplified successfully. A proper operating point is achieved by providing appropriate direct potentials at both the input and the output terminal pairs. *For biasing purposes only*, a junction transistor can be thought of as two junction diodes, one associated with the *p–n* junction of the emitter-base circuit, and the other associated with the *n–p* junction of the base–collector circuit. For transistor operation it will be shown that *the emitter–base diode is always forward-biased* and *the collector–base diode is always reverse-biased*.

A helpful rule for *p–n* junctions follows: "for forward-biasing connect supply positive to *p*-material." Naturally, the converse is true for reverse biasing. This rule is applied to the *p–n–p* transistor in the three practical configurations shown in Fig. 1–8. For each connection, the emitter terminal is made more positive

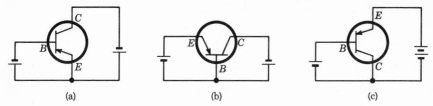

(a)   (b)   (c)

Fig. 1–8. Supply potential connections for normal transistor operation (*p–n–p*): (a) common-emitter; (b) common-base; (c) common-collector.

than the base, and the collector terminal is made more negative than the base. Naturally the magnitudes of these potentials differ considerably as evident from the values of quantities in Fig. 1–6(b) and 1–6(c). These magnitude differences are symbolically noted in Fig. 1–8 by the number of cells used in supply symbols.

Although the transistor can be visualized as two junction diodes to assist in the establishment of an operating point at some desired point in the active region of the collector characteristics, transistor operation, as we see in Chapter 2, is *not* that of two back-to-back diodes.

In some engineering applications, it is highly desirable that only one polarity of power supply be required for operating-point establishment. From Fig. 1–8 it is clear that for the common-emitter and common-collector stages only one such polarity is required; however, as shown in the figure the common-base stage would need both positive and negative supplies. This requirement may be amended if the emitter–base diode is biased by a supply located in the base lead, positive grounded, derived from the collector supply; only one polarity is then required.

When a single power supply of polarity *opposite* to the one shown in Fig. 1–8(a) or 1–8(c) is available, successful biasing is possible by locating the supply in the common lead and picking off a fraction of it for the emitter junction.

With regard to circuits, the major difference between *p–n–p* and *n–p–n* units can be appreciated from the practical connections of Fig. 1–9. Base current for a *p–n–p* transistor flows away from the base terminal; for an *n–p–n* unit it must flow into the base. Collector-voltage polarities are also opposites; the *p–n–p* type requires a negative collector potential; the *n–p–n* positive.

A summation of currents entering the transistor yields a very important relationship describing the *magnitudes* of the terminal currents:

$$I_E = I_C + I_B. \tag{1-3}$$

Equation (1–3) applies to either conductivity type and will play an important role in the discussions to follow. *The actual directions of these currents are as shown in Fig.* 1–9. The arrowhead in the transistor symbol is useful in describing

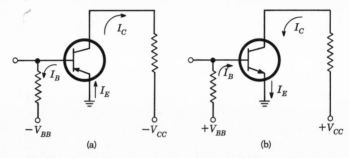

Fig. 1–9.   Biasing for transistors: (a) *p–n–p* unit; (b) *n–p–n* unit.

the direction of emitter current. A knowledge of the magnitude of the various currents of Eq. (1–3) is indispensable; such information may be gained from the curve of Fig. 1–6(b). At a specific collector potential, − 5 V for example, it is obvious that when base current is − 25 μA, collector current is − 1 mA. Therefore the magnitude of emitter current must be 1.025 mA; its direction will be into the transistor as noted in Fig. 1–9(a).

A general rule for junction triodes is valuable: *emitter current is the largest of the three currents, and is approximately equal in magnitude to collector current.* This rule is valid over most of the collector characteristics. It does not pertain to the case where $I_E = 0$, nor does it apply in the region of Fig. 1–6(c) where base current is positive.

1–7. Amplification.   An increase in the amplitude of an electrical signal may be achieved using passive elements exclusively. A transformer or an L-C network near resonance can be used to amplify voltage and/or current levels. However, in order for the power level of a signal to be increased, an *active device*, such as a transistor or a tube, must be employed. In an active device it is typical for a small incoming signal to control variations in a larger output or load current or voltage. Since power amplification can only occur when using devices that are biased, it follows that the difference between load power and input signal power is made up for by the power supplies.

Historically, transistors were first employed in the common-base mode. The Greek letter α (alpha) has been used to symbolize the current gain of a transistor, appropriately biased, and operated in that connection. A dc alpha, or static current-amplification factor, is defined by

$$\alpha_{dc} \equiv \left.\frac{I_C}{I_E}\right|_{V_{CB} = \text{const}} \tag{1-4}$$

It can be seen from Eq. (1–4) that the dc alpha may be determined at any specified V_{CB} by simply dividing the static value of I_C by I_E. Other accepted symbols for α_{dc} are h_{FB} and H_{FB}. Since it was noted in the preceding section that emitter current is normally the largest of the three currents, it follows that the value of α_{dc} is less than unity. Typical values of this parameter lie between 0.9 and 1.0, and vary somewhat with V_{CB} and I_E.

For small excursions in input and output quantities about the operating point, a small-signal α may be defined according to

$$\alpha \equiv \lim_{\Delta i_E \to 0} \left.\frac{\Delta i_C}{\Delta i_E}\right|_{v_{CB} = \text{const}} = \left.\frac{\partial i_C}{\partial i_E}\right|_{v_{CB} = \text{const}} \tag{1-5}$$

The restriction that v_{CB} be constant implies that the load on the transistor is simply a short-circuit to the time-varying portion of the signal. If this were not true, v_{CB} would vary with i_C. Hence α is the "short-circuit current-amplification factor of the transistor in the common-base configuration," and normally $0.9 < \alpha < 1.0$. Another symbol for the short-circuit current-gain parameter is h_{fb} (see Chapter 4).

For a transistor in the common-emitter connection, the short-circuit current-amplification factor is β (beta). The dc beta may be defined by

$$\beta_{dc} \equiv \left.\frac{I_C}{I_B}\right|_{V_{CE} = \text{const}} \tag{1-6}$$

This parameter is sometimes symbolized by h_{FE} or H_{FE}.

A small-signal current-amplification factor for this orientation is

$$\beta \equiv \lim_{\Delta i_B \to 0} \left.\frac{\Delta i_C}{\Delta i_B}\right|_{v_{CE} = \text{const}} = \left.\frac{\partial i_C}{\partial i_B}\right|_{v_{CE} = \text{const}} \tag{1-7}$$

Again, a load short-circuit is assumed. In practice, β takes on values up to 500; its value highly depends on the selected operating point. In place of β the symbol h_{fe} is often employed.

A pictorial definition of the difference between a dc and a small-signal parameter is available from study of Fig. 1–10. The current transfer characteristic for a common-emitter-connected p–n–p transistor is depicted. At $I_C = -2$ mA, $I_B = -50$ μA, so $\beta_{dc} = 40$. The small-signal current-amplification factor at that point is given by the slope of the curve; therefore $\beta = 48$.

Equation (1–3) relates the three transistor currents; the amplification factors are also related:

$$\beta = \alpha/(1 - \alpha). \tag{1-8a}$$

The complementary relationship is

$$\alpha = \beta/(\beta + 1). \tag{1-8b}$$

It is also of value to note that

$$\beta + 1 = 1/(1 - \alpha). \tag{1-8c}$$

Equations (1–8) apply to either the dc or small-signal parameters. In order to derive them one must assume that $v_{CB} = v_{CE}$ (Problem 1–12).

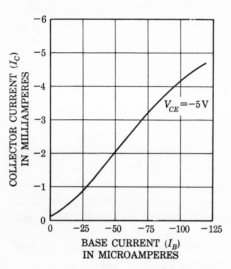

Fig. 1–10.   Transfer characteristics for a typical *p–n–p* transistor.

Although α does not exceed unity and thus load current is smaller than input current in the common-base configuration, power gain is nevertheless possible because of different impedance levels. The input resistance R_i generally is very low, of the order of 50 Ω, when the device is connected to a load R_L of 2000 Ω. Since power gain G is the ratio of signal power delivered to the load to signal power supplied to the input terminals,

$$G = \frac{P_o}{P_i} = \frac{I_c{}^2 R_L}{I_e{}^2 R_i} \cong \frac{\alpha^2 R_L}{R_i} \cong 40$$

with the quoted values.

The common-emitter configuration exhibits an input resistance that is higher than that of the common-base connection, and an output resistance that is lower, but because of the greater value of current gain ($\beta \cong 100$), considerable power gain can result. If R_i is assumed to be 2000 Ω, and a sample stage is feeding a 2000 Ω load, the resulting power gain is

$$G = \frac{I_c{}^2 R_L}{I_b{}^2 R_i} \cong \frac{\beta^2 R_L}{R_i} \cong 10{,}000.$$

For a transistor used as a common-collector amplifier, the current gain is approximately β/α but the input resistance is higher; 100,000 Ω would be a realistic value. Thus, for a load of 2000 Ω,

$$G = \frac{I_e{}^2 R_L}{I_b{}^2 R_i} \cong \left(\frac{\beta}{\alpha}\right)^2 \frac{R_L}{R_i} \cong 200.$$

The quantities α and β were previously defined as short-circuit current-amplification factors. Since, in the examples cited above, the load resistance was not zero, and consequently v_C was not constant, the preceding power-gain calculations were approximations. More exact expressions for circuit gains are presented in Chapter 5.

The amplification properties of a device or circuit can be specified by the numerical ratio of the magnitudes of output to input quantities or by the *decibel*, a logarithmic unit of power ratio. By definition, power gain in decibels is

$$\text{gain in dB} = 10 \log \frac{P_o}{P_i}, \tag{1-9}$$

where the subscript o again represents an output or load quantity and the subscript i, the quantity supplied to the circuit by a signal source. Should we wish to extend this definition to voltage and current quantities, then Eq. (1–9) becomes

$$\text{gain} = 10 \log \frac{V_o^2/R_o}{V_i^2/R_i} \quad \text{dB},$$

or

$$\text{gain} = 10 \log(I_o^2 R_o / I_i^2 R_i) \quad \text{dB}.$$

If $R_o = R_i$,

$$\text{gain} = 10 \log(V_o/V_i)^2 = 20 \log(V_o/V_i) \quad \text{dB}, \tag{1-10a}$$

and

$$\text{gain} = 20 \log(I_o/I_i) \quad \text{dB}. \tag{1-10b}$$

Equations (1–10a) and (1–10b) are correctly employed only for identical resistance levels. In transistor circuits the levels may be vastly different. Nevertheless it is customary to use the voltage and current equations in practice regardless of resistance levels.

As an example of the use of the decibel, the results of the three preceding gain calculations may be expressed in this unit. A power gain ratio of 10,000 is 40 dB, 200 is 23 dB, and 40 is equivalent to 16 dB.

1–8. Leakage Currents. Refer now to Fig. 1–7(a) and note that when the emitter is open, i.e., no emitter current is permitted, a small collector current does exist. This current, termed I_{CBO} (also I_{CO}), is the reverse or leakage current of the reverse-biased collector-to-base junction, and in germanium units is generally of the order of several microamperes. I_{CBO} may vary considerably among otherwise similar units, and is extremely temperature-sensitive. A slight increase is noted in I_{CBO} with collector voltage, but generally it is considered a constant for a particular transistor at a specified temperature. The circuit of interest is that of Fig. 1–11(a). The importance of the leakage current lies in the effect of its variations upon the operating point, a thorough discussion of which is reserved for Chapter 3.

If the collector of a transistor is unconnected as in Fig. 1–11(b) and a voltage applied from emitter to base in order to reverse-bias that junction, the resultant current is termed I_{EBO} (also I_{EO}). I_{EBO} is the reverse or leakage current of the emitter-to-base *p–n* junction. This junction is forward-biased in normal operation.

Leaving the base terminal unconnected and applying a potential from collector to emitter that serves to provide a reverse bias for the collector-to-base junction, as shown in Fig. 1–11(c), results in a current termed I_{CEO}. This current is larger in magnitude than either of the two simple reverse-leakage currents noted previously.

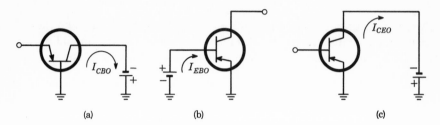

(a)   (b)   (c)

Fig. 1–11.   (a) I_{CBO} is collector–base current with emitter open; (b) I_{EBO} is emitter–base current with collector open; (c) I_{CEO} is collector–emitter current with base open.

Let us suppose that the small-signal current-amplification factor does not change in value over the usable current range of the collector characteristics. Under this assumption, it would be valid to relate α to the dc values of the currents within the device, provided that we include the leakage-current level. Thus, for this special case,

$$\alpha = \frac{\Delta I_C}{\Delta I_E}\bigg|_{V_{CB}=\text{const}} = \frac{I_C - I_{CBO}}{I_E}\bigg|_{V_{CB}=\text{const}} \tag{1-11}$$

We may rearrange this relation to give

$$I_C = \alpha I_E + I_{CBO} \tag{1-12}$$

at a specific value of V_{CB}. If we further assume that α and I_{CBO} do not change with V_{CB}, Eq. (1–12) could be used to *sketch* the collector characteristics of a common-base stage. Such a sketch would be a family of horizontal lines of constant I_E, and would be of use in graphical analyses.

To study the common-emitter characteristics, we substitute Eq. (1–3) into Eq. (1–12):

$$I_C = \alpha(I_C + I_B) + I_{CBO}. \tag{1-13}$$

Rearranging,

$$I_C = \alpha I_B/(1 - \alpha) + I_{CBO}/(1 - \alpha). \tag{1-14}$$

Using Eq. (1–8), we obtain

$$I_C = \beta I_B + (\beta + 1)I_{CBO}. \tag{1-15}$$

When $I_B = 0$, the resulting collector current is I_{CEO}. Therefore

$$I_{CEO} = (\beta + 1)I_{CBO}. \tag{1-16}$$

Equation (1–15) may be written

$$I_C = \beta I_B + I_{CEO}. \qquad (1\text{-}17)$$

Equation (1–17) is a mathematical description of the common-emitter collector characteristics. It represents a family of horizontal lines of constant I_B. Although Eq. (1–17) does not show the ever-present dependence of the characteristics upon V_{CE}, it is nevertheless of great value in sketching the output characteristics from knowledge of β and I_{CEO}.

1–9. Saturation and Cutoff. The common-emitter configuration has become the favorite of circuit designers, primarily because of the high degree of power amplification it provides. It therefore seems appropriate that a thorough study be made of this connection. In doing so, we find that the collector characteristics can provide more information concerning operation than is immediately apparent from examining a typical curve such as Fig. 1–6(b).

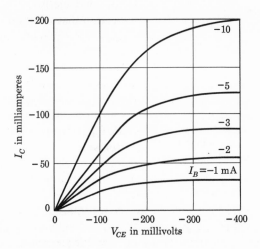

Fig. 1–12. Saturation region of a *medium-power p–n–p* transistor, common–emitter configuration.

Suppose that we investigate the low-voltage region of the collector characteristics. The region of the curve from zero to several hundred millivolts has been called the *saturation region* because incremental changes in base current do not cause the correspondingly large collector-current changes that are found at higher collector voltages. (This region is also referred to as the *bottomed* region.) Although Fig. 1–6(b) seems to indicate superimposed lines of constant base current at low values of V_{CE}, they are not actually superimposed when an expanded scale is used to depict that region of the characteristics, as in Fig. 1–12.

Both *p–n* junctions are forward-biased in the saturation region. Often used is a *saturation resistance*, symbolized by R_{CS}, which may be determined from the ratio of V_{CE} to I_C at any point in the saturated region. For germanium transistors, R_{CS} is generally less than 20 Ω, and in the majority of applications can be neglected; low-power silicon transistors, however, may exhibit a saturation resistance of several hundred ohms; the allowable operating portion of the characteristics is thereby limited. It is evident from the figure that the magnitude of the saturation resistance is dependent upon base current and therefore a value ascribed to R_{CS} pertains at the specified I_C and I_B.

Let us turn our attention to the low-current region of the collector characteristics. The symbol I_{CEO} has been introduced to designate collector current when I_B is zero, and our curves indicate the relations between I_C and V_{CE} when base current is leaving the base terminal of a *p–n–p* transistor. The question now

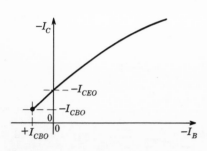

arises "can the transistor be operated with reverse base current?" If, to answer this question, we were to view a few typical collector characteristics, we should find no indication that operation is possible below I_{CEO}, because lines of constant base current are not usually drawn for that region. However, *the minimum collector current must be* I_{CBO}, for that is the reverse-leakage junction current. I_{CBO} flows *into* the base of a *p–n–p* transistor. Consequently we conclude that operation *is* possible to collector currents as low as I_{CBO}. Figure 1–13 is intended to clarify the relations among quantities of interest near *cutoff*.

Fig. 1–13. Portion of the transfer characteristic depicting leakage currents, common-emitter configuration, *p–n–p* transistor.

1–10. The Junction FET. The field-effect transistor or FET operates on the principle that the thickness and hence the resistance of a conducting channel of semiconducting material can be modulated or regulated by the magnitude of a potential applied to its input terminals. As an amplifier, the FET provides a higher input impedance than a conventional transistor, generates less self-noise, and has greater resistance to nuclear radiation. Two FET types exist, the *junction* type and the *insulated-gate* variety.

In its simplest form, the silicon junction FET has a single *p–n* junction; the junction is normally reverse-biased and forms the input pair of the three-terminal device. Consequently the device exhibits the high-impedance characteristic of a reverse-biased silicon diode. Output current flows through a bar or channel of *p*-type or *n*-type material, not through a junction as in the conventional transistor.

It may be noted from Fig. 1–14 that the terminals are referred to as *gate*, *source*, and *drain*.* Source and drain are usually interchangeable. The arrowhead

---

Grid, cathode, and *plate* are sometimes employed to designate these three terminals because of the similarity of this device to the vacuum-tube triode.

at the gate of the junction FET indicates the direction of conventional forward current, but because the gate–source junction of this device is normally reverse-biased, leakage current will be opposite to the direction of the arrow.

Circuitry for biasing a p-channel FET is shown in Fig. 1–15. The gate supply V_{GG} and the drain supply V_{DD} assure that the gate–source junction is reverse-biased. For all practical purposes, $|I_D| = |I_S|$ because I_G is a small leakage current that at room temperature may be of the order of 10^{-9} A.

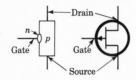
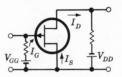

Fig. 1–14. Idealized construction of junction FET and circuit diagram for p-chan-
nel device.

Fig. 1–15. Biasing for p-channel junction FET.

Two separate power supplies are indicated in Fig. 1–15. It is possible to eliminate V_{GG} completely by adding a resistance between source terminal and ground so that the voltage drop across that element will provide the proper positive potential difference from gate-to-source. A more sophisticated form of biasing uses the V_{DD} supply, as well as the source-leg resistance and is discussed in Chapter 3.

Common-source static characteristics for a typical p-channel junction FET are shown in Fig. 1–16. The following observations may be made from a study of that graph:

1. Because input current is generally negligible, the input quantity of interest is V_{GS}. The FET is considered to be a voltage-controlled device.
2. It is possible to operate the device with some forward bias on the gate. This is evident from the line designated by $V_{GS} = -0.5$ V. If this forward voltage is exceeded, the gate current will become quite large and the advantage of high-input impedance lost.
3. For values of V_{DS} above the "pinch-off" voltage V_P, the device provides greater gain and output impedance. Consequently it is advantageous to operate at the higher drain voltages.

Input characteristics are those of a reverse-biased diode, and are not presented here. Operation in the common-drain mode would be very similar to the common-source characteristics shown. In a *dual gate* FET, additional control over the static characteristics is available from the potential applied to the second gate.

1–11. FET Parameters. To describe the amplification property of a field-effect transistor, the *transconductance* or *mutual-conductance* parameter is convenient. Mathematically,

$$g_m \equiv \lim_{\Delta v_{GS} \to 0} \frac{\Delta i_D}{\Delta v_{GS}}\bigg|_{v_{DS} = \text{const}} = \frac{\partial i_D}{\partial v_{GS}}\bigg|_{v_{DS} = \text{const}} \tag{1-18}$$

This parameter, also referred to as g_{fs}, is the small-signal output-current to input-voltage ratio, taken under short-circuit loading of the device. Typical values for g_m lie between 500 and 10,000 μmhos.

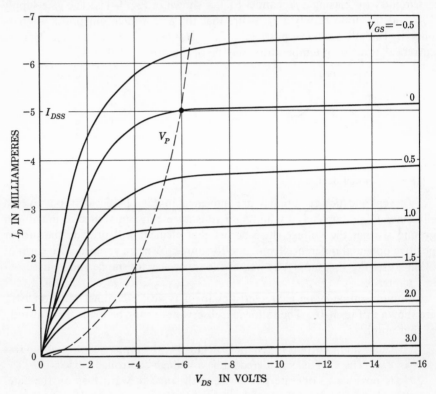

Fig. 1–16.   Common-source characteristics for a typical p-channel junction FET.

The voltage gain of a FET stage at low frequencies can often be successfully approximated by

$$|A_v| \cong g_m R_L. \qquad (1\text{-}19)$$

Equation (1–19) can be employed where the output resistance of the FET is large enough to be neglected and the input impedance is infinite.

To describe the quality of a FET, several static parameters are useful.

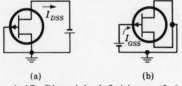

(a)   (b)

Fig. 1–17. Pictorial definitions of I_{DSS} and I_{GSS}.

1. ON *current* [I_{DSS}, *also* $I_{D(on)}$]. This parameter is the value of drain current, with $V_{GS} = 0$, usually specified with the drain voltage equal to V_P. To measure I_{DSS}, the simple circuit of Fig. 1–17(a) may be used; the level is noted in Fig. 1–16.

2. DC *Transconductance* (g_{FS}, *also* g_M). We shall use the definition

$$g_{FS} \equiv \left. \frac{I_D}{V_{GS}} \right|_{V_{DS}=\text{const}} \tag{1-20}$$

Thus g_{FS} describes the FET in a manner similar to the way in which h_{FE} describes the transistor.

3. *Pinch-off Voltage* (V_P).   The voltage applied between gate and source that reduces drain current to essentially zero is the pinch-off voltage. It is equal to the drain–source voltage at which the channel is effectively closed and I_D no longer increases with V_{DS}. Because an accurate measurement of V_P is difficult, it is often convenient to express performance relations in terms of quantities more easily measured.

4. *Gate Cutoff Current* (I_{GSS}).   The quality of the reverse-biased input junction is determined from measurement of the leakage current I_{GSS}. This parameter behaves in the same way as I_{CBO}, the leakage current of the diffusion transistor. I_{GSS} is pictorially defined in Fig. 1–17(b).

1–12. The Insulated-Gate FET.   A field-effect transistor may be constructed without a junction, using a potential difference applied between the channel and a gate located in close proximity to control channel conductance. Such an insulated gate unit is often referred to as an MOS or a MOST (*m*etal-*o*xide-*s*emiconductor *t*ransistor) or an IGFET (*i*nsulated-*g*ate FET). Because the gate and channel are separated by insulation, the input resistance of the MOS is superior to that of a junction FET, and is relatively unaffected by temperature.

In the fabrication of an *n*-channel MOS, the channel is often diffused into a substrate or foundation of *p*-material. Consequently, a *p–n* junction will exist in the structure. That junction is not used as a primary means of control over the source-to-drain current. However, a secondary effect is present that may be used if desired to alter the characteristics of the device.

Figure 1–18(a) depicts the idealized construction of an *n*-channel MOS and a circuit-diagram symbol for the device. This four-terminal device is often operated with the substrate lead connected to the source terminal.

Static source characteristics for an *n*-channel device are given in Fig. 1–18(b). Because there is no diode, it is possible to operate with either positive or negative values of V_{GS}. As shown in the diagram, the regions of operation are referred to as *enhancement* when the gate bias increases the conductance of the channel, and *depletion* when the reverse is true. As discussed in Chapter 2, a version of the MOS operates entirely in the enhancement mode.

The effect of a voltage applied between substrate and source terminals, V_{Subs}, is dependent upon the design parameters of the device itself. The effect of this voltage upon a particular MOS is given in Fig. 1–18(c).

Biasing considerations for insulated-gate devices are identical with those for the junction FET. To protect the oxide-insulation layer from static charge buildup, the gate should be returned to ground through a fixed, finite resistance and not left floating.

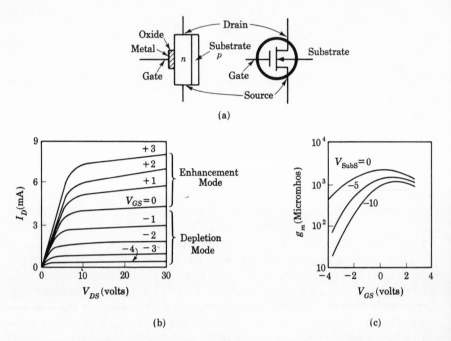

(a)

(b)

(c)

Fig. 1–18. *n*-channel MOST: (a) construction and circuit diagram symbol; (b) common-source characteristics; (c) g_m vs V_{GS} for various substrate–source voltages, V_{DS} constant.

1–13. Summary. The characteristics of conventional and field-effect transistors have been described by the various curves, definitions, and equations contained within this chapter. This material, while mainly descriptive, is a very important portion of the text. As the reader progresses, he will notice that the succeeding chapters serve mainly to clarify and extend the concepts introduced here, in order to gain a usable understanding of the devices for the purpose of applying them successfully.

It is possible for the reader with a solid grounding in vacuum-tube circuit techniques to employ the material thus far discussed for the design of workable transistor circuits. However, without a knowledge of the pitfalls inherent in semiconductor circuits, namely biasing stability, thermal runaway, and parameter variations, good circuit design is not probable.

Chapter 2 is an introduction to the physics of semiconductors. Every engineer who would work with transistors should have a knowledge of their physical operation in order to appreciate their limitations. Familiarity with the physical processes will enable the reader to cope more easily with the advances in the science of solid-state physics and the art of semiconductor device design that are to be expected in the coming decade.

PROBLEMS

1–1. The dynamic resistance of a diode is the slope of its characteristic at a particular point, while its static resistance is simply obtained by dividing the total value of V by I at a particular point. For the characteristic of Fig. 1–1(b), find the dynamic and static resistance at
    (a) 0.2 V, forward biasing;
    (b) 5 V, reverse biasing;
    (c) 600 μA, reverse biasing.

1–2. The device in the accompanying circuit is a Zener diode. Consider that its terminal voltage will remain constant at 20 V. The load is 1000 Ω and invarient but V will vary from 23 to 28 V. Select R so that the current through the diode will not exceed 60 mA when V takes on its maximum value. What will be the diode current when $V = 23$ V?

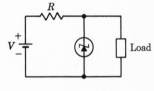

Problem 1–2.

1–3. Using information contained in Fig. 1–6, plot static transfer characteristics:
    (a) with collector current as ordinate and base voltage as abscissa for values of collector voltage of 0, 5, and 10 V;
    (b) with collector current as ordinate and base current as abscissa for values of collector voltage of 0, 5, and 10 V.

1–4. Explain the convention used in Fig. 1–6 that results in V_{CE}, I_C, and I_B having negative signs. What signs would be used for the currents of an n–p–n device? Would you expect *all* manufacturers and engineers to follow this convention?

1–5. Design a circuit to obtain the static characteristics curves for a common-base-connected low-power transistor.

1–6. Use Fig. 1–6(c) and the definition of the dynamic input resistance of the transistor as the slope of that characteristic to plot dynamic input resistance vs. base-to-emitter voltage for a constant collector voltage of -10 V.

1–7. By using the information contained in Fig. 1–8, draw diagrams similar to Fig. 1–9(a) and 1–9(b) for both p–n–p and n–p–n transistor types in the common-base and common-collector configurations.

1–8. Calculate β_{dc} from Fig. 1–6(b) at $V_{CE} = -5$ V. Does β_{dc} vary with collector voltage? Does β_{dc} vary with collector current?

1–9. A given transistor exhibits a short-circuit current amplification of 0.995 when used in a common-base circuit. Calculate its short-circuit current gain as a common-emitter amplifier and also as a common-collector amplifier.

1–10. Use Fig. 1–10 to determine β and β_{dc} at $I_B = -100\ \mu$A.

1–11. Express the ratio β/α solely as a function of β and solely as a function of α.

1–12. Derive Eqs. (1–8a), (1–8b), and (1–8c).

1–13. Calculate the approximate voltage gain for each configuration using the same numbers for α, β, R_i, and R_L as used in the text examples of Sec. 1–7.

1–14. Using Eqs. (1–3) and (1–12), derive an expression for I_E in terms of I_B and I_{CEO}, and from your derived expression predict and sketch the output characteristics for a transistor in the common-collector configuration. Discuss the spacing between lines of constant I_B and also discuss the $I_B = 0$ line.

1–15. Explain why I_B in Fig. 1–6(c) can take on positive values up to I_{CBO}. Draw the circuit to provide $V_{BE} = 0$ to assist your explanation.

1–16. A transistor known to have $\beta = 100$ and $I_{CBO} = 5$ μA is connected in a circuit as a common-emitter stage and a measurement of the collector current yields $I_C = 1$ mA with zero load resistance. Calculate I_E, I_B, α, and I_{CEO} under these conditions.

1–17. Calculate the dc collector saturation resistance R_{CS} from Fig. 1–12 for each displayed value of base current at $V_{CE} = 100$ mV.

1–18. A sound-amplifying system supplies a loudspeaker with 4 W of audio power when the system, which has an input resistance of 10,000 Ω, is supplied with a 0.2-V signal. The speaker is of the common 4-Ω variety and is assumed to be noninductive.
(a) Express the power gain in dB.
(b) Express the voltage gain in dB.
(c) Express the current gain in dB.
(d) Express the resistance-level ratio in dB by extension of Eq. (1–9), and subtract from the answer to part (c) in order to arrive at the answer to part (a).

1–19. By using the expression Eq. (1–17) that predicts the idealized collector characteristics, show that for a common-emitter oriented transistor, a base current of $-I_{CBO}$ causes a collector current of equal magnitude.

1–20. On a single sheet of graph paper, approximate the common-base and common-emitter collector characteristics for a transistor with $\alpha = 0.975$, $I_{CO} = 10$ μA, and $R_{CS} = 200$ Ω. Let collector currents range to 5 mA and collector-junction potentials to 20 V.

1–21. I_{CBO}, I_{CEO}, and I_{EBO} have been used to symbolize transistor leakage currents.
(a) Suggest the system being used that results in this three-subscript notation.
(b) Sketch circuits to independently measure each of these currents for an n–p–n transistor.

1–22. Draw circuits similar to Figs. 1–15 and 1–17 for an n-channel junction FET.

1–23. From the information available in Fig. 1–16, make the following plots:
(a) Transfer characteristics: V_{GS} as abscissa, I_D as ordinate, at $V_{DS} = -10$ V.
(b) g_m vs V_{GS}. [g_m is the slope of the curve in (a)].
(c) g_{FS} vs V_{GS}.

REFERENCES

1. Bardeen, J., and Brattain, W. H., "The Transistor, A Semiconductor Triode," *Phys. Rev.*, **74** (July, 1948).
2. Heil, O., "*Improvements in or Relating to Electrical Amplifiers and other Control Arrangements and Devices*," British Patent 439,457, September 26, 1939.
3. "IEEE Standard Letter Symbols for Semiconductor Devices," *IEEE Trans. Electron Devices*, **ED–11**, No. 8, (August, 1964).
4. Lilienfeld, J. E., U.S. Patents 1745175 (filed 10/8/26), 1877140, and 1900018.
5. Lo, A. W., *et al.*, *Transistor Electronics* (Prentice-Hall, Inc., Englewood Cliffs, New Jersey, 1955).
6. Pierce, J. F., *Transistor Circuit Theory and Design* (Charles E. Merrill Books, Inc., Columbus, Ohio, 1963).
7. Riddle, R. L., and Ristenbatt, M. P., *Transistor Physics and Circuits* (Prentice-Hall, Inc., Englewood Cliffs, New Jersey, 1958).
8. Ryder, J. D., *Electronic Fundamentals and Applications* (Prentice-Hall, Inc., Englewood Cliffs, New Jersey, 1964), 3rd ed.

9. Shea, R. F., *Principles of Transistor Circuits* (John Wiley & Sons, Inc., New York, 1953).
10. Shea, R. F., *Transistor Circuit Engineering* (John Wiley & Sons, Inc., New York, 1957).
11. Shockley, W., "A Unipolar 'Field-Effect' Transistor," *Proc. IRE*, vol. 40 (November 1952).

Fused-junction transistor without cover. (*Courtesy Raytheon Company, Semiconductor Division*).

Chapter 2

SEMICONDUCTOR PHYSICS AND DEVICES

Semiconductor devices have been used in electrical circuits since the *galena crystal* or "cat's whisker" of pre-vacuum-tube days. Dry rectifiers using *copper oxide* and *selenium* were widely accepted for battery charging and electronic rectification during the two decades prior to the introduction of the transistor and the junction diode; and thermistors and photoelectric devices of semiconducting materials long have been useful circuit components. Understanding of the operation of these earlier semiconductor devices is now more complete because of the vast research in solid-state physical phenomena that commenced in the late 1940's.

The elements *germanium* and *silicon* constitute the semiconductors of paramount importance today. The compound gallium arsenide has been used in the fabrication of tunnel diodes and transistors. It seems reasonable to speculate that other materials such as gallium phosphide, silicon carbide, indium phosphide, aluminum antimonide or possibly organic compounds will play a major role in electronics of the not-too-distant future.

At this point in the study of transistors it is appropriate that some attention be given to the principles of semiconductor physics, the applications of those principles, and the methods of transistor manufacture. Although it is theoretically unnecessary for a circuit designer to be aware of the physical processes involved, such knowledge is of very great assistance in appreciating transistor limitations, fully understanding circuit operation, and keeping abreast with developments in the field.

2–1. Structure. The fourth column of the periodic table includes silicon and germanium—they have four electrons in their outermost *orbit* or *shell*, and tend to form a crystal when in the pure elemental state. A crystal is a solid in which atoms are arranged in a definite order or pattern that is regularly repeated throughout the solid. Crystals may consist of different geometrical arrangements of atoms; the three-dimensional pattern repeated throughout the crystals of interest here is known as the *face-centered diamond cubic lattice*, a structure identical with that of the diamond form of carbon.

The distribution of the four valence electrons in the germanium or silicon atom is such that one electron is shared with each of the four neighboring atoms in the crystal. This condition, known as *covalent bonding*, results in a filled outer shell for each atom, for in addition to its own four electrons, each atom is sharing four other electrons with its neighbors, as in Fig. 2–1. When its outer ring contains eight electrons, the atom is "satisfied" or stable and no free electrons exist in the ideal structure at $0°$ K. This must mean that the crystal has insulating properties, since it is the presence of free charge carriers that is characteristic of conducting materials.

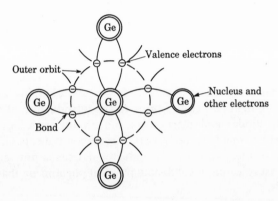

Fig. 2–1. Portion of the crystal structure of perfect germanium.

Pure germanium (or silicon) is referred to as an *intrinsic* semiconductor. Electrical conduction is possible because some covalent bonds are broken by thermal energy even at room temperature. An electric field or a light beam can also supply enough energy to break covalent bonds and liberate electrons to serve as charge carriers.

It is of course possible to measure and also calculate the number of broken bonds due to the addition of energy to an intrinsic semiconductor. At $300°$ K, which is about normal room temperature, the resistivity of pure germanium is about 50 Ω cm, with more than 10^{13} charge carriers per cubic centimeter of material. The resistivity of silicon at that same temperature is approximately 240,000 Ω cm, with some 10^{10} carriers per cubic centimeter.[2]

2–2. Impurities. A perfect crystal is not used for diode or transistor manufacture; the characteristics of such devices depend upon impurities within the crystal to alter its intrinsic conducting properties. An *extrinsic* semiconductor results from imperfections in the lattice structure, chemical imperfection due to foreign materials remaining after the refining process, or the controlled addition of known impurities, a process called *doping*. Impurities that are purposely added to elements in the fourth column of the periodic table (germanium and silicon) are elements from the third and fifth columns. Table 2–1 provides the portion of the periodic table that includes the elements of major importance to semiconductor work.

When a small number of arsenic atoms, for example, are added to a crystal of germanium, the lattice remains intact; that is, covalent bonding exists between all adjacent atoms. But since each arsenic atom has five electrons in its outermost orbit, it is apparent that an electron is left over from each atom of the impurity; one electron does not enter into the covalent bonding. This electron can be termed a free electron because it is easily detached from the arsenic atom. Fig. 2–2 depicts the situation. As would be expected, the resistivity of the crystal is decreased because of the presence of free electrons. *Donor* is the term most often applied to elements that, when added to pure germanium, serve to donate free electrons to the lattice. The composite material thus formed is *n-type* germanium, the *n* being an abbreviation for negative, the sign of charge on the electron. In *n*-type material electrical conduction is primarily an electron movement.

The addition of an impurity with three electrons in its outer orbit has an opposite effect upon the lattice. As shown in Fig. 2–3 there now are too few electrons to satisfy all the covalent bonds. Between each atom of the impurity and the surrounding atoms there will be a void of one electron; this absence of an electron is called a *hole*. *Acceptor* is used to specify elements which when added to

TABLE 2–1. PORTION OF THE PERIODIC TABLE INCLUDING ELEMENTS OF INTEREST TO SEMICONDUCTOR WORK.

Group 3	Group 4	Group 5
Boron$_{10.8}^{5}$	Carbon$_{12}^{6}$	Nitrogen$_{14}^{7}$
Aluminum$_{27}^{13}$	Silicon$_{28.1}^{14}$	Phosphorus$_{31}^{15}$
Gallium$_{69.7}^{31}$	Germanium$_{72.6}^{32}$	Arsenic$_{75}^{33}$
Indium$_{114.8}^{49}$	Tin$_{118.7}^{50}$	Antimony$_{121.8}^{51}$

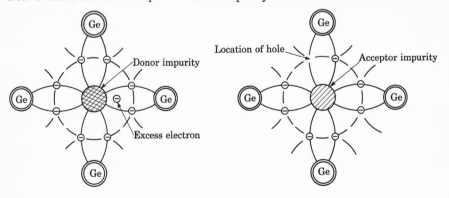

Fig. 2–2. The addition of a donor to the germanium crystal of Fig. 2–1 results in a free electron.

Fig. 2–3. The addition of an acceptor to the germanium crystal of Fig. 2–1 results in a hole.

an intrinsic semiconductor can result in holes in the lattice; acceptor meaning that the element will accept an electron, if one is available, to fill its commitments in the lattice. *p-type* material, then, has an excess of holes; *p* is an abbreviation for positive, the sign of a hole (since the charge on an electron is negative, the absence of an electron would seemingly be equivalent to a positively charged particle). In *p-type* materials electrical conduction is primarily a hole movement. The resistivity of pure germanium is decreased by the addition of acceptor impurities; thus the hole serves as an electrical carrier and is comparable in effectiveness to the free electron.

The movement of a free electron is random in a specimen of *n*-type material; the electron is free to wander. So it is with a hole in *p*-material, for electrons in neighboring bonds find it easy to fill the void, and the hole appears to move through the material. When such charge carrier movement is caused by an electric field, the process is referred to as *drift*. Holes naturally behave oppositely to electrons—they are attracted to negative charges.

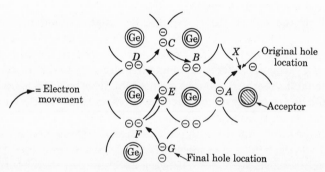

Fig. 2–4.   The movement of electrons to fill holes in the lattice results in hole movement.

A second process that results in carrier movement within a semiconductor is *diffusion*, the movement of carriers from regions of high concentration to regions of low concentration. Both holes and electrons will diffuse when an appropriate *concentration gradient* exists.

Hole movement can be appreciated from study of Fig. 2–4. If a hole is initially located in the outer orbit of the acceptor atom, as at *X* in the diagram, it is possible for an electron at *A* to move from its position to fill the hole, since it is in the same orbit, and no additional energy is required. After this movement, there is a hole at *A*. The electron at *B* can fill the new hole at *A*, so that the void is then located at *B*. In a like manner we may conceive of the hole reaching location *G* and beyond. We may conclude that hole movement is possible, that it is in the opposite direction to electron flow, and, significantly, it takes place within the valence shells of atoms. It is interesting to note that average hole drift velocity is about one-half that for electrons.

In securing a clear picture of semiconductor phenomena, it must be understood that the *impurities are immobile*; it is the free electrons and holes that are the carriers, for their movement dictates the movement of charge and hence what are called *electrical currents*. Electrons in *n*-type material and holes in *p*-type material are *majority* carriers, while any electrons in *p*-type material or any holes in *n*-type material are termed *minority* carriers. The net charge of a specimen of *p*-type or *n*-type material is normally zero, for neither electrons nor holes have been added to or removed from the atoms that constitute the crystal, and the atoms themselves are electrically neutral. The lattice may have an excess of electrons or holes because of the type of impurity added, but this excess is only relative to a perfect lattice structure.

2–3. Energy-Level Diagrams. Modern atomic theory stresses that for an atom of any element there is an integral number of orbits or levels to which electrons can belong, and each level represents a particular value of energy ascribed to the electrons "residing" there. To move an electron from one level to a higher energy level, the system must be furnished with an amount of energy equal to the energy difference between levels; this can be supplied from any convenient energy source. Electrons closest to the nucleus are in the lowest energy levels; those farthest from the nucleus have the highest energies. The higher the energy of a given electron, the less is its attraction to its nucleus.

Thus far in this discussion only a single atom has been considered. When a tremendously large number of atoms are congregated to form a solid, the energy-level picture of the individual atom is no longer valid, because of interactions between it and its neighboring atoms. The number of energy levels for a solid is very great, but they are generally very close. A number of close levels is termed an energy *band*; and each band, in a solid, is separated from other bands by a *forbidden gap*, a series of energies that electrons in that solid cannot possess. Not all solids have gaps in their energy-band picture, but semiconductors do.

From an energy-level standpoint the differences between insulators, conductors, and semiconductors can be appreciated. The width of the forbidden gap between the *valence band* of allowable energy levels and the *conduction band* of allowable energy levels is a key to that understanding. If a great deal of energy (in the form of heat or otherwise) must be added to a material to increase its conductivity to a reasonable value, then the forbidden gap of that material must be large, and consequently the material under normal conditions is an insulator. On the other hand if a negligible amount of added energy is needed to establish good electrical conductivity, a given specimen is classified as a conductor. A gap of intermediate width connotes a semiconductor. A pictorial representation of energy levels for different materials is Fig. 2–5. It must be borne in mind that whereas other gaps exist in a given atomic structure, it is the forbidden gap between the valence band (also called the filled band) and the conduction band (also referred to as the empty band) that is the important one.

In germanium or silicon, the gap is small enough so that, at room temperature, an appreciable number of interatomic bonds are broken by thermal energy, and a number of electrons will acquire sufficient energy to move from the valence band to the conduction band of the crystal. The forbidden gap for germanium is 0.72 electron volt, while for silicon a generally recognized figure is 1.1 electron volts. (The electron volt, eV, a unit of energy, is equivalent to 1.6×10^{-19} W-sec.)

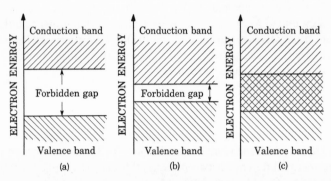

Fig. 2–5.   Representation of solids by energy-level diagrams: (a) insulator; (b) semiconductor; (c) conductor.

Let us consider the other elements of column four of the periodic table (Table 2–1). Carbon, in the diamond form, has a gap of 7 eV, and is therefore nonconductive up to very high temperatures. The crystalline form of tin, called gray tin, has a gap of only 0.1 eV and consequently is a stable crystal at very low temperatures only. Neither material may be used for transistor manufacture.

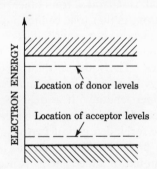

Fig. 2–6.   Locations of donor and acceptor levels in doped semiconductor.

The presence of electrons with conduction-band energies because of broken interatomic bonds results in holes in the valence band. A *pentavalent impurity*, that is a donor, when added to germanium, will add electrons to the crystal *without* adding any new holes. However, it is interesting to note that the energy-level system is further complicated by this donor; this impurity introduces new energy levels into the energy-band picture. The location of these new levels is slightly below the bottom of the conduction band for pure germanium (the gap was forbidden to electrons of the pure crystal only) (see Fig. 2–6). The total width of the gap was previously stated as 0.72 eV; the energy required to move an electron from a donor impurity into the conduction band is of the order of 0.01 eV, and since at normal ambient temperature the thermal energy is considered to be about 0.02 eV, it is concluded that almost all electrons are detached from donor atoms and have conduction-band energies.

The introduction of a *trivalent impurity* can also be investigated. As before, the presence of the impurity creates new energy levels. For acceptors, however, these levels are in the gap in the neighborhood of the top of the valence band of energies. Ambient temperature results in ionization of most acceptor atoms and thus an apparent movement of holes from the acceptor levels to the valence band. *Energy-level diagrams are plots of electron energies; energies for holes are highest near the valence band and decrease vertically upward.* Alternatively, one might say that electrons are accepted by the acceptors; these electrons are supplied from the valence band, leaving a preponderance of holes in the valence band.

Summarizing, then, under ambient conditions *n*-type material has a surplus of electrons, and electrical conduction is primarily a conduction-band electron drift; in a *p*-type material there is a hole surplus and electrical conduction is primarily a valence-band hole drift.

2-4. *p–n* Junctions. A *p–n* junction is created when *p*-type and *n*-type material are bonded to form a single crystal. The methods of junction manufacture are discussed in Sec. 2-7 and in other texts. Immediately after formation, carrier diffusion results in some electrons from the *n* region crossing the boundary while some holes from the *p* region are migrating to the other side. After crossing the junction, an electron from the *n* region finds itself in an area of high hole concentration. Recombination is probable and the electron as a carrier is therefore annihilated. A similar process can be visualized for holes from the *p* region crossing the junction. Since each region was originally electrically neutral, electron–hole recombinations on both sides and in the vicinity of the junction result in layers of ionized acceptors in the *p* region and ionized donors in the *n* region. Therefore the *p* region has experienced a net accumulation of negative charge and the *n* region a net accumulation of positive charge. This charge buildup continues until an equilibrium condition prevails and further carrier diffusion across the junction is discouraged by the repelling force between the carrier and the charge concentration across the boundary. The *p–n* junction in equilibrium is symbolized in Fig. 2–7(a).

Because of the accumulated charges in the vicinity of the *p–n* junction, a potential difference is evident. Figs. 2–7(b) and 2–7(c) are concerned with the distribution of charge and the potential picture. During the equilibrium process carriers in the neighborhood of the junction have been "swept out," and the area is referred to as the *depletion* or *transition* or *space-charge* region. The *potential hill* shown in Fig. 2–7(c) is a formidable obstacle for holes from the *p* region to surmount. Although not noted in the figure, a hill of equal magnitude also confronts electrons in the *n* region.

An energy level-diagram for the *p–n* junction is shown in Fig. 2–8. Because the *p* region has lost some high-energy holes and gained some high energy-electrons,

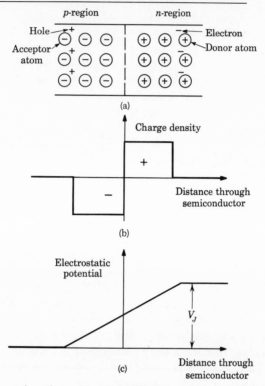

Fig. 2–7. The *p–n* junction: (a) after diffusion and recombinations; (b) charge distribution; (c) potential hill.

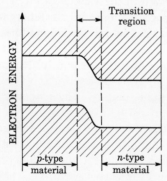

Fig. 2–8.   *p–n* junction energy-level diagram.

and therefore is no longer electrically neutral, its electron energy diagram will be relatively displaced above that of the *n* region by an amount of energy equal to qV_J, where q is the charge on the electron and V_J is the electrostatic potential difference across the junction.

In order for an electron to move from the *n* region to the *p* region, it would be necessary for it to have sufficient energy to climb the potential hill (the electron would have to invade the *p* region which has more of a negative charge than the *n* region). Likewise, when we consider holes in the *p* region, they would need to be supplied with external energy in order to climb the potential hill confronting them. Thermal agitation accounts for some carrier flow across the junction at ambient temperatures but any net movement of majority carriers is balanced by minority carriers. Minority carriers, although relatively few in number, find it easy to slide down the potential hills.

If a *reverse bias* is applied to the *p–n* junction as shown in Fig. 2–9(a) the potential hill for electrons in the *n* region becomes more difficult to climb. The only current possible results from the few minority carriers on each side of the

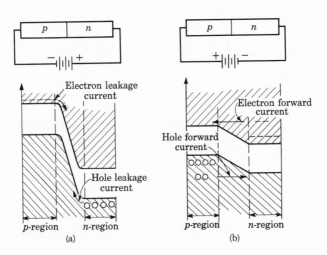

Fig. 2–9.   *p–n* junction with applied voltage: (a) reverse bias; (b) forward bias.

junction. The magnitude of this leakage or reverse current is dictated primarily by the junction temperature, because the major source of minority carriers is thermally broken covalent bonds.

Leakage current is almost independent of the magnitude of the reverse biasing voltage until the *avalanche* voltage or *Zener* voltage is exceeded. Reverse current then increases very rapidly. Avalanche breakdown occurs when the electric field across the junction produces ionization because resulting high-energy carriers collide with valence electrons. Zener breakdown appears to be a "field emission" phenomenon, the strong electric field in the junction region pulling carriers from their atoms.

Forward bias applied to a *p–n* structure facilitates the movement of majority carriers across the junction. Figure 2–9(b) indicates that the height of the potential hill has been reduced so that a portion of the available carriers can cross the junction with ease. Further reduction in the hill allows even greater numbers of carriers to cross. Although the reverse current still exists, it is negligible compared to the current associated with the movements of majority carriers.

The volt–ampere characteristic of the junction diode, shown in Fig. 2–10, can be described theoretically by the following relationship:

$$I = I_R(e^{qV/kT} - 1), \tag{2-1}$$

where I = junction current in amperes,

I_R = saturated value of reverse current in amperes,

q = charge on an electron, 1.602×10^{-19} coulomb,

V = potential difference in volts,

T = absolute temperature in degrees Kelvin,

k = Boltzmann's constant, 1.380×10^{-23} joule per °K.

This equation holds for both polarities of voltage, and agrees with experimental data.

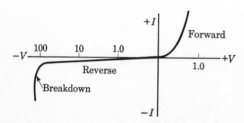

Fig. 2–10. Typical characteristic curve for a *p–n* junction (diode).

The effect of ambient temperature upon diode leakage or reverse current is important. Higher temperatures cause more electron–hole pairs to be thermally generated, and the resulting additional carriers cause larger leakage currents. In Chapter 1, I_{CBO} and I_{EBO} were introduced as leakage currents of *p–n* structures within the transistor. These currents are extremely temperature-sensitive; the degree of that sensitivity will be further discussed in Chapter 3.

In summary of the operation of a *p–n* junction diode, the following points are of interest. Joining *p*-type material to *n*-type material establishes a contact-potential hill which consequently limits random movement of majority carriers across the junction. Minority carriers, generated by thermal energy or otherwise can easily cross a reverse-biased junction, their flow being essentially independent of the magnitude of the bias, unless breakdown conditions are exceeded. With forward biasing, the height of the potential hill is reduced and majority carriers cross the junction in great number.

2–5. Transistor Operation. With understanding of *p–n* junction operation comes insight into transistor operation, for the common junction transistor is merely two rectifying junctions. The basic structure can take on either of the forms shown in Fig. 1–2, a *p–n–p sandwich* or an *n–p–n sandwich*. The emitter and collector regions form the two outside portions of the structure; between them is the thin base region. External circuitry is connected by relatively large metal contacts to each of the elements to ensure nonrectifying terminations. It was noted in Chapter 1 that under normal biasing conditions, the emitter–base junction is biased in the forward or high-conduction direction, while the collector–base junction is biased in the reverse direction.

Now consider Fig. 2–11(a), which shows an *n–p–n* transistor and its energy-level diagram in the absence of biasing. The energy barriers are apparent in the electron-energy diagram, and, as would be expected, there is no net flow of charges. The emitter junction can now be forward-biased, the collector junction reverse-biased with a positive potential through a load resistance for normal operation.

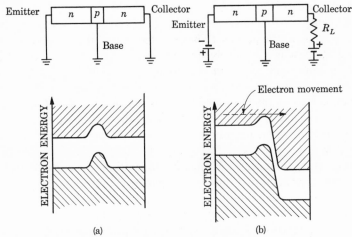

Fig. 2–11. The junction transistor with energy-level diagrams: (a) no bias voltages; (b) normal bias voltages.

Majority carriers, namely, electrons in the emitter *n* region, will move toward the base region because forward biasing has been applied to the emitter–base junction. They easily reach the base region and traverse the short distance through the base primarily by diffusion. At the collector junction they see the large potential hill created by the collector–base voltage. Because these electrons are minority carriers in the base region, they have no trouble with the reverse bias on the collector junction, and slide down the hill to the collector. Thus carriers from the emitter reach the collector when appropriate biasing is present. This is transistor amplification as noted in Chapter 1, namely, the passage of current from a low-resistance to a high-resistance circuit. When a time-varying signal is applied between base and emitter terminals, that signal just serves to modulate the static emitter–base potential, or, in other words, it alters the potential hill between emitter and base to allow a greater or lesser number of emitted charges to reach the collector.

The number of electrons reaching the collector from the emitter in the *n–p–n* transistor is less than the number *injected* by the emitter because of recombinations of electrons and holes in the base region. The number of recombinations must be kept low in order for the amplification efficiency to be high. Consequently the base region is made exceedingly thin, and the impurity density of the base wafer is controlled during manufacture; these measures reduce the time spent by electrons while diffusing through the base region and limit the number of holes with which recombination can take place. The value of alpha, the fraction of emitted charges which are collected, depends directly upon such recombinations. If the base is too wide, all emitted charges would recombine in that region and the device would simply function as a rectifier, with emitter and base as electrodes.

High-frequency performance also depends upon base thickness. Since an absence of strong electric fields is to be expected in that region, diffusion of carriers across the base is a relatively slow process and the distance traveled by a charge is an important factor in the ability of a transistor to follow high-frequency commands.

The junction regions are essentially devoid of carriers, and therefore are regions of high resistivity; almost the entire bias voltage drop occurs there, resulting in strong electric fields in the junction regions and weak fields in the remainder of the transistor.

The temperature limitation on transistor operation is clear when one considers that the normal concentrations of free carriers attributable to impurities are supplemented by thermally generated hole–electron pairs. At sufficiently high temperatures these thermally derived carriers can numerically "overpower" the impurity-derived carriers and make transistor action impossible.

Other currents exist in the sample n–p–n transistor. I_{CBO}, the collector-to-base current with the emitter unconnected, is composed of minority carriers from the collector (holes) moving toward the base. Holes flowing from base to emitter constitute another carrier flow; this, however, is purposely kept as low as possible, compared with the electron flow from the emitter, by control of the base impurity concentration. A summary of currents in the various sections of the transistor is given here:

1. I_C–primarily electrons from emitter. Also includes I_{CBO}, holes from collector moving to base and some electrons from base to collector.

2. I_E–primarily electrons from emitter to collector. Also some holes from base to emitter.

3. I_B–primarily holes that combine with the main stream of electrons diffusing through the base region. Also I_{CBO} as noted above, and holes from base to emitter.

To assist in visualizing these carrier movements, Fig. 2–12 is useful. The currents in connections external to the transistor are attributable to electron drift.

The principles of transistor operation are the same regardless of the circuit orientation of the device. In the common-emitter connection, the magnitude of the base–emitter voltage controls conduction in the collector–emitter path. Because load current does not come from the signal source located between base and emitter, a large current amplification is possible. Were the device perfect with no carrier recombinations in the base, base current would be negligible and operation would be that of an ideal input-voltage-controlled device.

It is now possible to explain why $I_C = I_{CEO}$ when no external base current is allowed. Because of the reverse collector–base potential, I_{CBO} exists. Recombinations in the base as exemplified by α require holes—these are available from I_{CBO}. Therefore, from Eq. (1–12)

$$I_C = \alpha I_E + I_{CBO} = I_E.$$

Solving for I_C we obtain

$$I_C = (\beta + 1)I_{CBO} = I_{CEO}. \tag{2-2}$$

The diode equation, Eq. (2–1), can be used to describe some aspects of transistor operation for, as we have seen, the transistor uses junction diodes for its building blocks. Nonlinearities in the volt–ampere curves, as evident from that equation, have resulted in the popular statement that the transistor is a current-amplifying device, for although voltage, current, and power gain can be achieved the device tends to amplify input current linearly. Therefore most transistor characteristics are plotted using currents; one who is versed in vacuum-tube amplification may find this approach quite different, but the results analogous.

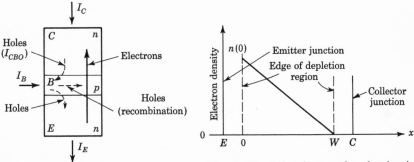

Fig. 2–12. Currents in *n–p–n* transistor.

Fig. 2–13. Minority carrier density in the base region of an *n–p–n* transistor.

2–6. Junction Transistor Capacitances. Two capacitance mechanisms degrade the high-frequency performance of the junction transistor. A *diffusion* or *storage* capacitance is associated with carrier diffusion through the base, while a *barrier, depletion, space charge,* or *transition* capacitance is present across every *p–n* junction and is caused by the uncovered charge layers that result from ionization of impurities.

Diffusion Capacitance. In order to study this effect, consider Fig. 2–13, which shows, somewhat idealized, the density of electrons in the base region of an *n–p–n* transistor. The distance between O and W represents the active section of the base; E and C represent the metallurgical emitter and collector junctions.

The density of minority carriers (electrons), injected into the base from the emitter, is assumed to vary linearly from $n(0)$ at the emitter junction to zero at the collector junction. The $n(0)$ level is dependent upon the forward bias applied to the input junction. Electrons reaching W are swept away; they continue to the collector region because of the normal reverse bias applied to the collector junction. A concentration gradient of minority carriers in the base is evident from the slope of the curve. In the absence of an electric field, carrier movement can result from diffusion when a concentration gradient exists. In this instance, electrons will diffuse through the base toward the collector according to the diffusion equation for electrons,

$$\mathbf{J}_n = qD_n\nabla n. \tag{2-3a}$$

The operator del (∇) implies the vector summation of the spatial derivatives of n. For a one-dimensional study, Eq. (2–3a) becomes

$$J_n = qD_n(dn/dx) \tag{2-3b}$$

with

J_n = current density due to electrons, A/m^2.
q = charge on the electron (considered as a positive number).
D_n = diffusion constant for electrons.
n = density of electrons, electrons/m^3.

The $|dn/dx|$ is simply $n(0)/W$, with W the base width, and $I = AJ$, with A the area of the base. Consequently, for no recombinations, the collector current is

$$|I_C| = AqD_n(n(0)/W). \tag{2-4}$$

The electron charge contained in the base region Q is determined by multiplying A by one-half the area of the triangle in Fig. 2–13. Thus

$$Q = \tfrac{1}{2} AqWn(0). \tag{2-5}$$

The *transconductance* of a transistor, g_m, is defined by.

$$g_m \equiv \left.\frac{\partial i_C}{\partial v_{EB}}\right|_{v_{CB}=\text{const}} \tag{2-6a}$$

If we assume that the diode equation (Eq. (2–1)) adequately describes the relation between i_C and v_{BE}, then upon differentiation of that expression we obtain the relation between g_m and static collector current:

$$g_m \cong qI_C/kT. \tag{2-6b}$$

We recall that capacitance is generally defined mathematically by $C \equiv dQ/dV$. Therefore the diffusion capacitance is

$$C_D = \frac{dQ}{dV_{BE}} = \frac{dQ}{dn(0)}\frac{dn(0)}{dI_C}\frac{dI_C}{dV_{BE}}. \tag{2-7}$$

When Eqs. (2–4) and (2–5) are appropriately differentiated, and Eq. (2–6) used, the expression for diffusion capacitance becomes

$$C_D = W^2 g_m / 2D_n. \qquad (2–8)$$

This rather large capacitance joins base and emitter in an equivalent-circuit representation of the transistor.

Einstein's relation for the electron diffusion constant is

$$D_n = (kT/q)\mu_n, \qquad (2–9)$$

where μ_n is the *mobility constant* for electrons in p material. Mobility is defined as the ratio of carrier drift velocity to electric-field intensity for carriers in the semiconductor (see Problem 2–6). Using typical experimental values for μ and room temperature for T, the diffusion constants are 31 and 94 cm^2/sec for minority carriers in germanium and silicon, respectively.

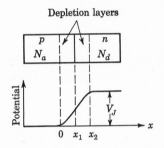

Barrier Capacitance. A capacitance is associated with every p–n junction, whether forward or reverse biased. Consider Fig. 2–14. An abrupt p–n junction exists at $x = x_1$ with the depletion layers extending to $x = 0$ and $x = x_2$. The acceptor density in the p region is N_a, and the donor density in n material is N_d. The contact potential

Fig. 2–14. Quantities defined for study of barrier capacitance.

is V_J, and V_1 and V_2 will be used to designate the electrostatic potentials in the p and n regions, respectively.

The spatial variation of potential in a region containing charge is predicted by *Poisson's equation.* For one-dimensional geometry this relation is

$$d^2 V/dx^2 = -\rho/\varepsilon \qquad (2–10)$$

The charge density in the region is ρ and ε is the permittivity of the material. For the p region, $\rho = -qN_a$, and $\rho = qN_d$ for the n region. Equation (2–10) may be integrated twice for each region. The boundary conditions for evaluation of integration constants are

$$dV_1/dx = 0, \; x = 0, \qquad V_1 = 0, \; x = 0,$$

$$dV_2/dx = 0, \; x = x_2, \qquad V_2 = V_J, \; x = x_2.$$

At the metallurgical junction x_1, it must be true that $dV_1/dx = dV_2/dx$ and $V_1 = V_2$. We also consider the permittivities of the regions to be equal. From the steps discussed above, it follows that

$$x_1 = [N_d/(N_a + N_d)]x_2. \qquad (2–11)$$

If this value for x_1 is substituted into the expression for V_2, one obtains

$$x_2 = [2\varepsilon V(N_a + N_d)/qN_aN_d]^{1/2}. \tag{2-12}$$

In Eq. (2–12), $V = V_J$ when no external field is applied: $V = V_J + |V_a|$ when V_a is a reverse bias; $V = V_J - |V_a|$ for a forward bias of V_a. It is evident from Eq. (2–12) that *the barrier thickness decreases with forward bias and increases with reverse bias.*

In order to obtain an expression for barrier capacitance, we recall that $C = dQ/dV$. In the p region, $|Q_p| = qN_a(x_1 - 0)A$; $|Q_n| = qN_d(x_2 - x_1)A$ in the n region. Taking $(dQ_n/dx_2)(dx_2/dV)$ yields

$$C_T = \varepsilon A/x_2 = KV^{-1/2}. \tag{2-13}$$

At the forward-biased emitter junction, C_T is quite small and usually can be neglected compared to the diffusion capacitance C_D. The major effect of C_T is felt between collector and base.

For a junction linearly graded in impurity density, an analysis yields the transition capacitance proportional to $V^{-1/3}$.

Base width modulation. The static collector-to-base voltage, V_{CB}, causes the collector depletion region to extend into the physical base by an amount equal to $C - W$ in Fig. 2–13. Any changes that occur in v_{CB}, as may be caused by a signal superimposed upon the static level, also affect the width of the depletion region. The total charge therein contained is thereby altered because a change in base width changes the slope of the minority-carrier density curve. If diffusion is considered to be the sole mechanism dictating the value of collector current, that current must change in accordance with any variation in v_{CB}. This phenomenon gives rise to the major portion of the output resistance of the transistor. It must be accounted for in any equivalent circuit used to describe the device.

The change in i_C caused by v_{CB} variations is also felt at the transistor's input, for base current is considered to be linearly related to collector current by β. To signify a change in i_B caused by change in v_{CB}, the collector and base may be considered to be joined by a resistive element. This element is in addition to the collector–base barrier capacitance.

Further discussion of the effects of base-width modulation is reserved for the treatment of the hybrid-π equivalent circuit in Sec. 4–9.

2–7. Transistor Fabrication. The quality level of commercial transistors is presently high, largely because of improvements in manufacturing techniques during the past decade. Several different methods of fabrication are of importance and it is reasonable to assume that new methods will develop because of intense competition among transistor manufacturers.

The method of manufacture is seldom a basis for selection of a particular transistor for a given circuit application. Although the manufacturing method does account for important operational differences, it is a study of characteristics and not of fabrication that eventually determines the transistor to be used.

Three basic mechanisms for doping semiconductors provide the basis for the various types of conventional transistors. Either the *growing*, the *alloying*, or the *diffusing* of impurities into semiconductor material can be employed. These techniques can be used individually or combined in the fabrication of a single transistor.

The growing of junctions is accomplished by starting with a small *seed* of material cut from a previous operation. The seed is touched to the surface of a bath or *melt* of molten semiconductor and is slowly pulled from the melt. The size of the original seed grows because melt in the the vicinity of the seed adheres to it and freezes during withdrawal. The characteristics of the melt can be changed during the pulling operation by adding impurities. The completed crystal is cut into diodes or transistors and leads are welded to the proper areas. In appearance, a *grown-junction transistor* resembles Fig. 1–2 and its dimensions are typically $0.01 \times 0.01 \times 0.1$ in. When manufactured as described, this device is also referred to as a double-doped transistor.

The *rate-grown transistor* is a device whose structure depends upon variations in growth rate. It is possible to dope a melt with both donors and acceptors, and grow single crystals from it. The crystal will be n-type if grown at a high rate and p-type if grown at a low rate because impurities differ in their solubility characteristics. By proper control of the growth rate, it is possible to produce alternate p and n regions in a single crystal. A variation on this theme is the *meltback* transistor in which a doped bar containing both donors and acceptors is melted at one end, and upon freezing a thin base region is formed.

The *alloy-* or *fused-junction transistor* has been widely used. A wafer of base material (generally n-type germanium) is held in a jig between two pellets of impurity (indium, for example). The structure is heated until the impurity melts ($155°C$ for indium), and the molten impurity penetrates the base material, dissolving some of it. During cooling, crystal regrowth results in a completed three-layer structure as shown in Fig. 2–15(a). By control of temperature, time, and pellet size, it is possible to achieve various operating characteristics, but since rather high junction capacitance results from the process, the alloy-junction transistor generally does not perform well at the higher frequencies.

The *surface-barrier transistor*, when first introduced, extended the operating frequency range of transistors. A very thin base wafer (0.0002 in.) with small electroplated contacts forming rectifying junctions resulted in a transistor operable to frequencies in excess of 100 Mc/sec. This construction and operation was achieved by a manufacturing process that subjected a small piece of germanium to two jets of electrolyte, such as a solution of indium-chloride, which impinged upon opposite faces of the germanium base slab. Etching of the semiconductor was accomplished by passage of current through the electrolyte streams and the germanium. When the proper base thickness was achieved, current polarities were reversed and the jets plated metal emitter and collector contacts on either side of the base.

Improvements in the above-mentioned procedures were made by the addition of impurity diffusion techniques to the basic processes. These variations are known as *grown-diffused, diffused-alloy,* or *drift, alloy-diffused, micro-alloy* (MAT), and *micro-alloy diffused* (MADT) transistors. In all instances, except for the MAT, the improved structures sport base regions with graded impurity profiles for superior high-frequency performance.

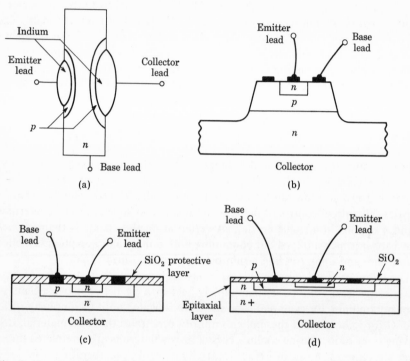

Fig. 2–15. Transistor fabrication: (a) alloy-junction; (b) mesa; (c) planar; (d) epitaxial.

In the *diffusion* process, impurities of one conductivity type are made to diffuse at high temperature into the surface of a bar of opposite type, resulting in the formation of a *p–n* junction. The discussion in this section is concerned with the diffusion of impurities into a solid; this should not be confused with the diffusion of carriers noted earlier in connection with currents in a transistor base. These processes are, however, mathematically equivalent.

As an example of the diffusion process, consider that specimens of *n*-type silicon are placed in a furnace, and BCl_3 (boron chloride) admitted in a carrier gas (such as nitrogen). A chemical surface reaction will take place that liberates boron so that it may form acceptor layers on the silicon wafers. *A p–n junction is formed in a diffused structure when donor and acceptor impurity concentrations are equal.* On one side of the junction donors will predominate; on the other acceptors. Because the diffusion process always results in graded impurity concentrations, a built-in accelerating field exists that improves high-frequency performance. Further discussion of this internal electric field is given in Sec. 2–8.

In the *mesa* or *diffused base* transistor, P_2O_5 (phosphorous pentoxide) may be diffused into an *n*-type silicon collector region to form the base region. The emitter can be of aluminum alloyed into the base. Acid etching of appropriate areas of the entire structure results in a plateau or mesa as shown in Fig. 2–15(b). In the *double-diffused* transistor, the emitter is also diffused instead of being alloyed.

The *planar* construction uses diffusion and surface passivation that protects surfaces and junction edges from contamination. Leakage currents are low because SiO_2, an insulator, is formed on the exposed surfaces [see Fig. 2–15(c)]. An *epitaxial* transistor has a thin layer of low-conductivity material for its collector, with the remainder of the collector region of high conductivity as shown in Fig. 2–15(d). The epitaxial layer allows high voltage ratings, while the $n+$ region helps reduce the saturation resistance of the device.

2–8. High-Frequency Considerations. Limitations on the high-frequency performance of junction transistors are caused by diffusion capacitance, space-charge capacitance, and *base-spreading resistance*, the ohmic or bulk resistance of the base material. Efforts to reduce these effects have been carried on since the beginnings of transistor technology. The use of graded-base regions as noted in Sec. 2–7 has solved a significant part of the high-frequency problem.

Graded-base devices generally provide improved high-frequency performance because the existence of the associated *built-in electric field* in the base allows both drift and diffusion mechanisms in the transport of minority carriers across that region. To show that a field exists due to an impurity gradient in the *p*-type base of an *n–p–n* transistor, consider that the acceptor density N_a varies with the distance from the emitter junction. Then dN_a/dx is nonzero, and, if the condition is as shown in Fig. 2–16, that derivative is negative.

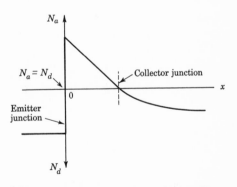

Fig. 2–16. Impurity concentration profile.

The *hole* current density in the *p*-type base will depend in the general case upon both diffusion and drift. A mathematical relation for diffusion current density is given by Eq. (2–3). Drift is described by Ohm's law; in a very general form,

$$\mathbf{J} = \sigma\mathbf{E} \qquad\qquad (2\text{–}14)$$

with σ the conductivity of the material and **E** the applied field. For holes in the base, the current density in the x or longitudinal direction is

$$J_p = -qD_p(dp/dx) + \sigma_p E_x \tag{2-15}$$

with σ_p the conductivity for holes in the p material, and p the density of holes. In a high-quality device, the net hole currents crossing the junctions must be very small. We set Eq. (2–15) to zero and further assume low-level injection of electrons from the emitter. This allows $p = N_a$. The field intensity in the base is then available from Eq. (2–15):

$$E_x = (qD_p/\sigma_p)(dN_a/dx). \tag{2-16}$$

This equation gives the strength of the built-in field, E_x, caused by dN_a/dx. The effect of this field upon electrons traversing the base is evident when we consider that the electron-current density must not only contain the normal diffusion term, but also a drift term due to E_x. Thus electron current in the base is, for $\sigma_n = \sigma_p$,

$$J_n = qD_n(dn/dx) - qD_p(dN_a/dx). \tag{2-17}$$

The effect of a negative dN_a/dx is to require, for a given current level, less stored charge (the area of the triangle of Fig. 2–13). The diffusion capacitance is thereby reduced, and improved high-frequency performance assured.

Another approach to the problem of extending transistor performance to high frequencies has been the development of the *junction tetrode*, or *double-base transistor*, shown in Fig. 2–17. If two connections are made to opposite sides of the base region of an ordinary junction transistor, and a biasing potential is applied between those two terminals, certain operational advantages are obtained. The interbase bias voltage is made large enough so that only a portion of the emitter junction is operating as an emitter; the remainder of the emitter is cut off. Effective base resistance is thereby reduced because all transistor action occurs adjacent to one base contact; reduction in base resistance directly extends the maximum allowable operating frequency of junction transistors.

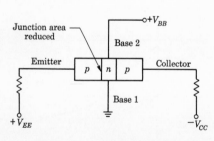

Fig. 2–17.   Junction tetrode.

2–9. The Field-Effect Transistor.   A brief discussion of the static characteristics and definitions of important parameters of the FET was given in Chapter 1. A sketch useful for describing the physical behavior of the junction form of this device is shown in Fig. 2–18. The source end of the p-type bar is grounded and the drain end connected to supply potential V_{DD}. These connections are nonrectifying; the gate connection is, however, a p–n diode. The conductance of the drain–source path is a direct function of the effective dimensions of the bar. For a simple geometry, the conductance of a bar of semiconducting material is

$$G = q\mu_h p WT/L \qquad (2\text{--}18)$$

with

 q = electronic charge,
 μ_h = hole mobility,
 p = density of holes.

The conductance of the specimen can be controlled most easily by variation of the effective physical dimension T.

It has previously been pointed out that the depletion region at a reverse-biased junction widens with increased potential. Reverse biasing of the FET junction is dependent upon both V_{DD} and V_{GG}, and the contour of the depletion region present in the physical configuration of Fig. 2–18 is wide near the drain and

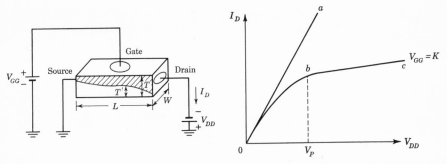

Fig. 2–18. FET simplified, biasing for p channel.

Fig. 2–19. Generation of output characteristics.

narrow near the source end of the bar, as shown by the shaded area in the figure. The channel of the bar below the shaded area represents a path of relatively high conductance. The effective height of that channel, T', is highly dependent upon the reverse bias on the junction. If sufficient bias is applied, the channel will be "pinched off"; the resistance of the source–drain path will then become very high.

Knowledge of these basic physical phenomena can be used to predict the output characteristics of the device. The line o–a in Fig. 2–19 represents the ohmic resistance of the bar material; the V–I characteristic would follow this line if conductance were not altered by the effect of increased drain–supply potential V_{DD} upon the height of the depletion layer. At point b we have pinch-off; for potentials higher than V_P the bar remains in the pinched-off state and only a slight dependence of I_D upon V_{DD} can be noted. The drain–source voltage that results in virtual saturation of I_D is V_P; at V_P the space-charge layer has widened so that the bar is essentially closed off. For voltage levels above V_P, most of the potential drop in the channel is confined to a narrow nozzle-like section near the drain.

The device exhibits a high value of output resistance as evidenced by the flatness of the characteristic above V_P; below V_P a significantly lower output resistance is apparent. Operation usually takes place at values of V_{DS} above pinchoff; this region is sometimes referred to as the "pentode" region—below V_P the device is often said to be in its "triode" region.

Operation of the insulated-gate FET relies upon the same principles as the junction device. A charge on the gate electrode repels like charge in the adjacent section of the channel, thus depleting the channel of its mobile carriers. However, the MOS differs from its junction relative because it is capable of operating with either polarity of gate voltage; by application of a positive voltage to the gate of an n-channel device, the drain current is increased because of the additional mobile carriers available for conduction in the channel.

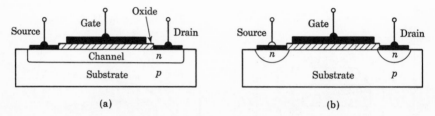

(a)   (b)

Fig. 2–20.   MOS units: (a) depletion type; (b) enhancement type.

If the channel is electrically conductive in the absence of gate–source voltage, the MOS is referred to as a *depletion type*. If the channel is conductive only when gate voltage is present, it is an *enhancement type*. The basic differences between these MOS types are noted in Fig. 2–20. In the depletion version, a discrete channel is noticeable. The enhancement device relies upon attraction of mobile carriers from the substrate to form a channel of carriers to enhance conduction between drain and source.

2–10. Controlled Rectifiers. Although similar in physical size and external appearance to conventional power diodes, the *controlled rectifier* has an additional terminal, called the *gate*, that can be used to *turn on* the anode–cathode circuit. A small gate signal can control a large output, or anode current; thus this device, often called the *silicon controlled rectifier*, or SCR, provides amplification characteristics not available with conventional rectifiers.

The SCR is a switching device, for it provides either an *on* or an *off* state for its load current; its anode–cathode conductance is either *high* or *low*, respectively. The device is normally *off*, but can be switched *on* by an appropriate gate signal.

We shall be concerned with an n–p–n–p structure, where the symbols for semiconductor type correspond to *cathode, gate* or *control layer, blocking layer,* and *anode,* respectively. As shown in Fig. 2–21, anode and cathode junctions as well as a control junction exist in the structure.

When the device is reverse biased, positive on cathode, both anode and cathode junctions can block the applied voltage. Because the blocking layer and anode layer are only lightly to moderately doped, whereas the cathode and control layers are rather heavily doped, almost the entire applied voltage appears across the anode junction.

Normal biasing, positive on anode, cathode negative, results in the control junction being reverse biased, while the other two junctions are forward biased. Only a small leakage current is evident until the device is turned *on*.

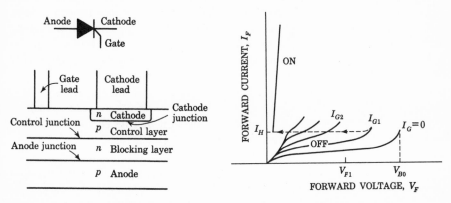

Fig. 2–21. SCR symbol and construction.   Fig. 2–22. Anode characteristics of an SCR.

Turn-on can occur by pulsing the gate with a sufficiently high current or voltage (positive with respect to cathode). This results in a cloud of holes being injected into the control layer near the gate lead. Simultaneously, a cloud of electrons moves into the control layer from the cathode. These electrons, now in the control layer, are attracted to the control-junction barrier; the barrier repels the gate-injected holes and they consequently diffuse toward the cathode junction. As the hole cloud nears the cathode junction an additional electron cloud is injected into the control layer because of the positive space-charge; therefore, two mechanisms are causing electron injection into the control layer.

The electrons attracted to the control junction have no difficulty in sliding down the associated potential hill and reaching the anode. The control-junction barrier is normally sufficiently high so that carrier multiplication by collision takes place there. At the same time, holes from the anode area move toward the cathode. Carrier multiplication also takes place at the control barrier. The resulting high hole-carrier density on the *p* side of the cathode junction attracts more electrons, and the process continues until the original potential wall at the control junction is completely broken down, and the device is in full conduction.

The SCR cannot be turned off by gate signals—the anode voltage must be reduced sufficiently for anode current to drop to zero.

The static forward characteristics of a typical SCR are shown in Fig. 2–22. In the off condition there is anode current, the level of which is generally lower than the holding current I_H, and the anode–cathode potential drop across the SCR may be as large as the forward breakover voltage V_{BO}. V_{BO} is the voltage required to "fire" the device with zero gate current. For other gate-current values, the unit will fire at values of V_F lower than the breakover level. Firing, or turning on, is depicted in the figure by the horizontal dashed line. When fired, the forward current then assumes a value dictated primarily by the power supply and load resistance present in the cathode–anode circuit.

The holding current is the minimum value of forward current that the SCR can sustain. After being fired, should the anode voltage be reduced, the anode current will proportionately decline until the level I_H is reached. For any further reduction in V_F, forward current will drop to zero. Typical values for I_H range from 1 to 100 mA; these values are generally small, however, compared to the corresponding maximum average forward currents for these devices, which range to 150 A.

According to the preceding discussion of turn-on by gate current, we would expect the gate–cathode characteristics to be those of a forward-biased diode, similar to the emitter of a conventional transistor. If we again refer to Fig. 2–22, we note that at a specific value of V_F, say V_{F1}, which essentially represents the load-circuit power supply in a simple circuit, *the SCR could not be turned on by gate currents lower than I_{G2}.* Thus the interrelations between I_G and V_F are apparent. However, because of unit-to-unit production variations, and the large influence of temperature upon the characteristics, the circuit designer must know the limits of the gate characteristics in order to assure that his SCR will always be fired when a known gate signal is given.

Variations to the basic SCR have resulted in devices called silicon *gate-controlled switches* (GCS). The behavior of one type of GCS is similar to the standard SCR in the first quadrant of its output characteristics, and *also* in the third quadrant. Thus in operation the device resembles two paralleled SCR's with their anodes and cathodes joined. Referred to as a "Triac," this switch can be triggered by gate pulses of either polarity in either first or third quadrant.

2–11. The Unijunction Transistor. This device resembles the FET in that it has only one p–n junction, but differs from the FET because in normal operation that junction is forward biased. A physical sketch and a circuit-diagram symbol with appropriate biasing are shown in Fig. 2–23. The unijunction transistor, sometimes referred to as a double-base diode, consists of a lightly-doped bar, in this case n-type silicon, with a junction located near its center. The resistance between base 1 and base 2 is the *interbase resistance R_{BB}*, and is of the order of 5 to 10 kΩ where the emitter is open or the junction reverse-biased. With V_{BB} applied, the voltage on the n side of the emitter junction is ηV_{BB}. The fraction η is referred to as the *intrinsic stand-off ratio*; it generally has a value of from 0.5 to 0.75 indicating that the emitter is somewhat closer to base 2 than base 1.

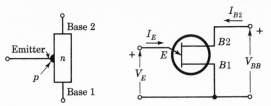

Fig. 2–23.   Unijunction transistor construction and circuit diagram symbol.

In Fig. 2–24, the static emitter characteristics of a typical unit are shown. For values of V_E below ηV_{BB}, the emitter junction is reverse biased, and only a low level of emitter current is possible. An increase of the emitter–base 1 voltage so that the junction is forward-biased, as at V_p, permits hole injection into the bar. These holes are repelled by base 2, but their presence in the bar increases its conductivity between emitter and base 1. This increased conductivity results in a reduced voltage drop V_E required to support a given current level I_E. If we think of the device as being fed from a current source I_E, then any increase in that current will increase the conductivity and the drop V_E will decrease. This process can continue until we reach the valley, with coordinates V_v and I_v. For values of emitter current greater than I_v, the emitter portion of the device behaves as a conventional forward-biased p–n junction diode, as evidenced by the $I_{B2} = 0$ curve in Fig. 2–24.

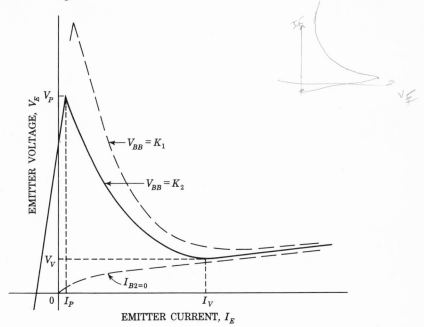

Fig. 2–24.   Static emitter characteristic for a unijunction transistor.

Between the peak and valley points on the emitter characteristic, the unijunction transistor has a *dynamic negative resistance*, because the *slope* of the characteristic is negative. A negative resistance is particularly useful in the generation of time-varying waveforms (oscillation); negative resistance can also be useful for amplification. Further discussion of the unijunction transistor is presented in Chapter 13.

2-12. The Tunnel Diode. A two-terminal device that exhibits a region of incremental negative resistance is the *tunnel diode*, also referred to as the Esaki diode, after its inventor. Tunnel diodes are usually made of germanium or gallium arsenide.

In the tunnel diode both *p* and *n* regions are very heavily doped and consequently the depletion region is extremely narrow. It is possible for carriers to *tunnel* through the potential barrier if it is narrow enough (typically 10^{-6} cm) and if available energy levels or states exist on the other side.

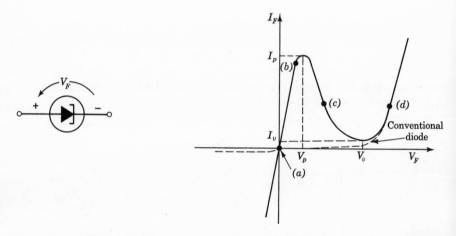

Fig. 2–25.   Circuit-diagram symbol for tunnel diode and typical *V–I* characteristic.

A circuit-diagram symbol for the tunnel diode is shown in Fig. 2–25. In normal operation the device is forward biased, plus on *p* material. The volt–ampere characteristic of a typical tunnel diode is also given in Fig. 2–25. The negative resistance region is noted in the vicinity of (c). For high levels of forward voltage above the valley V_v, the device behaves in a manner similar to a conventional diode. For reverse voltages, a high reverse current is evident.

The physical operation of the tunnel diode will be considered with reference to the regions (a), (b), (c), and (d) of the volt–ampere characteristic. The corresponding energy-level diagrams are given in Fig. 2–26. In the absence of biasing, as at (a) in Fig. 2–25, a contact potential is established as exists at any *p–n* junction. Forward biasing of the junction as in (b) of the figure allows the level of conduction-band electrons to be opposite empty states in the *p* material.

Quantum-mechanical tunneling takes place through the thin barrier as noted by the arrow. In (c) of Fig. 2–26, corresponding to the (c) portion of the characteristic, further forward biasing reduces the forward current below its peak value

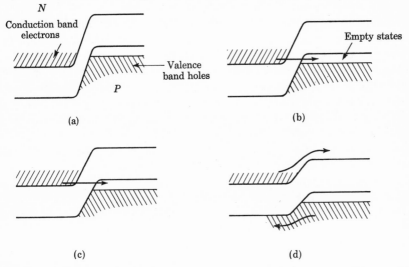

(a)   (b)

(c)   (d)

Fig. 2–26. Energy-level diagrams for tunnel diode, letters refer to points on the characteristic of Fig. 2–25.

because of the reduced number of available states in the p-region valence band opposite conduction levels in the n region. For a sufficiently large forward bias as at (d), the device operates as a conventional diode.

Gallium arsenide units differ from germanium tunnel diodes in that their peak and valley voltages are about double those of germanium. For a typical germanium unit, $V_p = 75$ mV, $V_v = 330$ mV, $I_p = 20$ mA, and $I_v = 2$ mA.

If, in the process of manufacturing a tunnel diode, less doping is used, the peak current is lowered. The peak current may be slightly greater than, or may be made equal to the valley current. Such a device is referred to as a *back* or *backward diode*. A typical characteristic is shown in Fig. 2–27.

A back diode, if used in the reverse direction, has a higher conductance than a conventional forward-biased diode. If used in its forward direction, it can serve as a low-voltage regulator. When connected in series with other components such as tunnel diodes, the composite V–I curve may be of interest.

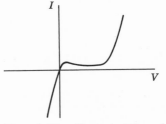

Fig. 2–27. Characteristic of a back diode.

2–13. Metallic Contact Devices. It has long been known that rectification or diode action can result from a metal–semiconductor contact. It is also possible to achieve an *ohmic* or *nonrectifying* contact between these materials, and all the devices discussed thus far employ such contacts.

Whether a particular contact is or is not rectifying depends upon the particular metal and semiconductor used. To formulate a general rule to be followed in determining the behavior of a contact, the *work function* of a material may be used as the test characteristic. The work function of a material may be defined as the amount of energy that must be added to an electron to cause it to be emitted from the surface of the material, or to permit it to escape completely from the domination of its parent. If we designate the work function of the metal as Φ_m and of the semiconductor as Φ_s, a contact will be ohmic if $\Phi_m < \Phi_s$ and rectify if $\Phi_m > \Phi_s$.[22] An ohmic condition can also result if the metal and the semiconductor can alloy, for it is then possible to achieve a gradual transition between materials. There are exceptions to these rules.

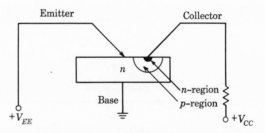

Fig. 2–28. Point-contact transistor.

Commercial rectifiers using metal-to-semiconductor contact for their operation include the selenium and copper oxide rectifiers and point-contact (crystal) diodes. The selenium rectifier uses the junction between selenium and cadmium, lead, or tin. The same metals are often used in contact with cuprous oxide in the copper oxide rectifier. A point-contact diode is made from a small slab of semiconducting material, germanium for example, and a fine wire (whisker) that is sharpened to a point at one end. When a suitable spot for rectification is found on the surface of the slab, the unit is pulsed with a current to weld the wire to the slab. Naturally, the power-handling capacity of such a device is limited by the wire size.

Historically, the first transistors were of the point-contact type. Because of the many advantages of junction transistors, the point-contact transistor is no longer used.

A point-contact transistor is shown in Fig. 2–28. The collector is often a phosphor bronze wire. The *n* and *p* regions are introduced into the germanium base by *forming*, the passage of large current pulses through the contact in the back direction. The emitter–base diode also makes use of point-contact fication. Point-contact devices can exhibit α of greater than unity, for the structure behaves more like four layers of semiconductor material than three as in the conventional p–n–p or n–p–n structures.

2–14. Microelectronics. The term *microelectronics* is generally used to describe the spectrum of technologies that are used to produce complete electronic circuits or circuit modules of extremely small size. In addition to microminiaturization, the techniques of microelectronics may afford other advantages over circuits assembled by conventional means, including improved uniformity and reliability, decreased weight and power consumption, and lower total cost. Microelectronic assemblies are generally characterized by the absence of discrete circuit elements; the elements are not necessarily recognizable to the untrained eye nor are they separable from the assembly as a whole.

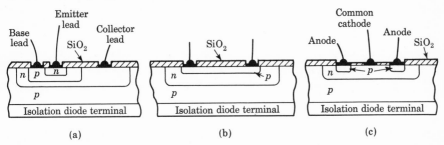

Fig. 2–29.   Integrated circuit elements: (a) transistor; (b) resistance; (c) diode pair.

An *integrated circuit* or *microcircuit* is a device that will perform the function of a complete circuit or of a major fraction of a circuit fabricated by conventional means, in which the circuit elements, both passive and active, are included or integrated into a single solid wafer of semiconductor material. A procedure for the fabrication of an integrated circuit is the selective diffusion of appropriate impurities into a single silicon wafer in order that the functions of a collection of individual elements be simulated.

In the general area of microelectronics is included the thin-film circuit, in which layers of conductive, insulative, semiconductive, or ferromagnetic film materials are deposited in a pattern upon a passive substrate (a substrate is the base material or core of a microcircuit used for physical support, and may be passive, such as glass, or active, such as silicon). The examples of microcircuits given in this section will not be of thin-film circuits.

The procedure being used to fabricate integrated circuits has evolved from the methods developed for planar transistors. An integrated-circuit transistor is shown in Fig. 2–29(a). Transistors can be made by starting with a polished wafer of n-type silicon, for example, and forming a layer of SiO_2 over its surfaces by exposure to oxygen at high temperature. The wafer is then coated with a photo resist and exposed to ultraviolet light through a mask to outline the areas for the circuit elements. Photo development and etching of the SiO_2 defines the important areas on the surface of the wafer. Diffusion of p-type impurity through the channels opened in the protective layer on the top surface and also the entire bottom surface results in the bottom layer of p material shown in the figure. The junction between this p region and the remaining n-type material forms the isolation diode to be subsequently discussed.

Repeating the photographic sequence of operations noted above with the diffusion of appropriate impurities can result in the p-type base and the n-type emitter regions shown in the figure.

After completion of the masking, etching, diffusion, and oxidation sequences noted above, it is necessary to make interconnections among the various elements on the silicon wafer. Holes are made in the outer oxide layer and the wafers placed in a high-vacuum chamber in which aluminum is being evaporated or boiled. The aluminum deposits in a thin coat over the entire wafer. This layer is masked and selectively etched to form the pattern of connections. Because many integrated circuits are made at the same time on relatively large wafers, a final step in the process is the cutting of the wafer into individual microcircuits.

In order to separate adjoining circuit elements, the additional diffused p layer forms an isolation p–n junction or diode tied to the collector of the transistor. The isolation diode will be reverse-biased; thus adjoining elements will be isolated by this diode. The transistor collector is brought out at the top as shown.

An integrated circuit resistor is shown in Fig. 2–29(b). The resistance is simply that of the p region between the contacts. Its value is primarily dictated by the distance between contacts and the impurity density of that region.

Two diodes with a common n-type cathode are depicted in Fig. 2–29(c). The common cathode also serves as the cathode of the isolation diode. If the diodes are back-biased, they may be used as low-valued capacitances. Capacitance can also be obtained by using SiO_2 as a dielectric between silicon and an electrode such as deposited aluminum. The capacitance of such a structure is controlled by plate area and dielectric thickness.

It is possible to produce isolated integrated circuit elements without the parasitic isolation diode. One such method, dielectric isolation, proceeds with impurity diffusion into an n substrate, followed by oxide growth over the entire top surface. The original substrate is then removed, and a new substrate of polycrystalline silicon grown on *top* of the previously formed oxide layer. The assembly is then inverted so that the new growth forms the foundation. Between this substrate and all active areas is a layer of oxide to provide the necessary isolation.

2–15. Allied Semiconductor Devices. A family of active and passive circuit elements is available to the circuit designer, and it is indeed likely that the size of this family will grow to great proportions. Let us briefly examine the *silicon capacitor, thermistor, varistor,* and *photodiode.*

At a p–n junction the depletion or transition region widens with reverse potential and this in effect moves the two conduction areas apart and decreases the junction capacitance just as if the junction were two metal plates separated by a dielectric with a variable thickness. A silicon device that uses this phenomenon is called the *silicon capacitor* or *varactor*. A typical variation is 120 to 22 pF for potentials from 0.1 to 25 V (1 pF = 1 picofarad = 10^{-12} farad). The varactor, or *variable reactor*, finds application in parametric amplifiers, where the nonlinearity of its capacitance–voltage characteristic may be used for amplifying microwave signals.

The thermistor is a thermally sensitive resistance, the temperature coefficient of which is large and negative. For many years thermistors, basically semiconductors, have been used to temperature-compensate circuits. As an example of sensitivity to ambient temperature, it is possible for a 10,000 Ω unit at 0° C to be 200 Ω at 100° C and 10 Ω at 300° C.

A resistor that exhibits a nonlinear relationship between the voltage applied to it and the current that it passes is called a *varistor*. The forward V–I curve of a diode presents such a nonlinear characteristic. Commercial varistors are available in high and low voltage and current ranges.

Just as semiconductors are sensitive to heat energy, so are they also light sensitive. A *photodiode* consists of a single p–n junction. Light energy will create electron–hole pairs and if such a diode is biased in the reverse direction, its conductivity will be altered by the incidence of light. The junction *phototransistor* is a three-layer structure, n–p–n for example, with only the two outer terminals brought to external terminations. Point-contact photosensitive devices are also available.

PROBLEMS

2–1. Does Eq. (2–1) predict reverse breakdown? Explain your answer.

2–2. Evaluate the exponent in Eq. (2–1) at normal ambient temperature (300° K).

2–3. Sketch a curve, similar to Fig. 2–10, that compares silicon and germanium diodes. How does the width of the forbidden gap affect diode characteristics?

2–4. Sketch the forward characteristic of a diode with a reverse saturation current of 10 μA for voltages to 1 V. Calculate at least three points on the forward curve. Consider the temperature to be 300° K.

2–5. The term *mobility* is used to designate the ease of carrier drift in a solid. Mobility is the ratio of drift velocity to electric field intensity:

$$\mu = \frac{v_d}{E} \frac{\text{cm/sec}}{\text{V/cm}} .$$

Prove that the conductivity of a specimen can be expressed as $nq\mu$, n representing the density of free electrons that are assumed to be the only carriers.

2–6. In intrinsic germanium, hole mobility (μ_p) is 1800 cm²/Vsec and electron mobility (μ_n) is 3800 cm²/Vsec. If the measured conductivity of a specimen is 0.01 (Ω cm)$^{-1}$, calculate the density of electron–hole pairs (see Problem 2–5).

2–7. Calculate the resistivity of a silicon specimen doped with 10^{16} donors per cm³. The sample is 1 in long and has a 2×2-mm cross section. Determine the resistance of the bar between contacts placed at the ends of the long dimension and also between contacts placed at opposite sides of the short dimension. Consider electron mobility to be 1200 cm²/Vsec at 300° K.

2–8. The number of thermally generated hole-electron pairs in intrinsic germanium is given by

$$n_i = 10^{16}T^{3/2}e^{-E_g/2kT} \text{ (cm)}^{-3}.$$

For temperatures of 200°, 300°, and 400° K, calculate the density of pairs. E_g is the width of the forbidden gap.

2–9. A sample of germanium exhibits an intrinsic resistivity of 0.6 Ωm. Find the current density in an applied field of 1 V/m if there are 10^{18} donors and 4×10^{17} acceptors/m³ added to the specimen. Mobilities for electrons and holes in germanium are to be considered as 3800 and 1800 cm²/V-sec.

2–10. Describe the operation of a *p–n–p* transisistor by drawing an energy-level diagram similar to Fig. 2–11.

2–11. Why do minority carriers exist? Does your reasoning explain the difference in I_{CBO} between silicon and germanium devices?

2–12. Explain why semiconductor devices made of silicon can operate at higher ambient temperatures than can germanium devices.

2–13. Consider the common-base output characteristics that depict I_{CBO} ($I_E = 0$) as well as curves for other values of I_E. Since I_{CBO} is caused by minority carriers and the remainder of the characteristic family results from majority-carrier movement, explain why both cause collector current in the same direction. A diagram may clarify your explanation.

2–14. Explain clearly why a common-base-connected transistor can exhibit transistor action with the collector-base junction voltage reduced to zero.

2–15. The dependence of alpha upon base thickness has been investigated, with the following theoretical conclusions:

$$f_{\alpha b} = 2.6/W^2 \text{ for germanium } p–n–p,$$

$$f_{\alpha b} = 5.6/W^2 \text{ for germanium } n–p–n,$$

and

$$f_{\alpha b} = 1.8/W^2 \text{ for silicon transistors,}$$

where $f_{\alpha b}$ stands for the "alpha cutoff frequency," the frequency at which α has declined to use $1/\sqrt{2}$ of its low-frequency magnitude, and W is base width in inches.[22] Compare operation of the three transistors with base widths of 1/2, 1, and 2 mils.

2–16. Derive Eqs. (2–6b) and (2–8).

2–17. Derive Eqs. (2–11) and (2–12).

2–18. Explain, using a physical argument, why turn-on can occur in an SCR with no applied gate signal.

2–19. Explain why a large reverse current exists in tunnel diodes.

REFERENCES

1. Bradley, W. E., "Principles of the Surface-Barrier Transistor," *Proc. IRE*, **41** (December 1953).
2. DeWitt, D., and Rossoff, A. L., *Transistor Electronics* (McGraw-Hill Book Co., Inc., New York, 1957).

3. Dunlap, Jr., W. C., *An Introduction to Semiconductors* (John Wiley & Sons, Inc., New York, 1957).
4. Gaertner, W. W., *Transistors: Principles, Design and Applications* (D. Van Nostrand Co., Inc., Princeton, New Jersey, 1960).
5. Gentile, S. P., *Basic Theory and Application of Tunnel Diodes* (D. Van Nostrand Co., Inc., Princeton, New Jersey, 1962).
6. Gray, P. E., *et al.*, *Physical Electronics and Circuit Models of Transistors* (John Wiley & Sons, Inc., New York, 1964).
7. Hunter, L. P., *Handbook of Semiconductor Electronics* (McGraw-Hill Book Co., Inc., New York, 1962), 2nd ed.
8. Levine, S. H., *Principles of Solid-State Microelectronics* (Holt, Rinehart and Winston, Inc., New York, 1963).
9. Lo, A. W., *et al.*, *Transistor Electronics* (Prentice-Hall, Inc., Englewood Cliffs, New Jersey, 1955).
10. Integrated Electronics Issue, *Proc. IEEE*, **52** (December, 1964).
11. Middlebrook, R. D., *An Introduction to Junction Transistor Theory* (John Wiley & Sons, Inc., New York, 1957).
12. Phillips, A. B., *Transistor Engineering* (McGraw-Hill Book Co., Inc., New York, 1962).
13. Pierce, J. F., *Transistor Circuit Theory and Design* (C. E. Merrill Books, Inc., Columbus, Ohio, 1963).
14. Shive, J. N., *Properties, Physics, and Design of Semiconductor Devices* (D. Van Nostrand Co., Inc., Princeton, New Jersey, 1959).
15. Shockley, W., *Electrons and Holes in Semiconductors* (D. Van Nostrand Co., Inc., New York, 1950).
16. Shockley, W., "A Unipolar 'Field Effect' Transistor," *Proc. IRE*, **40** (November, 1952).
17. Staff, *The Controlled Rectifier*, Vol. 1, International Rectifier Corp., El Segundo, California, 1962.
18. Transistor Issue, *Proc. IRE*, **40** (November, 1952).
19. Transistor Issue, *Proc. IRE*, **46** (June, 1958).
20. *Transistors I*, Radio Corporation of America, Princeton, New Jersey, 1956.
21. Valdes, L. B., *The Physical Theory of Transistors* (McGraw-Hill Book Co., Inc., New York, 1961).
22. van der Ziel, A., *Solid State Physical Electronics* (Prentice-Hall, Inc., Englewood Cliffs, New Jersey, 1957).
23. Warschauer, D. M. *Semiconductors and Transistors* (McGraw-Hill Book Co., Inc., New York, 1959).

Chapter 3

THE OPERATING POINT

This chapter begins the treatment of the transistor as an important part of the practical electronic circuit. Up to this point the transistor has been considered as an isolated component; now it is necessary to incorporate it into a complete circuit to do a specified job. Our first consideration will be the practical establishment of a suitable operating point; because several different circuits may be used, a comparison of the performance of the various circuits will be made. The discussion initially presented in this chapter will consider the conventional transistor, common-emitter oriented. Biasing of the FET, common-source connection, will follow. This material may easily be extrapolated to cover other connections of these devices.

Establishing the proper operating point for a transistor stage and maintaining that operating point despite unit-to-unit manufacturing variations, aging, or ambient-temperature variations is of prime importance in modern electronic circuit design. To establish an operating point in a common-emitter circuit, the necessary direct potentials and currents must be provided to locate at suitable coordinates in the active region of the collector characteristics. After an operating point is attained, time-varying excursions of input signal (base current, for example) of limited magnitude should cause output signal (collector current) variations of similar waveshape. If the corresponding output excursions are *clipped* or in other ways do not satisfactorily duplicate the input signal, then the operating point is probably unsatisfactory and must be repositioned on the collector characteristics.

An operating point can be defined by a particular I_B and V_{CE}, or I_B and I_C, or I_C and V_{CE}, for specifying any of these quantity pairs will dictate a point on the output characteristics. The operating point is often referred to as the *quiescent* or Q point.

3-1. The Static Load Line. The *static* or *dc load line* is a line drawn on the collector characteristics that is the locus of possible operating points for the device in the particular circuit under consideration. Its use in circuit analysis and design is to provide a picture of the suitability of the operating point.

60

Consider the general circuit of Fig. 3–1. A summation of voltages in the collector–emitter loop yields

$$V_{CC} = I_C R_C + V_{CE} + I_E R_1 - V_{EE}. \qquad (3\text{–}1a)$$

Since I_C and I_E are approximately equal, Eq. (3–1a) can be written as

$$V_{CC} = I_C(R_C + R_1) + V_{CE} - V_{EE}. \qquad (3\text{–}1b)$$

Solution for I_C yields

$$I_C = \frac{V_{CC} + V_{EE}}{R_C + R_1} - \frac{V_{CE}}{R_C + R_1}. \qquad (3\text{–}2)$$

The collector characteristics relate I_C to V_{CE}. Equation (3–2) can be drawn as a straight line on those same coordinates having a slope of $-1/(R_C + R_1)$ and I_C axis intercept at $(V_{CC} + V_{EE})/(R_C + R_1)$. When Eq. (3–2) is superimposed upon the collector characteristics, it is called the dc load line. The operating point, or Q point, must lie on this line and *also on the I_B line determined by base-biasing circuitry.*

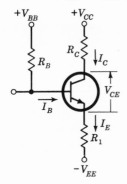

Fig. 3–1.   General transistor biasing circuit.

For circuits using a bypassed or un-bypassed emitter resistor R_1, the value of that resistance must be added to R_C to establish the load-line slope and I_C intercept. The load line originates at a point on the V_{CE} axis equal to $V_{CC} + V_{EE}$. Often the V_{EE} supply is not used. When such is the case, the line starts at V_{CC}.

The general rules for drawing the dc load line for a common-emitter amplifier stage can be summarized as follows*:

1. Sum all resistance in the emitter–collector circuit. The negative reciprocal of this total will be the slope of the line.

2. Sum all potential sources in the emitter–collector circuit. This will locate a point on the V_{CE} axis of the collector characteristics.

3. The I_C axis intercept is determined by dividing the sum from step 2 by the sum given in step 1.

4. Draw a straight line between the points determined in steps 2 and 3.

Example.   A common-emitter stage works into a resistive load of 5000 Ω and has a bypassed emitter resistor of 1000 Ω. The collector supply potential is 12 V. Draw the dc load line and locate an operating point at $I_C = 1$ mA.

---

*These rules must be modified when a circuit node is located between either collector or emitter power supply and the transistor (see Problem 3–3).

Summing resistance in the emitter–collector circuit results in 6000 Ω. The load line will have a V_{CE} intercept at $V_{CC} = 12$ V and an I_C intercept at $V_{CC}/(R_C + R_1)$ or 2 mA. The line and Q are located as in Fig. 3–2.

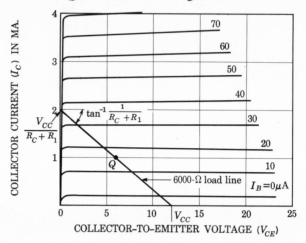

Fig. 3–2.   DC load line on collector characteristics for the example cited in the text.

3–2. Bias Stability.   It is imperative in good circuit design that once an operating point is decided upon it should not significantly vary when the transistor characteristics change because of unit-to-unit production differences, or because of ambient temperature effects.   Since it was noted that several different coordinates (I_B, I_C, V_{CE}) may be used to specify an operating point, a question arises concerning which coordinate is the most important in providing a stable operating point.

As an example of the problem at hand, consider Fig. 3–3.   The operating point

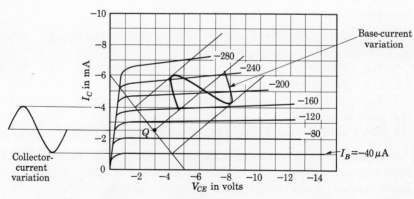

Fig. 3–3.   Typical operation of the stage of Fig. 3–1.   A sinusoidal base current results in a corresponding collector current of larger amplitude.

is located at Q. A time-varying base current of about 120 μA peak-to-peak is causing a collector-current variation of 3 mA peak-to-peak. The collector current is a faithful reproduction of the base signal and no clipping of the waveform due to saturation or cutoff is evident. *This is Class-A operation.*

If a transistor of the same type but having different electrical characteristics (leakage, gain, or saturation) were inserted into the circuit, or if a different ambient temperature were encountered, operation as shown in Fig. 3–4 may

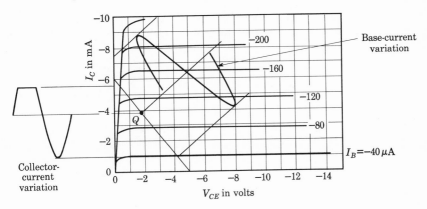

Fig. 3–4.   Typical operation of the stage of Fig. 3–1 operating at the same base current as in Fig. 3–3. The transistor characteristics represent a higher gain unit.

result. Although the Q point is still at $I_B = -100$ μA, the introduction of a sinusoidal base-current signal of the same amplitude as previously considered (120 μA peak-to-peak) now results in a clipped collector-current waveform. The stage is being driven into the saturation region of the characteristics and output no longer follows input. The major difference between the two curves is that Fig. 3–4 describes a higher-gain unit. Because of the generally wide manufacturing tolerances on the parameters (β_{dc} in this instance), the problem discussed here is real, and must be solved by the circuit designer.

"How can we provide an operating point that will minimize the effects of manufacturing, aging, and temperature and thus limit distortion caused by these factors?" Study of Figs. 3–3 and 3–4 tends to show that *stabilization of I_B is not the desired remedy* to this problem, for I_B was held constant in the above example. Note that the other operating-point coordinates did shift. *If some point along the curve axes were to have been held constant, such as a particular value of I_C, then more satisfactory operation would have resulted.* If, in Figs. 3–3 and 3–4, the Q point had been maintained at $I_C = -2.5$ mA instead of $I_B = -100$ μA, clipping would not have occurred. Gain will not be stabilized by this proposal, but methods for gain stabilization are available and will be treated later; our concern in this chapter is operating-point stability and suitability.

Because various circuit arrangements may be used to bias transistor stages, it is necessary to evaluate them. A widely accepted means of bias network evaluation is the study of the relative stability of I_C with respect to changes in the dc parameters of the device. Section 3–3 contains a brief discussion of those parameters.

3–3. Parameter Variations. In Chapter 1 it was shown that the transistor collector current is made up of two components, a leakage-current portion and an amplified input-current portion:

$$I_C = \beta I_B + I_{CEO}. \tag{3-3}$$

We may use these ideas to formulate an equivalent electrical circuit for a tran-

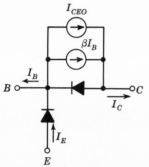

sistor, a model that may be used in analyzing transistor circuits mathematically, (see Fig. 3–5).

It has been noted that the emitter-base diode is always biased in the forward direction. Variations in the forward properties of that diode, while generally large, can often be adequately swamped by external circuit resistance. The collector–base diode is always biased reversely; its variations will also be great, but because of the high value of resistance it presents, and the fact that this resistance accounts for the

Fig. 3–5. DC equivalent circuit for common-emitter-connected transistor.

slope of the collector characteristics, a more-or-less second-order effect, we shall neglect it in the discussion that follows.

Let us center our attention upon the current generators of the equivalent circuit. The alpha parameter may differ by a few percent from unit to unit and therefore its tolerance would appear to be of little consequence in considering bias stability. A major contributor to instability is the $(1 - \alpha)$ term (as found in β); this term must somehow be swamped or its effects minimized. For a transistor with an α of 0.97, $1 - \alpha$ is 0.03. If α is 0.99 for a substitute transistor used in the given circuit, the $(1 - \alpha)$ term is now 0.01. Thus, with the numbers cited a 67% change occurs in $(1 - \alpha)$ while α changes by less than 2%.

Of great importance is change in I_{CBO}. For germanium transistors I_{CBO} generally varies according to the formula[3]

$$I_{CBO} = A_0 e^{0.08(T - T_0)} \tag{3-4}$$

where A_0 is the measured value of I_{CBO} at the reference temperature, T is the operating temperature of the collector junction in degrees Centigrade, and T_0 is the reference temperature in degrees Centigrade, usually 25° C. The constant 0.08 represents an average determined from a large number of transistor tests. Typical of the variation to be expected in I_{CBO} is that shown as Fig. 3–6, which represents I_{CBO} vs. temperature for sample germanium and silicon transistors.

About an 8 % change per °C is to be expected in the leakage current of germanium units. Generally, silicon transistors exhibit less temperature sensitivity.

Now in summary, the important unit-to-unit variations will be in the magnitude of the amplification factor and the magnitude of the leakage current. Consequently, the zero input-current line of the characteristics will differ, as will the spacing between lines of constant input current. Temperature changes will have some effect upon h_{FE}; the variation is given in Fig. 4–16. Leakage current is

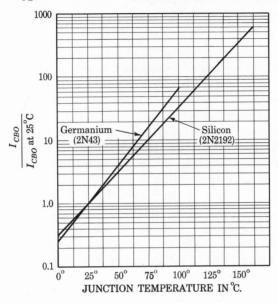

Fig. 3–6. Typical variation of I_{CBO} with temperature.

highly dependent upon temperature. The resultant change in characteristics will be a ladder effect, with the height of the first rung (leakage) dependent upon temperature. The upper rungs move up or down with the first.

3–4. Circuit Studies. The selection of an operating point depends upon a number of factors. Among these factors are the maximum signal excursions to be handled by the stage under consideration, the load on the stage, the available supply potentials, and the tolerable distortion in the signal. Gain can be optimized by appropriate choice of an operating point. Many manufacturers provide a "recommended operating point," and for low-power transistors this is often at $I_C = 1$ mA, $V_{CE} = 5$ V, but operation may just as well center about other points, and it is not necessary to follow the recommendation. No specific rules will be given here for selecting a point; rather by study of sample designs the reader will acquire a feeling for a choice based upon all the factors of the circuit design.

The selection of a biasing circuit can be made after study of the various schemes that have proven useful. A number of these circuits are presented in the paragraphs that follow; they may be compared along the following lines:

1. Sensitivity to temperature and to manufacturing tolerances;
2. sensitivity to changes in supply voltages;
3. number of supplies required;
4. current drain on supplies;
5. number of circuit components;
6. input resistance presented to signal;
7. amount of degeneration (loss of gain).

Naturally, in any particular circuit all of the above factors will not be of equal importance, but, as we have previously seen, item No. 1 can cause great difficulty and our major attention will be directed toward stabilizing the operating point.

Our study of the bias stability problem will commence with investigations of I_C, for we wish to make I_C independent of I_{CBO} and $(1 - \alpha)$. When this is accomplished it still is possible that ac stage gain will vary because of certain influences, as stated in a subsequent chapter. However, a part of the over-all problem will be solved if an amplifying stage can be prevented from being prematurely and unpredictably driven into saturation or cutoff.

What causes I_C to vary? In the following analysis of biasing methods one is impressed by the similarity of the equations for I_C—they all contain terms that include α, $(1 - \alpha)$, and I_{CBO}. It will be seen that the effects of the $(1 - \alpha)$ terms can often be minimized. On the other hand terms involving I_{CBO} are not easy to remove from the expressions for I_C. The relative merits of each of the circuits considered here can be studied.

The following assumptions are used for simplification of analysis of common-emitter stages:

1. The base-to-emitter voltage, V_{BE}, is negligible. In other words, the drops across the swamping resistors R_1 and R_2 are much greater than V_{BE}. If a more detailed study of behavior is required, corrections to the analyses may be made. In almost all instances V_{BE} will lie below 0.8 V and generally below 0.2 V for low-power germanium transistors.

2. The collector-to-emitter voltage V_{CE} has negligible effect upon collector current. Thus, for the purposes of these analyses, I_C is composed of two components according to Eq. (3–3), and depends upon collector voltage only insofar as I_B is dependent upon that voltage.

3. The short-circuit current amplification factor β is constant over the range of possible operating points.

A circuit stability factor S has been defined and widely accepted and will be employed here.[7] It is a measure of the bias stability or circuit sensitivity to temperature. Mathematically,

$$S \equiv \Delta I_C / \Delta I_{CBO} \cong \partial I_C / \partial I_{CBO}. \qquad (3\text{–}5)$$

We are primarily interested in the ratio of the change ΔI_C caused by ΔI_{CBO}, but for simplicity the partial derivative will be employed. The value of the stability factor lies in its use as a measure of comparison among circuits. S as defined here cannot attain a magnitude below unity; the closer to unity the less sensitive the operating point will be to temperature changes. A transistor stage adequately biased with $S = 10$ and subjected to a temperature that changes I_{CBO} by 40 μA will experience a resulting change in the operating point I_C of 400 μA. It is the circuit designer's responsibility to determine if a 400 μA change is tolerable in light of expected signal magnitudes, etc.

Other static stability factors are occasionally of value. For variations in V_{BE}, V_{BB}, and α, one could use

$$S_v \equiv \partial I_C/\partial V_{BE}, \qquad M \equiv \partial I_C/\partial V_{BB}, \qquad N \equiv \partial I_C/\partial \alpha.$$

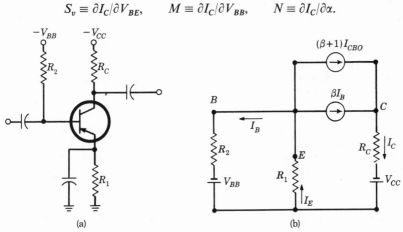

Fig. 3–7. Fixed biasing: (a) typical common-emitter amplifying stage with fixed biasing; (b) dc equivalent circuit for (a).

Before considering the first of our sample circuits, it is necessary to state that names have been ascribed to the various biasing circuits in order more clearly to compare their performance. These names are by no means universally used; however, a system of nomenclature seems to be of value here.

3–5. Fixed Bias. Consider the practical common-emitter amplifying stage of Fig. 3–7(a) and its dc equivalent circuit of Fig. 3–7(b). Coupling capacitors are shown in order to isolate this stage from preceding and succeeding circuitry. The direct supply voltages for both the collector V_{CC} and the base V_{BB} are normally the same source, and therefore the circuit requires only one supply, a practical advantage over some alternate biasing circuits. *This circuit essentially sets a constant base current*, and thus extreme sensitivity to gain variations is to be expected. The resistances R_1 and R_2 improve performance by swamping variations in the input resistance of the transistor. These resistors have other important functions, which will be discussed.

Basic equations for this circuit are

$$I_C = I_E - I_B,$$

$$I_C = \beta I_B + (\beta + 1)I_{CBO},$$

$$V_{BB} = I_E R_1 + I_B R_2. \qquad\qquad\Bigg\} \qquad (3\text{-}6)$$

These three equations may be solved for I_C:

$$I_C = \frac{\alpha V_{BB} + I_{CBO}(R_1 + R_2)}{R_1 + R_2(1 - \alpha)}. \qquad (3\text{-}7)$$

The effects of variations in α and I_{CBO} can now be considered. To minimize effects of the $(1 - \alpha)$ term, we must set

$$R_1 \gg R_2(1 - \alpha). \qquad (3\text{-}8)$$

The requirement posed by Eq. (3–8) is practical only if V_{BB} is a low-voltage source separate from V_{CC}. If it is necessary to utilize V_{CC} for both supplies, then Eq. (3–8) cannot be satisfied. When employing fixed biasing we must often be content with a stage whose operating point is sensitive to changes in α and, in fact, a circuit with fixed bias is also extremely sensitive to changes in I_{CBO}, as will be shown. However, this circuitry offers certain advantages; a minimum of components are needed, and input resistance is not measurably reduced by the bias scheme, for although R_2 parallels the transistor, it is generally of a sufficiently large magnitude so as not to affect the ac input resistance of the stage. The need for only one power supply is also a necessity in certain applications.

Differentiation of Eq. (3–7) with respect to I_{CBO} yields the following relation for stability factor:

$$S = \frac{\partial I_C}{\partial I_{CBO}} = \frac{R_1 + R_2}{R_1 + R_2(1 - \alpha)}. \qquad (3\text{-}9)$$

As has been stated, R_2 is generally of very large value, particularly, if base current is obtained from V_{CC}, and consequently a fixed biased stage is often adversely affected by any leakage current variations. Formulas for the M and N stability factors are given in Table 3–1.

The foregoing relations are of little value unless typical magnitudes of the components and parameters are assumed. Therefore, let us consider a practical amplifying stage having the following characteristics:

$$I_C = 1 \text{ mA}, \qquad\qquad R_C = 4700 \ \Omega,$$

$$V_{BB} = V_{CC} = 9 \text{ V}, \qquad R_1 = 1000 \ \Omega,$$

$$\alpha = 0.988.$$

The specified collector current was achieved with R_2 at a value of 600,000 Ω. The stability factors are therefore:

$$S = 73.3 \ \mu A/\mu A \text{ and } M = 120 \ \mu A/V.$$

The sensitivity to alpha (N) cannot be determined from regular measurements of an operating stage because cutoff current I_{CBO} appears in the expression for N; this transistor, when tested independently, exhibited an I_{CBO} of 2 μA. Thus

$$N = 0.0913 \text{ A/unit} = 913 \ \mu A/0.01 \text{ unit.}$$

We shall use these numbers to compare fixed biasing with other biasing schemes.

A few words are appropriately awarded to discussion of R_1. This resistor is technically unnecessary, for a fixed-bias stage will operate satisfactorily without bypassed emitter resistance. (The bypass capacitor is required to eliminate ac degeneration in R_1, because that element is common to both the input and output loop. The capacitor is chosen according to the discussion of Sec. 6–3 so that its reactance is low at the lowest frequency the amplifier is called upon to handle.) It is obvious from Eq. (3–7) that R_1 helps to swamp the $(1 - \alpha)$ term and thus N is decreased, as well as S.

DC degenerative feedback is provided by R_1, for, if we assume an increase in I_C, the resulting increased drop across R_1 tends to provide a *reduced* forward bias on the emitter junction, thus tending to lower the collector current. With $R_1 = 0$ in the sample circuit noted above, R_2 must increase to 740,000 Ω to provide the same collector current, and the stability factors become

$$S = 83.4 \ \mu A/\mu A,$$

$$M = 111 \ \mu A/V,$$

$$N = 990 \ \mu A/0.01 \text{ unit.}$$

It might appear that if R_1 could be made extremely large, all problems would be solved. R_1, however, is an important factor in the dc load line for the stage and will help determine signal-handling capabilities. The values of R_1 and R_C therefore are subject to ac considerations and compromise; further discussion is reserved for later in the chapter.

In summary, fixed biasing provides a simple and inexpensive means for establishing an operating point. The stability of the operating point is extremely poor when compared with that of other circuits. Bypassed emitter resistance improves the stability of the selected point.

3–6. Single-Battery Bias. This form of biasing differs from the fixed-bias case by the simple addition of a resistance between base terminal and ground as shown in Fig. 3–8. The additional resistance R_3 can be chosen so that the equivalent series base–circuit resistance (R_2 in Fig. 3–7) is considerably reduced; therefore, large improvements in the stability factors are possible.

Equations may be written for this circuit as was done for fixed biasing, or

Thevenin's Theorem may be used to arrive at the expression for collector current:

$$I_C = \frac{\alpha R_3 V_{BB} + I_{CBO}[R_1(R_2 + R_3) + R_2 R_3]}{R_1(R_2 + R_3) + (1 - \alpha)R_2 R_3}. \tag{3-10}$$

The sensitivity factor to changes in I_{CBO} is, from Eq. (3-10),

$$S = \frac{R_1(R_2 + R_3) + R_2 R_3}{R_1(R_2 + R_3) + (1 - \alpha)R_2 R_3}. \tag{3-11a}$$

If we consider R_3 small compared to R_2, then Eq. (3-11a) becomes

$$S = (R_1 + R_3)/[R_1 + R_3(1 - \alpha)] \quad (\text{for } R_2 \gg R_3). \tag{3-11b}$$

The assumption used here, that $R_2 \gg R_3$, is not necessarily true for all circuits. Generally R_2 is 2 to 10 times greater.

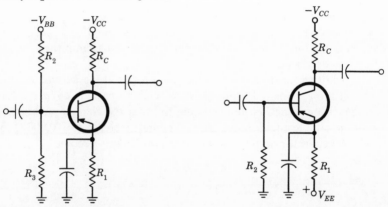

Fig. 3-8.　Single-battery biasing.　　　　Fig. 3-9.　Emitter biasing.

The sample stage considered in the preceding section was also biased by the method of this section. The desired operation point was achieved with values of R_2 of 50,000 Ω and R_3 of 8000 Ω, although an infinite number of combinations of these resistances is possible because the two form sort of a voltage divider. Using the complete formula, Eq. (3-11a),

$$S = 7.3 \ \mu A/\mu A.$$

Thus in this circuit, single-battery biasing is approximately 10 times as stable with respect to I_{CBO} as is fixed biasing. This represents a significant improvement, at the cost of just one resistive element. From the formulas of Table 3-1, we obtain $M = 126 \ \mu A/V$ and $N = 85 \ \mu A/0.01$ unit. A significant improvement in N is obtained.

A degree of freedom exists in the single-battery bias arrangement for, as has been mentioned, a large number of combinations of R_2 and R_3 are possible.

Several of the usable combinations for the sample stage are listed here; each pair results in the operating point at $I_C = 1$ mA:

R_2	10 kΩ	20 kΩ	50 kΩ	100 kΩ	200 kΩ	300 kΩ
R_3	1.5 kΩ	3.1 kΩ	8 kΩ	18 kΩ	44 kΩ	86 kΩ

The R_2 and R_3 elements form a *loaded voltage divider*. The divider is said to be loaded because the static base current is drawn from the junction of those two resistances. For circuit-design purposes it is possible to neglect I_B only when that current is extremely small. This condition exists when the transistor has an extremely large value of h_{FE}.

In summarizing the case for single-battery bias, we may say that operating-point stability is considerably improved over that of fixed bias at the expense of one additional resistor. Only one dc supply is required and bypassed emitter resistance is again recommended.

3-7. Emitter Bias. If the base of the common-emitter configuration is grounded, or returned to ground through a resistor of moderate size, and the emitter is connected to a separate potential supply as shown in Fig. 3-9, a most stable operating point can be achieved. R_1 and R_2 again help to swamp variations in the input diode. Solution of the appropriate loop and nodal equations yields

$$I_C = \frac{\alpha V_{EE} + I_{CBO}(R_1 + R_2)}{R_1 + R_2(1 - \alpha)} \tag{3-12}$$

The stability-factor equations are identical with those for fixed biasing except that V_{EE} appears, rather than V_{BB}. Although the equations are alike, numerical values of the components will differ.

In the emitter-biased stage, a constant level of emitter current is being set, rather than constant base current. The potential at the base will be close to ground, differing only by the small drop $I_B R_2$. The voltage at the emitter terminal, V_E, is approximately the same as at the base because V_{BE} is always less than 1 V. Consequently,

$$I_E = (V_{EE} - V_E)/R_1 \tag{3-13a}$$

or

$$I_E \cong V_{EE}/R_1 \quad \text{(for } R_2 \text{ small).} \tag{3-13b}$$

In this connection then, R_1 dictates the desired emitter (or collector) current, and R_2 *serves just as a return for base current*. For biasing purposes R_2 could be a short circuit, but no ac amplification would then result.

To compare emitter biasing with the previously discussed methods, we shall assume that a 9 V supply is used for V_{EE} and that I_C is again required to be 1 mA. If R_2 is chosen to be 10,000 Ω, and $R_1 = 9000$ Ω according to Eq. (3-13b), then

$$S = (R_1 + R_2)/[R_1 + R_2(1 - \alpha)] = 2.08 \ \mu\text{A}/\mu\text{A}.$$

This compares very favorably with the typical numbers obtained for fixed biasing and single-battery biasing. Sensitivity to supply-voltage variations is about the same as that provided by the other schemes, but α variations have practically no effect upon the emitter-biased stage.

Suppose that transformer coupling is used between the preceding circuitry and the stage under consideration. The secondary of the transformer in Fig. 3–10 places the base terminal at dc ground, assuming negligible dc resistance of the winding. The equation for the operating point for this arrangement is

$$I_C = (\alpha V_{EE} + I_{CBO}R_1)/R_1. \tag{3–14}$$

The corresponding S factor equals unity; thus the ultimate in operating-point stability can be achieved.

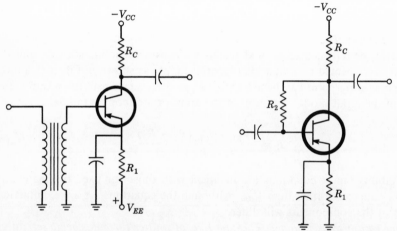

Fig. 3–10. Typical common-emitter am-
plifying stage with emitter biasing.   Fig. 3–11. Self-biasing.

General conclusions to the discussion of emitter biasing— although the need for two dc supplies of opposite polarity is often a definite disadvantage, a highly stable operating point is guaranteed.

3–8. Self-Bias. Self-bias gets its name from the fact that the collector terminal is connected through an external resistor to the base terminal. This connection is shown in Fig. 3–11. Because a lower voltage is available at the collector than with fixed biasing directly connected to V_{CC}, the value of R_2 will necessarily be smaller.

The constant no-signal collector potential V_C establishes the operating point at a particular level of base current. Should the collector static characteristics change for any reason, the base current will change somewhat because V_C, which can be said to be driving I_B, changes when the characteristics change. Thus with this circuit *a constant I_B is not being set*, because I_B will shift with output-circuit

TABLE 3-1.　SUMMARY OF BIASING EQUATIONS.

	Fixed Bias	Single-Battery Bias	Emitter Bias	Self-Bias
I_C	$\dfrac{\alpha V_{BB} + I_{CBO}(R_1+R_2)}{R_1+R_2(1-\alpha)}$	$\dfrac{\alpha R_3 V_{BB} + I_{CBO}[R_1(R_2+R_3)+R_2R_3]}{R_1(R_2+R_3)+(1-\alpha)R_2R_3}$	$\dfrac{\alpha V_{EE} + I_{CBO}(R_1+R_2)}{R_1+R_2(1-\alpha)}$	$\dfrac{\alpha V_{CC}+I_{CBO}(R_2+R_1+R_L)}{R_1+R_L+(1-\alpha)R_2}$
$S=\dfrac{\partial I_C}{\partial I_{CBO}}$	$\dfrac{R_1+R_2}{R_1+R_2(1-\alpha)}$	$\dfrac{R_1(R_2+R_3)+R_2R_3}{R_1(R_2+R_3)+(1-\alpha)R_2R_3}$	$\dfrac{R_1+R_2}{R_1+R_2(1-\alpha)}$	$\dfrac{R_2+R_1+R_L}{R_1+R_L+(1-\alpha)R_2}$
$M=\dfrac{\partial I_C}{\partial V}$	$\dfrac{\alpha}{R_1+R_2(1-\alpha)}$	$\dfrac{\alpha R_3}{R_1(R_2+R_3)+(1-\alpha)R_2R_3}$	$\dfrac{\alpha}{R_1+R_2(1-\alpha)}$	$\dfrac{\alpha}{R_1+R_L+(1-\alpha)R_2}$
$N=\dfrac{\partial I_C}{\partial \alpha}$	$\dfrac{\left\{\begin{array}{l}(R_1+R_2)V_{BB}\\+I_{CBO}(R_1+R_2)R_2\end{array}\right\}}{[R_1+R_2(1-\alpha)]^2}$	$\dfrac{\left\{\begin{array}{l}(R_3 V_{BB}+I_{CBO}R_2R_3)\\\times(R_1R_2+R_1R_3+R_2R_3)\end{array}\right\}}{[R_1(R_2+R_3)+(1-\alpha)R_2R_3]^2}$	$\dfrac{\left\{\begin{array}{l}(R_1+R_2)V_{EE}\\+I_{CBO}(R_1+R_2)R_2\end{array}\right\}}{[R_1+R_2(1-\alpha)]^2}$	$\dfrac{\left\{\begin{array}{l}(R_1+R_L+R_2)V_{CC}\\+I_{CBO}(R_2+R_1+R_L)R_2\end{array}\right\}}{[R_1+R_L+(1-\alpha)R_2]^2}$

variations. The compensating effects of self-bias are desirable, but from an ac standpoint some gain will be lost because of signal feedback through R_2. Self-biasing can take on several forms: the circuit may be as shown in Fig. 3–11; the base may be returned to ground using an additional resistor; or R_2 on occasion has been split into two components, with a capacitor to ground from the junction.

Solution of the dc equations for I_C yields

$$I_C = \frac{\alpha V_{CC} + I_{CBO}(R_1 + R_2 + R_C)}{R_1 + R_C + (1 - \alpha)R_2}.$$ (3–15)

Therefore,

$$S = \frac{R_1 + R_2 + R_C}{R_1 + R_C + (1 - \alpha)R_2}.$$ (3–16)

These equations are quite similar to those applicable to fixed biasing. However, as noted, R_2 is smaller in the self-biased circuit. The sample stage was biased at 1 mA with $R_2 = 240,000 \ \Omega$. Therefore $S = 28.6 \ \mu A/\mu A$, $M = 115 \ \mu A/V$, $N = 316 \ \mu A/0.01$ unit.

Conclusions to the discussion of self-bias operation are that only one supply voltage is necessary and that connecting the base resistor to the collector terminal rather than directly to the collector supply results in a more stable operating point.

3–9. Other Means of Setting the Operating Point.   Biasing circuits not included in this discussion have been used in various applications. Several are apparent in circuits considered in later chapters, and each may be studied on its own merits. It is felt, however, that the circuits previously described here are useful in the vast majority of applications, that their relative merits have been adequately explored, and that when new circuits are considered these methods can serve as a basis of comparison. The rather special biasing requirements for dc amplifiers and power amplifiers are treated in the text under those titles.

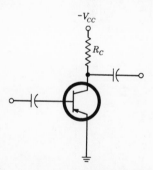

Fig. 3–12.   Cutoff biasing.

In the low-signal-level stages of some transistor circuits, it may be advantageous to maintain as high an input impedance as possible, or to achieve a most economical design. By providing no path for quiescent base current we can still achieve Class-A operation if so desired. The diagram of Fig. 3–12 shows a circuit biased near cutoff, at $I_B = 0$. Since the collector current *is* I_{CEO}, the operating point is highly sensitive to temperature. As stated in Chapter 1, it is possible to swing to I_{CBO} as a lower limit on collector current, but distortion is prevalent in this low-current region.

Nevertheless, consider a stage with $I_{CBO} = 10 \mu A$ and $\beta = 39$. Then the output current capability of such a stage is $I_{CEO} - I_{CBO}$ or 390 μA peak. The allowable input signal would be 390/39 or 10 μA peak.

A newcomer to the transistor field with vacuum-tube experience may wonder why the cathode-biasing technique employed in tube circuitry is not applicable to transistor circuits. Cathode bias for a tube is illustrated in Fig. 3–13(a). DC plate current I_b causes a potential drop across R_1 of the indicated polarity. Since negligible current flows in R_g, the resulting grid-to-cathode bias is simply $I_b R_1$. Capacitor C_1 is chosen to have a small reactance compared with the resistance of R_1 at the lowest operating frequency.

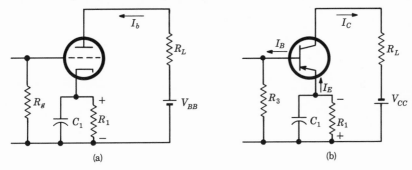

(a)   (b)

Fig. 3–13.   (a) Cathode biasing for vacuum tube; (b) similar circuit for transistor stage.

A similar transistor circuit is that of Fig. 3–13(b). If an emitter current is *assumed*, then the $I_E R_1$ drop would be of the polarity shown. *This would tend to reverse-bias the emitter–base diode rather than provide the forward bias required for normal Class-*A *operation.*

3–10. Design of Biasing Circuitry. The discussions in the preceding sections of this chapter serve mainly for comparative analysis of the various biasing circuits. Emphasis was placed upon the S factor; this factor is of particular interest in circuits that are subjected to wide temperature variations. From studies of this type, it can be generally concluded that the single-battery bias arrangement, if well designed, is satisfactory for most applications.

The semiconductor material used in the transistor being considered will have an effect upon the tolerable S. The leakage current in silicon devices is so low that in many single-battery biased circuits operating below 70° C, the R_3 element can be omitted with no serious performance deterioration.

The expressions for I_C *derived for the various circuits are of value only when the dc beta is accurately known.* For any circuit that tends to set a constant level of base current, the collector current is, of course, equal to β_{dc} times that level. Because a constant base current is not being set with emitter biasing, the equation for I_C will give excellent results regardless of the transistor's current-gain parameter.

A very valuable method of bias circuit design uses the *extremal analysis* technique discussed in the next section. This method is based upon the worst cases or extremes in characteristics to be encountered in the application of a particular transistor type. It enables the circuit designer to use the single-battery bias scheme with absolute certainty that the circuit will not drift from a given locus of Q points when variations in β_{dc}, I_{CBO}, or V_{BE} are encountered.

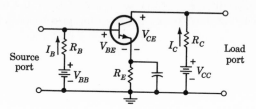

Fig. 3–14.   General amplifying stage.

To describe extremal analysis it is convenient to consider a more general network for transistor biasing. Quantities are defined in Fig. 3–14. To relate this circuit, with elements V_{BB} and R_B, to the single-battery bias scheme of Fig. 3–8, with R_2 connected to V_{CC}, Thevenin's theorem may be employed with the result that

$$R_2 = R_B V_{CC}/V_{BB}$$

and

$$R_3 = R_B/[1 - (V_{BB}/V_{CC})].$$

(3–17)

Normally V_{CC} is known; R_2 and R_3 can be obtained from Eq. (3–17) after V_{BB} and R_3 are determined.

3–11. Extremal Analysis. Figure 3–15 depicts two superimposed sets of collector characteristics. They may represent a specific transistor at differing ambient temperatures, or the expected variations caused by production variables and temperature in the characteristics of a single transistor type.

Let us suppose that Q_1 and Q_2 represent the limits beyond which we dare not allow the direct collector current I_C to travel because of signal size, distortion, or any other consideration. The corresponding excursions in I_C and I_B will be symbolized by ΔI_C and ΔI_B. When Q_1 is considered as the normal or reference point, ΔI_B will be a negative quantity.*

A summation of potential differences around the base–emitter loop of the general stage shown in Fig. 3–14 gives

$$V_{BB} = I_C R_E + I_B(R_B + R_E) + V_{BE}.$$

(3–18)

*In order to eliminate the confusion associated with the differing polarities of quantities in *p–n–p* and *n–p–n* types, the equations presented here will deal with magnitudes in so far as possible. Thus ΔI_B is negative because the magnitude of I_B declines between Q_1 and Q_2.

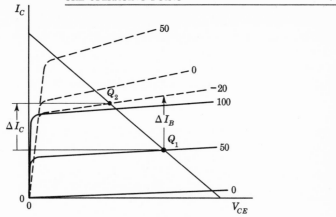

Fig. 3–15. Collector characteristics at temperature extremes.

The base–emitter voltage drop V_{BE} is a function of temperature and manufacturing tolerances. When considering only the effect of temperature, one is confronted with input-characteristic extremes as shown in Fig. 3–16. A mathematical relation for the linear portion of the T_1 curve is

$$V_{BE}(T_1) = V_{BE1} + r_1 I_B. \tag{3–19}$$

At a more elevated temperature T_2, the relation is

$$V_{BE}(T_2) = V_{BE1} + \Delta V_{BE} + r_2 I_B. \tag{3–20}$$

The incremental resistances r_1 and r_2 represent the slopes of the I_B–V_{BE} characteristics. These resistances are usually swamped by R_B and R_E and are therefore of little consequence. Subtraction of Eq. (3–19) from Eq. (3–20) gives

$$V_{BE}(T_2) - V_{BE}(T_1) \cong \Delta V_{BE}. \tag{3–21}$$

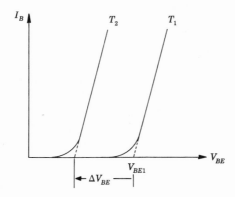

Fig. 3–16. Input characteristics at temperatures T_1 and T_2.

It is to be noted that ΔV_{BE} is a negative quantity as used here. It will be used to represent the change in V_{BE} resulting from all causes.

The operating-point excursion from Q_1 to Q_2 in Fig. 3–15 may result from unit replacement and/or temperature change. If we consider V_{BB} and the resistance values as invariant, the applicable base–emitter loop equation at Q_2 is

$$V_{BB} = (I_C + \Delta I_C)R_E + (I_B + \Delta I_B)(R_B + R_E) + V_{BE} + \Delta V_{BE}. \qquad (3\text{–}22)$$

Subtraction of Eq. (3–18) from Eq. (3–22) yields the following relation among the quantity increments:

$$\Delta I_C R_E + \Delta I_B(R_B + R_E) + \Delta V_{BE} = 0. \qquad (3\text{–}23)$$

If this relation is solved for R_E, we obtain

$$R_E = -\frac{\Delta V_{BE}}{\Delta I_B + \Delta I_C} - \frac{\Delta I_B}{\Delta I_B + \Delta I_C} R_B. \qquad (3\text{–}24)$$

In a more compact form, Eq. (3–24) becomes

$$R_E = A + BR_B. \qquad (3\text{–}25)$$

Because of the significance of Eq. (3–25), it will be referred to as the *general biasing relation*.

Equation (3–25) does not permit solution for either R_B or R_E, but allows an additional constraint to be used for determination of biasing elements. The additional constraint may be imposed by supply-voltage fluxuations, or by ac considerations such as input resistance or gain.

Example. The specifications for a particular transistor stage are:

1. Load is 1000 Ω, resistive. Source resistance = 1000 Ω.
2. Stage should be capable of supplying a 0.5 mA (peak) signal to the load.
3. $V_{CC} = -15$ V.
4. Maximum supply drain = 1.5 mA.
5. Transistor type 2N2614 to be used.
6. Temperature range: 25° to 50° C.

For extremal analysis, data are taken on a representative sample of the selected transistor type for the plot shown in Fig. 3–17. Superimposed are the characteristics of the lowest-gain unit to be considered, and those of the highest-gain unit at the maximum specified temperature. A dc load line may be drawn using the known constraints: the given value of V_{CC} and the signal-size requirement. The current drain of this stage is to be limited to 1.5 mA or less. In order to handle a signal of satisfactory size, it is necessary that the extremal operating points be located away from saturation and cutoff.

If Q_1 is chosen at $|I_C| = 0.75$ mA and $|V_{CE}| = 11.25$ V on the 5000 Ω dc line, allowable collector-signal current will be approximately 0.6 mA as evidenced by the vertical distance from Q_1 to cutoff. Since the specification is 0.5 mA, this choice for Q_1 seems reasonable. For Q_2 we choose 1.5 mA, 7.5 V. Thus one sees from the graph that

$$\Delta I_B = -7.5 \ \mu A \text{ (from 5 to 2.5 } \mu A \text{ in opposite direction)}$$

and

$$\Delta I_C = 0.75 \text{ mA.}$$

There remains the problem of finding V_{BE}. It has been shown that a distinct correlation exists between the value of V_{BE} and the magnitude of the thermal coefficient of that voltage,[10] but there is no correlation between h_{FE} and V_{BE}.

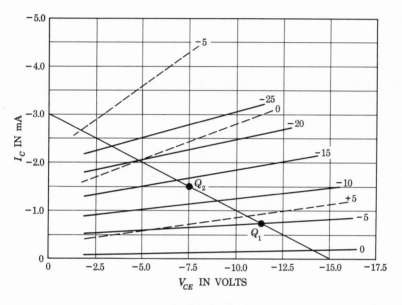

Fig. 3–17. Characteristics of extremal units.

In order for the biasing of the stage to reflect conservative engineering judgment, the following rules must apply:

(1) The value of V_{BE} to be used in Eq. (3–18) to find V_{BB} is the highest value that could pertain to any low-gain unit at the reference temperature.

(2) The value of ΔV_{BE} to be used in Eq. (3–24) is the difference between the value of V_{BE} used in (1) and the lowest value of V_{BE} for any unit at the highest temperature.

From test data, the largest value for any unit at 25° C is 0.160 V. The lowest value of V_{BE} at 50° C is 0.107 V. Therefore

$$\Delta V_{BE} = -0.053 \text{ V.}$$

With these numbers in Eq. (3–24), the general biasing relation is found to be

$$R_E = 71.4 + 0.01 R_B.$$

The constants A and B are fairly low-valued in this example because the temperature extremes are not widely spaced, and ΔI_C is rather large. It is also true that this transistor has a high current-transfer ratio, a factor that controls ΔI_B to a large extent.

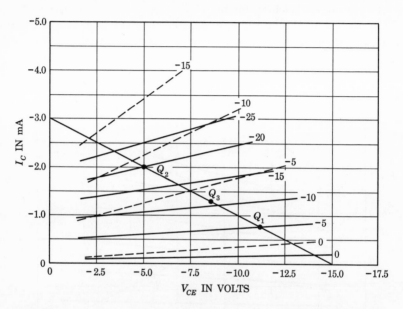

Fig. 3–18. Characteristics of extremal units—production variations only.

Figure 3–18 depicts the characteristics of high- and low-gain units *at the reference temperature*. The spread in characteristics is caused exclusively by manufacturing tolerances. A 5000 Ω static load line and quiescent points Q_1 and Q_2 have been chosen as shown. Between those points, $\Delta I_C = 1.25$ mA and $\Delta I_B = +3$ μA. If for simplicity we assume that ΔV_{BE} is zero, then, from Eq. (3–23),

$$\Delta I_C R_E = -\Delta I_B R_B.$$

Solution for R_B requires a negative value of resistance. In this instance, the selected ΔI_C is too large. If ΔI_C were decreased to 0.5 mA, so that $\Delta I_B = -1$ μA, as at Q_3, then a satisfactory relation is obtained:

$$R_E = 2(10^{-3}) R_B.$$

We see from this example that certain requirements are nonrealizable.

3–12. Biasing the FET. The FET amplifying stage must be biased at a suitable point in the I_D–V_{DS} plane. The selected operating point must simultaneously satisfy signal size or distortion, power supply, and gain, bandwidth, or other requirements. In order for the discussion of FET biasing to be most general, it is focused upon the junction device. Biasing principles for MOS units are analogous, with several exceptions.

It was noted in Chapter 1 that the junction FET can operate successfully with zero gate-source voltage; consequently, an elaborate biasing network is not a necessity. But biasing at $V_{GS} = 0$ has several disadvantages—the allowable signal size is limited, power-supply current drain would be high, and the drain-load resistance R_D would be of rather low value in order to escape the region of triode-like operation. In addition, the Q point would be rather unstable because of large unit-to-unit variations. For these reasons, operation at $V_{GS} = 0$ is not generally employed.

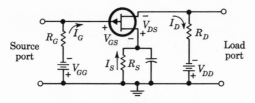

Fig. 3–19.   General biasing network.

Self-bias.   The generalized biasing network is shown in Fig. 3–19. Because the input junction is reverse-biased rather than forward-biased as with the conventional transistor, *the voltage drop $I_S R_S$ is of the correct polarity so that it can be used for V_{GS}.*

Consider that the entire gate-source voltage will be obtained from the drop across R_S. The applicable network is that of Fig. 3–19 *with the V_{GG} supply omitted.* If I_G is very small or essentially zero, the R_G element may be arbitrarily selected to complete the loop so that the $I_S R_S$ voltage is available to the gate. Around the gate-source loop, one obtains

$$V_{GS} = I_S R_S. \tag{3–26}$$

Locating the desired Q point on the output characteristics of the device completely specifies the quiescent values of V_{GS} and I_D, and R_S may be obtained from Eq. (3–26). ($I_D = I_S$ for all practical purposes).

With this form of biasing, the designer has no freedom to choose R_S; he must comply with Eq. (3–26). Because good operating-point stability requires that the value of R_S be high, self-biasing as described here does not provide a highly stable operating point.

Modified Self-biasing.   Unit-to-unit variations are especially severe with FET's. Temperature effects on the static characteristics are also a problem to be overcome. Again, successful circuit design requires that consideration be given to the stability of the operating point once it is set.

The modified self-bias circuit is that of Fig. 3–19, *including* V_{GG}. Kirchhoff loop equations can be written for the gate–source loop and for the drain–source loop of the stage. The resistance R_S is again included because that element is of value in setting the bias as well as in stabilizing it. Under the assumption that $I_D = I_S$, we have, for the input loop,

$$V_{GG} = -I_G R_G + I_D R_S - V_{GS}. \tag{3–27}$$

It is convenient to define a static stability factor for FET biasing circuits as was done for the conventional transistor. To describe the common-source characteristics, we shall use a very approximate mathematical description, namely,

$$I_D \cong I_{DSS} - g_m V_{GS}. \tag{3–28}$$

Equation (3–28) contains a small-signal parameter, g_m. In this section for simplicity of analysis, we shall treat g_m as a constant, although it is to be recognized that in most practical devices g_m will vary appreciably when considering the entire I_D–V_{DS} plane. A relation is available for V_{GS} from Eq. (3–27); if it is substituted into Eq. (3–28), and terms collected, we obtain,

$$I_D = [I_{DSS} + g_m(I_G R_G + V_{GG})]/(1 + g_m R_S). \tag{3–29}$$

Now a static stability factor may be defined and evaluated as follows:

$$S_F \equiv \partial I_D/\partial I_{DSS} = 1/(1 + g_m R_S). \tag{3–30}$$

The stability factor S_F is not a direct function of V_{GG}; however, *in the circuit that employs the separate V_{GG} supply, R_S can be considerably larger than in the completely self-biased circuit.* To prove this statement we again assume $I_G R_G$ to be negligible. Then rearrangement of Eq. (3–27) yields

$$V_{GS} = I_D R_S - V_{GG}. \tag{3–31}$$

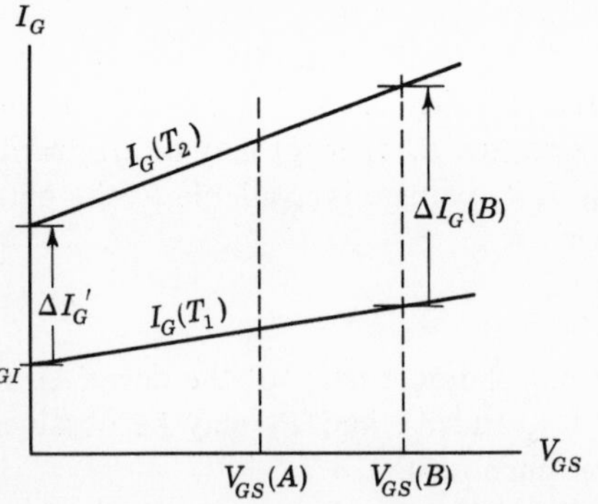

Fig. 3–20. Input characteristics at temperatures T_1 and T_2.

The predominant term is $I_D R_S$. However, because of the subtraction of V_{GG}, for given V_{GS} and I_D the source resistance R_S must be of a larger value than in the exclusively self-biased circuit. A lower value of S_F results.

3–13. FET Extremal Analysis. Let us study FET biasing from the extremal analysis standpoint. Idealized input characteristics of a junction FET are shown in Fig. 3–20 at two temperatures, T_1 and T_2 ($T_2 > T_1$). The curves may be represented by

$$I_G(T_1) = I_{G1} + y_1 V_{GS}, \tag{3–32a}$$

$$I_G(T_2) = I_{G1} + \Delta I_G' + y_2 V_{GS}. \tag{3-32b}$$

The incremental admittances y_1 and y_2 are implied by the slopes of the curves. The change in I_G due to temperature is obtained by subtracting Eq. (3–32a) from Eq. (3–32b):

$$\Delta I_G = \Delta I_G' + (y_1 - y_2)V_{GS}. \tag{3-33}$$

When an FET is subjected to temperature extremes, the biasing network will invariably cause the gate–source potential V_{GS} to change. The most extreme change in I_G occurs at the highest gate–source bias, $V_{GS}(B)$ in Fig. 3–20; therefore to be on the conservative side, Eq. (3–33) can be approximated by

$$\Delta I_G \cong \Delta I_G(B). \tag{3-34}$$

It is again convenient to consider the output characteristics of the active device at the two extremes, or "worst cases," to be expected. In Fig. 3–21 these cases

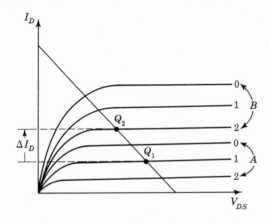

Fig. 3–21. Output characteristics for extremal units.

are shown as A and B. If Q_1 and Q_2 represent the limits placed upon the operating point because of distortion, power-supply drain, or signal-size considerations, and Q_1 considered as the reference, then ΔI_D, the allowable excursion in I_D, is a positive quantity, as is the excursion ΔV_{GS}.

The equation describing Q_1 quantities is

$$V_{GG} = -I_G R_G + I_D R_S - V_{GS}. \tag{3-35}$$

At Q_2, we have

$$V_{GG} = -(I_G + \Delta I_G)R_G + (I_D + \Delta I_D)R_S - (V_{GS} + \Delta V_{GS}). \tag{3-36}$$

Subtracting Eq. (3–35) from (3–36) gives

$$-\Delta I_G R_G + \Delta I_D R_S - \Delta V_{GS} = 0. \tag{3-37}$$

The desired relation between biasing elements is obtained by solving this relation for R_S:

$$R_S = (\Delta V_{GS}/\Delta I_D) + (\Delta I_G/\Delta I_D)R_G. \tag{3-38}$$

This similarity between this formula for R_S and the general biasing relation for the conventional transistor is noted. In a more compact form, Eq. (3–38) is

$$R_S = A' + B'R_G. \tag{3-39}$$

Further discussion of Eq. (3–37) is necessary in order to employ the equation successfully. Let us first examine the effect of *manufacturing tolerances exclusively* by considering that units A and B of Fig. 3–21 represent extremals. It is usually valid to treat $\Delta I_G R_G$ as negligible compared with the other terms in Eq. (3–37); hence, A' is the only term of importance in Eq. (3–38). If the excursion in I_D is sufficiently limited, both ΔV_{GS} and ΔI_D are positive numbers. The result is a requirement for a finite, positive R_S.

Now turning our attention to the temperature problem, we note that unit A must be the low-gain unit at high temperature, and unit B the high-gain unit at low temperature because temperature effects in the FET are opposite to those in a transistor. Below the temperature range where $\Delta I_G R_G$ is of importance we obtain $R_S = \Delta V_{GS}/\Delta I_D$. It may be concluded that the temperature and manufacturing-tolerance problems may be solved concurrently, at least in considering the variation allowed in I_D.

When the temperature is so elevated that $\Delta I_G R_G$ becomes a significant term in Eq. (3–37), ΔV_{GS} will be reduced. A limit is approached when the drop across R_G becomes rather large, for then the operating point seeks the vicinity of $V_{GS} = 0$. This effect can be overcome, to some extent, by the use of a low-valued gate-biasing resistance, for then the $\Delta I_G R_G$ product is diminished. However, such compensation may be undesirable from the viewpoint of amplification properties, for the increase in I_D results in increased g_{fs}, the small-signal transconductance parameter, and may be used to compensate for the falloff in g_{fs} that occurs with increased temperature.

Example. Let it be required that an FET stage be biased at

$$I_D = 1 \text{ mA}, I_G = 10^{-9} \text{ A}, V_{GS} = 0.8 \text{ V}.$$

Manufacturing tolerances and temperature effects dictate

$$\Delta I_D = 1 \text{ mA}, \Delta V_{GS} = 0.2 \text{ V}, \Delta I_G = 10^{-6} \text{ A}.$$

The supply voltage $V_{DD} = 25$ V. The problem is to determine R_G, V_{GG}, and R_2 and R_3 of Fig. 3–22(a).

From Eq. (3–38)

$$R_S = 200 + 0.001R_G.$$

If R_S is chosen arbitrarily to be 2700 Ω, then

$$R_G = 2.5 \times 10^6 \ \Omega.$$

From Eq. (3–35) we obtain

$$V_{GG} = 1.9 \text{ V.}$$

Referring to Fig. 3–22(a), we note that

$$R_3 = 2.7 \times 10^6 \ \Omega \text{ and } R_2 = 32.8 \times 10^6 \ \Omega$$

With this form of biasing, the input resistance of the stage is essentially R_3. When the change in I_G is not a problem, R_3 can be considerably larger than the value obtained in this example. A method of eliminating high-resistance values uses three resistances and is shown in Fig. 3–22(b). The element in series with the gate can equal R_G and the R_2–R_3 divider may use low-valued elements to provide V_{GG}.

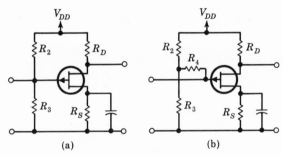

Fig. 3–22.   Biasing schemes.

The discussion of the dc portion of the transistor stage is now concluded and in the ensuing chapter ac operation will be of primary concern. However, whenever a complete stage is to be analyzed or designed, the interrelations between ac operation and quiescent conditions must be considered. We shall see that the operating point is an important part of each circuit to be studied.

PROBLEMS

3–1. Draw dc load lines of 500 and 1000 Ω on a sketch of the 2N2614 collector characteristics (Appendix I), starting from $V_{CE} = -10$ V. Locate operating points at $I_B = -50 \ \mu$A for each line. What angle, in degrees, does each load line make with the horizontal?

3–2. A vertical load line and a horizontal load line indicate what kinds of loads?

3–3. Establish rules for drawing the dc load line for the self-biased stage, Fig. 3–11.

3–4. Derive an equation for θ, the angle between the dc load line and the horizontal, as a function of R and the scale factors of the plot.

3–5. Draw diode equivalent circuits similar to Fig. 3–5 for a transistor connected common-base and connected common-collector.

3–6. A transistor has a leakage current I_{CBO} of 10 μA at 25° C. Use Eq. (3–4) to calculate the temperature rise necessary for I_{CBO} to double its 25° C value. Will this same temperature rise pertain to a doubling of I_{CEO}?

3–7. Confirm Eqs. (3–7) and (3–9) for fixed bias.

3–8. Confirm Eqs. (3–10) and (3–11a) for single-battery bias.

3–9. Confirm Eq. (3–12) for emitter bias.

3–10. Confirm Eq. (3–15) for self-bias. In writing the necessary equations note that I_C breaks into two components, I_B and the current through R_C.

3–11. Discuss each biasing scheme of this chapter from the standpoint of (a) input resistance to alternating signals; (b) dc power-supply drain.

3–12. A certain fixed-bias stage with $R_2 = 110,000$ Ω and $\beta = 50$ is operating from a 10 V supply and must exhibit a stability factor (S) of 10. Calculate the R_1 required. Is this a reasonable answer?

3–13. Include V_{BE} in the equation for I_C for fixed biasing.

3–14. Calculations with laboratory confirmation indicate that, in a particular fixed-bias stage using silicon transistors, $R_1 = 1000$ Ω, $R_2 = 100,000$ Ω, $\alpha = 0.98$, and $I_{CO} = 0.1$ μA when the collector current is 3.27 mA. For a production run, resistors with $\pm 20\%$ tolerance are to be used. Calculate the operating point (I_C) shift if each resistor is at the upper end of its allowable range, and also at its lowest possible value.

3–15. A stage is to be designed with single-battery biasing. $I_E = 2$ mA, $I_B = 50$ μA, $V_{BE} = 0.2$ V, $R_1 = 1$ kΩ, $V_{BB} = 10$ V. If $R_3 = 10$ kΩ, what value must R_2 take on in order for the operating point to be at the coordinates given?

3–16. To set an operating point for a single-battery biased common-emitter stage at 1 mA, the following data were taken of usable combinations of R_2 and R_3. The circuit feeds a 3600 Ω load and R_1 is 1000 Ω. The transistor has a β of 80 and I_{CO} of 7 μA. $V_{BB} = V_{CC} = 12.4$ V.

R_2	R_3
200 kΩ	115 kΩ
150 kΩ	60 kΩ
110 kΩ	35 kΩ
40 kΩ	10 kΩ
21 kΩ	5 kΩ

Compare the various resistance pairs to determine which pair will result in a stage that shows a minimum of sensitivity to I_{CO} variations.

3–17. Using the same circuit as in the preceding problem, but with a $\beta = 22$ transistor, determine if a higher stability is achieved because required resistance values are lower. $R_2 = 18$ kΩ when $R_3 = 5$ kΩ, and $R_2 = 32$ kΩ when $R_3 = 10$ kΩ, for example.

3–18. Design an emitter-biased circuit in which the collector current does not change more than 0.5 mA for an increase of 200 μA in I_{CO}. The available supplies are $+15$ and -15 V and the operating point must be at -10 V and -1.5 mA. I_{CO} is initially negligible, $\alpha = 0.98$ and is substantially constant.

(a) What values should R_1 and R_2 be? What potential exists from base to emitter? The transistor is germanium.

(b) If α changed to 0.96 because of the same temperature variation that changed I_{CO}, would the values calculated in (a) be correct in order to limit the change in I_C to 0.5 mA? If not what can be done to the original design?

3–19. Derive the expression for I_C for a stage biased as shown in the accompanying figure.

3–20. Confirm Eqs. (3–17).

3–21. Consider the circuit of the accompanying figure. Under which of the following conditions would you expect damage to the transistor? In each instance where damage would probably occur, briefly explain the cause.

(a) Polarity of 30 V source reversed.

(b) Polarity of 0.5 V source reversed.

(c) Emitter lead opened at point A.
(d) When inserted, the collector and emitter leads are interchanged.
(e) When inserted, the base and emitter leads are interchanged.
(f) A *p–n–p* transistor is substituted.

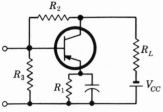

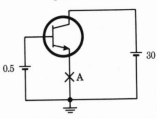

Problem 3–19.

Problem 3–21.

3–22. A 9 V power supply, positive ground, is to be used to supply dc to an *n–p–n* amplifying stage. The desired operating-point coordinates are $I_C = 0.2$ mA, $V_{CE} = 5$ V, and elements R_1 and R_3 need not be used. If $h_{FE} = 100$ for the transistor used, find R_2 and R_C. I_{CBO} is negligible.

3–23. Determine the operating-point coordinates I_E and V_{CE} of the video amplifier shown in the figure. Consider $I_{CBO} = 0$, $V_{BE} = 0$, and $h_{FE} = 50$.

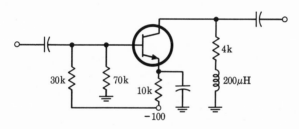

Problem 3–23.

3–24. Consider the common-base circuit of the figure. We desire $I_E = 1$ mA and $V_{BC} = 5$V. The load is 5000 Ω.

(a) Calculate the necessary values of V_{CC} and V_{EE} if R_1 is 1000 Ω.
(b) Derive an expression for I_C in terms of the circuit parameters.
(c) Derive an expression for $\partial I_C/\partial I_{CO}$.
(d) From your answer to (c), how can you achieve high stability in this circuit?
(e) What effects would a bypassed base resistance have upon the operation of this circuit?
(f) How would it be possible to operate a common-base circuit from one supply? Think.
(g) Discuss the circuit from the standpoint of ac power lost in R_1 if the ac input resistance of the transistor is 50 Ω.

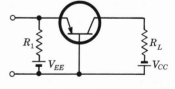

Problem 3–24.

3–25. For the common-collector circuit shown, $I_E = 1$ mA, $|I_B| = 100$ μA, $V_{EC} = 10$ V, and the load is 1000 Ω.

(a) Find R_2 if $V_{BB} = V_{EE}/2$.
(b) Derive an expression for I_E in terms of the circuit parameters.

(c) Derive an expression $\partial I_E / \partial I_{CO}$.

(d) From your answer to (c), how can high stability be achieved with this circuit?

(e) What effects would a bypassed collector resistance have upon this circuit?

3–26. The various biasing circuits (except self-bias) may be analytically treated by considering the transistor's base supply from a Thevenin equivalent viewpoint. The generalized diagram of the accompanying figure can then be used for analysis of the different biasing techniques by altering or deleting elements in the figure. For example, for fixed bias from a single supply, $V_2 = 0$, $R_b = R_2$ and $V_1 = V_{CC}$.

(a) Derive an expression for I_C for the generalized biasing circuit.

(b) For fixed bias, single-battery bias, and emitter bias, make a listing of the values of V_1, V_2, and R_b in terms of V_{CC}, V_{EE}, R_2, and R_3.

(c) Confirm Eqs. (3–7), (3–10), and (3–12). Consider that $V_{BB} = V_{CC} = V_{EE}$.

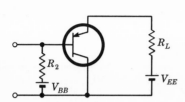

Problem 3–25.

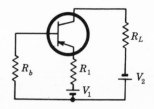

Problem 3–26.

3–27. Determine the general biasing relation with numerical coefficients using values given in the text and in Fig. 3–17, but with Q_2 at 1 mA. Repeat with Q_2 at 2 mA.

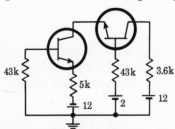

Problem 3–28.

3–28. Consider the circuit of the figure. Determine the voltage between each transistor terminal and ground. The transistors are identical, $h_{FE} = 49$, $V_{BE} = 0.28$ V, and I_{CBO} is negligible.

3–29. The p-channel FET, described by Fig. 1–16, is to be biased at $V_{GS} = 1.0$ V, $V_{DS} = -8$ V. The only available supply is -30 V, and the gate current can be considered negligible. Design the stage by specifying values of R_D, R_S, and gate resistances for the following cases: (a) Self-bias, (b) Modified self-bias. Compare the S_F factors of your two circuits.

3–30. Bias the circuit of the example of Sec. 3–13, considering that $\Delta I_G = 0$ and that $\Delta I_D = 10^{-4}$; use the circuit of Fig. 3–22(a). Repeat for the circuit of Fig. 3–22(b).

REFERENCES

1. DeWitt, D., and Rossoff, A. L., *Transistor Electronics* (McGraw-Hill Book Co., Inc., New York, 1957).

2. Lo, A. W., *et al.*, *Transistor Electronics* (Prentice-Hall, Inc., Englewood Cliffs, New Jersey, 1955).

3. Hunter, L. P., *Handbook of Semiconductor Electronics* (McGraw-Hill Book Co., Inc., New York, 1962), 2nd ed.

4. Riddle, R. L., and Ristenbatt, M. P., *Transistor Physics and Circuits* (Prentice-Hall, Inc., Englewood Cliffs, New Jersey, 1958).
5. Mulligan, J. H. Jr., and Shamis, S. S., "Transistor Amplifier Stages with Prescribed Gain and Static and Dynamic Sensitivity," *Communication and Electronics*, No. 55, (July, 1961).
6. Murray, R. P., "Design of Transistor RC Amplifiers," *IRE Trans.*, **AV-6**, No. 3 (May–June, 1958).
7. Shea, R. F., "Transistor Operation: Stabilization of Operating Point 5," *Proc. IRE*, **40** (November, 1952).
8. Shea, R. F., *Transistor Circuit Engineering* (John Wiley & Sons, Inc., New York, 1957).
9. Staff, Texas Instruments, Inc., *Transistor Circuit Design* (McGraw-Hill Book Co., Inc., New York, 1963).
10. Tuszynski, A., "Correlation Between the Base–Emitter Voltage and Its Temperature Coefficient," *Solid-State Design*, **3**, No. 7, (July, 1962).

Chapter 4

EQUIVALENT CIRCUITS AND THEIR PARAMETERS

The impedance levels that a transistor circuit presents to a signal source and load and the signal amplification it provides may be determined either graphically or analytically. Graphical techniques are generally employed for analyzing high-signal-level stages and for checking the suitability of the operating point. The normal procedure for analyzing stages that are required to handle signals of small amplitude exclusively is to calculate performance using mathematical equations involving the small-signal parameters supplied by the manufacturer or determined by test.

An electrical *equivalent circuit* or *model* will be used to represent the active device, either transistor or FET. Although these devices are basically nonlinear, over a limited range of their operating characteristics the relations between significant currents and voltages may be assumed to be linear. The small-signal equivalent circuits based upon that assumption will be studied in this chapter.

4–1. Equivalent Circuits. A large number of different equivalent circuits for the transistor have been proposed, and it is conceivable that as transistors enter higher-frequency regions of operation, or are manufactured by new processes, new equivalents will be born. Exactness in representation is somewhat responsible for the many equivalents, for an electrical model for any device is subject to many refinements. However, any equivalent circuit employed is an approximation to actual behavior because an exact equivalent, if available, would be unwieldy. Therefore, because of nonlinearities of characteristics and the lumping of distributed parameters, great accuracy in the calculation of the performance of transistor circuitry is unwarranted; simplifying assumptions should be utilized whenever applicable.

Once an acceptable model is selected from a technical standpoint to represent a device, it will remain the same regardless of the circuit configuration in which the device is employed, i.e., common-base, common-emitter, or common-collector. The equivalent circuit of a transistor derived for the common-base configuration can be used when employing the device in some other configuration

90

just by connecting the three terminals of the transistor equivalent circuit to the proper places in the network.

It is sometimes more convenient to utilize alternate nomenclature when considering the various configurations. Thus β, the current-amplification factor relating excursions in collector current to those of base current, is most likely to be employed in discussing the common-emitter configuration (and also common-collector), while α, the ratio of variations in collector current to those of emitter current, is most often used in working with common-base stages. With the normal tools of circuit theory, it is possible to arrive at several different representations because of the interrelations among parameters.

Early work with transistors used the *current-generator equivalent* tee representation. The *hybrid equivalent* circuit, because of the ease of measurement of its parameters, has gained wide acceptance. The *y parameters* are also easily measured and have become more-or-less standard for describing higher-frequency devices, and are being used for the FET. The *hybrid-π* equivalent circuit is extremely useful for studies of the high-frequency behavior and gain sensitivity of common-emitter stages. Our attention in this and future chapters will be directed toward circuit analysis and design employing these four representations for the active device.

4–2. Matrix Parameters. A two-terminal-pair or two-port network may be treated as a black box and general equations written relating the terminal quantities V_1, I_1, V_2 and I_2. A general representation of such a device is shown in Fig. 4–1. Within the box is a linear, active, bilateral network—here a transistor. Because the external conditions are measurable, the device within the box can be characterized by a set of four parameters; these parameters are the coefficients in the pair of simultaneous equations that may be written to relate the external quantities.

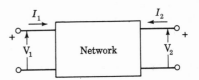

Fig. 4–1. General network showing reference directions for external quantities.

For example, the box of Fig. 4–1 can be described by

$$V_1 = z_{11}I_1 + z_{12}I_2;$$
$$V_2 = z_{21}I_1 + z_{22}I_2, \tag{4-1}$$

Eqs. (4–1) can be written in matrix form:

$$\begin{bmatrix} V_1 \\ V_2 \end{bmatrix} = \begin{bmatrix} z_{11} & z_{12} \\ z_{11} & z_{22} \end{bmatrix} \begin{bmatrix} I_1 \\ I_2 \end{bmatrix}. \tag{4-2}$$

The elementary rules of matrix algebra, as given in Appendix II, provide for an expansion of Eq. (4–2) that yields Eqs. (4–1). For some purposes, a shorthand form of Eq. (4–2) is useful:

$$[V] = [z][I]. \tag{4-3}$$

Matrix methods are of value in solving certain transistor circuit problems. They are used specifically in Secs. 5–11 and 8–4.

Returning to Fig. 4–1, it can be noted that five other equation pairs may be written to relate the terminal quantities:

$$I_1 = y_{11}V_1 + y_{12}V_2;$$
$$I_2 = y_{21}V_1 + y_{22}V_2. \tag{4-4}$$

$$V_1 = h_{11}I_1 + h_{12}V_2;$$
$$I_2 = h_{21}I_1 + h_{22}V_2. \tag{4-5}$$

$$I_1 = g_{11}V_1 + g_{12}I_2;$$
$$V_2 = g_{21}V_1 + g_{22}I_2 \tag{4-6}$$

$$V_1 = a_{11}V_2 - a_{12}I_2;$$
$$I_1 = a_{21}V_2 - a_{22}I_2. \tag{4-7}$$

$$V_2 = b_{11}V_1 - b_{12}I_1;$$
$$I_2 = b_{21}V_1 - b_{22}I_1. \tag{4-8}$$

The above relationships may also be written in matrix form (see Problem 4–1). *The positive directions of currents and voltages are defined as shown in Fig. 4–1.*

For each of the above equation pairs, it is possible to draw an equivalent electrical circuit, a circuit that could be considered to be the contents of the box of Fig. 4–1. The equivalent circuit that satisfies Eqs. (4–1) is shown in Fig. 4–2 and has been called the *z* equivalent. In a like manner equivalent circuits for the other equations can be drawn, and many variations are possible, particularly when one considers the equivalence of sources.

Further study of the *z* equivalent is of value. Each of the *z* parameters must have the dimensions of impedance, but it is to be noted that $z_{12}I_2$ and $z_{21}I_1$ are *dependent* voltage sources. If I_2 were to be caused to equal zero, by open-circuiting the output-terminal pair, z_{11} could be referred to as the *input impedance with output open-circuited*. Mathematically

$$z_{11} = \frac{V_1}{I_1}\bigg|_{V_2 = 0}. \tag{4-9}$$

In a similar manner, with open terminations, the other *z* parameters are referred to as transfer and output impedances.

With V_2 short circuited the current transfer ratio of the *z* parameter circuit is

$$I_2/I_1 = -z_{21}/z_{22}. \tag{4-10}$$

For a common-emitter-connected transistor this ratio is equal to β and for common-base it equals $-\alpha$. Because the *z* parameters are determined from open-circuit measurements, and it is virtually impossible to provide such terminations for transistors while retaining the required dc levels necessary for biasing, the z parameters are not particularly useful for transistor studies.

4–3. The Hybrid Equivalent Circuit. The *hybrid or h* parameters have become the most used for describing the characteristics of the transistor. They are the coefficients in Eqs. (4–5). Repeated here,

$$V_1 = h_{11}I_1 + h_{12}V_2; \tag{4–11}$$

$$I_2 = h_{21}I_1 + h_{22}V_2. \tag{4–12}$$

The h-parameter equivalent circuit can take on the form of Fig. 4–3 in order to satisfy Eqs. (4–11) and (4–12). Since the defining equations must obey Kirchhoff's Laws, h_{11} must be an impedance, and h_{22} an admittance while h_{12} and h_{21} are dimensionless. *For low-frequency analysis of junction transistors, h_{11} and h_{22} will be resistive.*

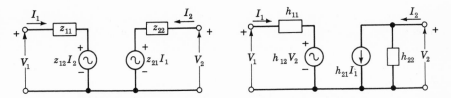

Fig. 4–2. *z*-parameter equivalent circuit.   Fig. 4–3. *h*-parameter equivalent circuit.

The ease of measurement of the h parameters has contributed to their widespread adoption. If the output terminals are ac short-circuited, then $V_2 = 0$ and

$$h_{11} = V_1/I_1. \tag{4–13}$$

Also

$$h_{21} = I_2/I_1. \tag{4–14}$$

Opening the ac input circuit reduces I_1 to zero and gives

$$h_{12} = V_1/V_2, \tag{4–15}$$

and

$$h_{22} = I_2/V_2. \tag{4–16}$$

Therefore h_{11} is called the "input impedance with output short-circuited," and h_{22} is the "output admittance with input open-circuited." Likewise, h_{12} is the "voltage feedback ratio with input open-circuited," and h_{21} is the "current amplification with output short-circuited." It is interesting to note that $h_{21} = \beta$ when we consider a common-emitter-connected transistor and $h_{21} = -\alpha$ for a transistor in the common-base mode, because h_{21}, α, and β are defined for short-circuit loading. A negative sign precedes α because of the direction assigned to I_2 in Fig. 4–3; in the common-base configuration, current flowing into the emitter terminal actually results in collector current out of the collector terminal.

The short and open circuits referred to in the preceding paragraph for the measurement of transistor parameters may be accomplished in the laboratory by the insertion of suitable capacitors and inductors. A large-valued capacitor across an output terminal pair will short-circuit an ac signal, but will not disturb quiescent conditions. Likewise, a large-valued choke in an input bias current supply will essentially open that circuit to ac.

In order to standardize transistor nomenclature, the Institute of Electrical and Electronics Engineers recommend the following parameter symbols:

$$h_i = h_{11} \text{ (Input impedance),}$$

$$h_r = h_{12} \text{ (Reverse voltage feedback ratio),}$$

$$h_f = h_{21} \text{ (Forward current transfer ratio),}$$

$$h_o = h_{22} \text{ (Output admittance).}$$

The values of parameters will depend upon the circuit configuration employed; consequently, a second subscript is added to the h parameters to designate the orientation. Thus h_{ib}, h_{rb}, h_{fb}, and h_{ob} describe common-base performance, while h_{ie}, h_{re}, h_{fe}, and h_{oe} are used for common-emitter-connected transistors, and h_{ic}, h_{rc}, h_{fc}, and h_{oc} are the applicable parameters for common-collector work. Since the symbols with numerical subscripts do not specify the transistor connection employed, one occasionally finds h_{11b}, etc., used as well as h_{11e}, etc., and h_{11c}, etc. Figure 4–4 depicts circuits employing the recommended nomenclature.

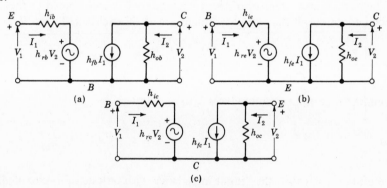

Fig. 4–4. h-parameter equivalent circuits: (a) common-base; (b) common-emitter; (c) common-collector.

The equivalent circuits of Fig. 4–4 for the three standard configurations do not differ, because they all must satisfy the defining equations. Only the parameter nomenclature varies because of configuration, and it is therefore possible to derive performance equations in terms of general parameters, h_i, h_r, h_f, and h_o and then, with these formulas, calculate circuit operation by inserting the specific parameters that correspond to the circuit configuration being analyzed. The performance equations will be derived in Chapter 5.

Before leaving the hybrid equivalent, we note typical values of these parameters for the purpose of evaluating the effects of certain approximations useful in the derivation of mathematical relations. For a junction transistor, specifically the 2N3242, the following common-emitter parameters are typical at $V_{CE} = 12$ V, $I_C = 10$ mA, measured at a frequency of 1 kc/sec:

$$h_{ie} = 600 \, \Omega, \qquad h_{fe} = 175,$$
$$h_{re} = 1.25 \times 10^{-4}, \qquad h_{oe} = 75 \times 10^{-6} \text{ mho.}$$

These correspond to the following common-base values:

$$h_{ib} = 3.6 \, \Omega, \qquad h_{fb} = -0.994,$$
$$h_{rb} = 1.45 \times 10^{-4}, \qquad h_{ob} = 0.45 \times 10^{-6} \text{ mho.}$$

The equivalent common-collector parameters are

$$h_{ic} = 600 \, \Omega, \qquad h_{fc} = -176,$$
$$h_{rc} = 1, \qquad h_{oc} = 75 \times 10^{-6} \text{ mho.}$$

Common-base and common-collector parameters are not listed in Appendix I under this transistor type; they are obtained using the relations of Table 4–1.

4–4. The y-Parameter Equivalent Circuit. The defining equations were given in Eqs. (4–4). In matrix form

$$\begin{bmatrix} I_1 \\ I_2 \end{bmatrix} = \begin{bmatrix} y_{11} & y_{12} \\ y_{21} & y_{22} \end{bmatrix} \begin{bmatrix} V_1 \\ V_2 \end{bmatrix}. \qquad (4\text{–}17)$$

All of the y parameters are obtained from short-circuit measurements. They are primarily applicable at high frequencies where obtaining a valid open circuit is especially difficult because of the effects of stray capacitances upon measured parameter values.

The y equivalent circuit is shown in Fig. 4–5. Two dependent current generators are apparent in the diagram. Should a two-voltage-generator model be desired, source interchanges could

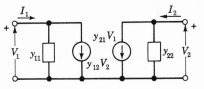

Fig. 4–5. y-parameter equivalent circuit.

be employed and the result would be analagous to Fig. 4–1 and the z equivalent. The y parameters are often employed to describe a transistor at a particular frequency. For example, at 30 Mc, $V_{CE} = 20$ V, and $I_C = 20$ mA, the following values apply to a sample type 2N697 transistor:

$$y_{ie} = (22.5 + j14.7)10^{-3} \text{ mho}, \qquad y_{fe} = (36.6 - j91.6)10^{-3} \text{ mho},$$
$$y_{re} = (-0.8 - j0.38)10^{-3} \text{ mho}, \qquad y_{oe} = (1.7 + j5.7)10^{-3} \text{ mho.}$$

The y parameters are also used for the FET. Further discussion is reserved for Sec. 4–11.

4–5. Current-Generator Equivalent Tee. Another means of representing the small-signal characteristics of the transistor is to use a "T" model, a network comprised of a resistance in each of the three branches associated with the triode. To simulate the amplification provided by the device when properly biased and terminated, a dependent generator is added to the resistive tee. Thus the *current-generator equivalent tee* contains elements r_e, r_c, and r_b in the emitter, collector, and base branches, respectively, and a current generator αI_e connected across r_c, as shown in Fig. 4–6(a). The resistances of the tee model represent bulk resistance, semiconductor "barrier" resistance, and the internal feedback caused by base-width modulation.

The tee equivalent was first employed for common-base connected devices. In Fig. 4–6(a) a time-varying emitter current I_e entering the emitter terminal causes the collector current I_c to instantaneously leave the device. Because no phase reversal is observed in the common-base connection, the current gain factor α must be a positive quantity.

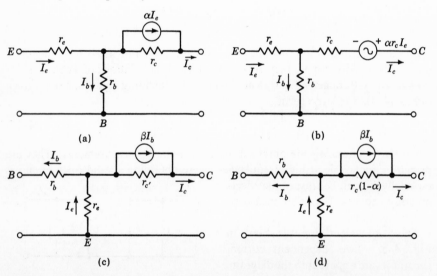

Fig. 4–6.   (a) Common-base current-generator equivalent circuit; (b) common-base voltage-generator equivalent circuit; (c) common-emitter equivalent of (a); (d) common-emitter equivalent with all parameters in terms of (a).

For circuit studies it is often convenient to replace the current generator and parallel resistance with an equivalent voltage-generator, series-resistance combination according to the Thevenin and Norton Theorems. The result of this interchange is the circuit of Fig. 4–6(b). The interchange of sources is a useful tool, and it is recommended that the reader review his ability to perform this task. Simply, when making a source interchange, the value of the source resistance (or impedance) does not change but its location does, and a current generator of I

becomes a voltage generator of magnitude IR. To reverse the procedure, a voltage generator of V becomes a current generator of V/R.

For the common-emitter connection, the equivalent circuits of Figs. 4–6(a) and 4–6(b) apply, but it is necessary to interchange the branches that include r_e and r_b. It is customary, however, to think of the collector current generator as dependent upon the input quality I_b rather than I_e as in Fig. 4–6(c). To change from αI_e paralleling r_c to βI_b paralleling some new resistance r_c', we recall the summation of currents

$$I_e = I_c + I_b. \tag{4–18}$$

Then in making a source transformation of αI_e, the resulting voltage generator can be written as $\alpha(I_c + I_b)r_c$. But in series with this generator is r_c, and consequently an $I_c r_c$ voltage drop. If we combine the rise $\alpha I_c r_c$ with the drop $I_c r_c$, then $I_c r_c(1 - \alpha)$ is the composite drop due to collector current and $\alpha I_b r_c$ the total rise. Transforming these into a current-generator equivalent yields, for the generator,

$$V/R = (\alpha I_b r_c)/[r_c(1 - \alpha)] = \beta I_b,$$

and the resistance paralleling this source is

$$r_c' = r_c(1 - \alpha). \tag{4–19}$$

The generally accepted circuit for common-emitter studies is Fig. 4–6(d). A common-collector equivalent is presented in Sec. 5–3.

It is obvious from Fig. 4–6 that the T model as given here is applicable to low-frequency studies exclusively. A T-equivalent modified for high-frequencies studies would include collector barrier capacitance and frequency-dependent current-amplification factor.

4–6. Parameter Interrelations. When using hybrid parameters it is somewhat cumbersome to provide a complete set of 12 parameters for each transistor type. Consequently, it has become more-or-less standard for manufacturers to supply just one set of four parameters. The user can either mathematically solve for the other sets, or can rearrange the applicable equivalent circuit by transferring terminals. Both methods will be employed in subsequent paragraphs.

Our goal is to derive a series of relations among the three sets of h parameters. To study the other connections, we shall rearrange the terminals of the common-base circuit of Fig. 4–4(a). This repositioning is shown in Fig. 4–7. In (a) of that figure, we have the equivalent common-emitter circuit in terms of common-base parameters. To find h_{ie} and h_{fe}, recall that

$$\left.\begin{array}{l} h_{ie} = V_1/I_1 \\ h_{fe} = I_2/I_1 \end{array}\right\} \text{ for output short-circuited.}$$

The output short-circuit results in the network of Fig. 4–8(a). A further simplification to that of Fig. 4–8(b) can be made with a knowledge of typical parameter

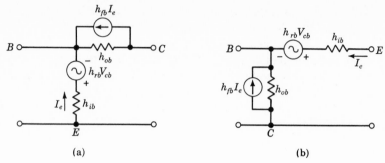

(a)   (b)

Fig. 4–7.   Repositioning of the terminals of the common-base circuit of Fig. 4–4(a)
for (a) common-emitter analysis; (b) common-collector analysis.

values: h_{rb} normally has a value of 10^{-3} or 10^{-4}, and h_{ob} usually represents a
resistance of 10^5 or 10^6 Ω. These two parameters will be removed for simplicity
and then

$$-I_1 = I_e + h_{fb}I_e,$$
$$V_1 = -I_e h_{ib}. \tag{4–20}$$

Since

$$h_{ie} = V_1/I_1 = (-I_e h_{ib})/[-I_e(1 + h_{fb})], \tag{4–21}$$

then

$$h_{ie} = h_{ib}/(1 + h_{fb}). \tag{4–22}$$

We know that

$$h_{fe} = I_c/I_1 = (I_e h_{fb})/[-I_e(1 + h_{fb})]. \tag{4–23}$$

Therefore

$$h_{fe} = -h_{fb}/(1 + h_{fb}). \tag{4–24}$$

In a similar manner equations for h_{re} and h_{oe} as well as the common-collector
parameters may be derived (see Problems 4–7 and 4–8). Table 4–1 presents a
summary of these relations among parameters.

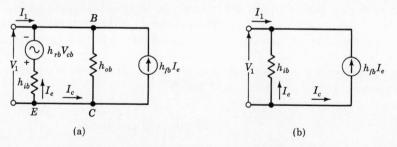

(a)   (b)

Fig. 4–8.   Circuits for derivation of relationships between common-base and common-
emitter parameters: (a) Fig. 4–7(a) with output short-circuited; (b) further simplification.

TABLE 4–1.   APPROXIMATE RELATIONS AMONG h PARAMETERS.

Relations between common-base and common-emitter parameters	Relations between common-base and common-collector parameters
$h_{ie} = h_{ib}/(1 + h_{fb})$	$h_{ic} = h_{ib}/(1 + h_{fb})$
$h_{re} = \dfrac{h_{ib}h_{ob} - h_{rb}h_{fb} - h_{rb}}{1 + h_{fb}}$	$h_{rc} = 1$
$h_{fe} = -h_{fb}/(1 + h_{fb})$	$h_{fc} = -1/(1 + h_{fb})$
$h_{oe} = h_{ob}/(1 + h_{fb})$	$h_{oc} = h_{ob}/(1 + h_{fb})$

To derive relations among the sets of matrix parameters, procedures that include shorting and opening of the ports may be employed. Matrix interrelations are given in Appendix II.

T and h Parameters. The T and h parameters must be related, for the two equivalent circuits were used to describe the same device—the transistor; the gain and impedance-level equations must be identical, whether expressed in r's or h's. Our goal at this point is to find relations between the two sets of parameters. To simplify the problem we shall consider only the common-base h parameters; Table 4–1 will then give us h parameters for the other configurations, if desired.

It has already been noted that

$$h_{fb} = -\alpha. \tag{4–25}$$

The input resistance for the common-base stage with load short-circuited is h_{ib}. If the T circuit is solved for its input resistance with collector-to-base shorted, we obtain

$$R_i = r_e + [r_b r_c (1 - \alpha)]/(r_b + r_c). \tag{4–26}$$

Equating h_{ib} to R_i of Eq. (4–26) yields the following relation between parameter sets:

$$h_{ib} \cong r_e + r_b(1 - \alpha) \tag{4–27}$$

when one assumes $r_c \gg r_b$.

The output resistance of a common-base stage with input open is $1/h_{ob}$ in hybrid terms and approximately r_c in the T circuit. Therefore,

$$1/h_{ob} \cong r_c. \tag{4–28}$$

Formulas for input and output impedance levels and amplificational properties of terminated two-port networks are available in Chapter. 5.

It can be noted from the common-base T equivalent that the voltage fed back with input open can be approximated using simple voltage division by $r_b/(r_c + r_b)$. Consequently,

$$h_{rb} \cong r_b/r_c. \tag{4–29}$$

These equations are tabulated in Table 4–2 along with T parameters in terms of h's.

TABLE 4–4. APPROXIMATE RELATIONS BETWEEN h PARA-
METERS AND T PARAMETERS.

$$h_{tb} = r_e + r_b(1 - \alpha) \qquad\qquad r_e = h_{tb} - \frac{h_{rb}}{h_{ob}}(1 + h_{fb})$$

$$h_{rb} = r_b/r_c \qquad\qquad r_b = h_{rb}/h_{ob}$$

$$h_{fb} = -\alpha \qquad\qquad r_c = 1/h_{ob}$$

$$h_{ob} = 1/r_c \qquad\qquad \alpha = -h_{fb}$$

Curves and Parameters.   Because either a set of curves or a set of parameters may be used to specify an active circuit element such as the transistor, the curves and parameters must be related. For the common-emitter connection with collector voltage and base current as independent variables, the functional relationships among variables are

$$v_{BE} = f(i_B, v_{CE}),$$
$$i_C = f(i_B, v_{CE}). \tag{4–30}$$

A differential change in the *total value* of base voltage is

$$dv_{BE} = \frac{\partial v_{BE}}{\partial i_B} di_B + \frac{\partial v_{BE}}{\partial v_{CE}} dv_{CE} \tag{4–31}$$

and a differential change in i_C is

$$di_C = \frac{\partial i_C}{\partial i_B} di_B + \frac{\partial i_C}{\partial v_{CE}} dv_{CE}. \tag{4–32}$$

The rms values of *small* ac signals can represent differential changes:

$$di_C = I_c, \qquad dv_{CE} = V_{ce},$$
$$di_B = I_b, \qquad dv_{BE} = V_{be}.$$

The operating range over the characteristics may be considered as linear if the changes are small; therefore, the partial derivatives are constants. Symbols have already been assigned to them. Thus Eqs. (4–31) and (4–32) become

$$V_{be} = h_{ie}I_b + h_{re}V_{ce}, \tag{4–33}$$
$$I_c = h_{fe}I_b + h_{oe}V_{ce}. \tag{4–34}$$

In Chapter 1 a pictorial definition of beta was given, and it was shown to be the incremental ratio of collector current to base current at a constant value of v_{CE}.

From collector characteristics the slope of the lines of constant total base current yields h_{oe}; the validity of this statement is evident from Eqs. (4–32) and (4–34):

$$h_{oe} = \left.\frac{\partial i_C}{\partial v_{CE}}\right|_{i_b = 0} \tag{4–35}$$

To determine the two remaining parameters of the set graphically, one must have the input characteristics of base current vs base-to-emitter voltage for various collector-to-emitter potentials. Such a curve is Fig. 1–7(b). h_{ie} is the slope of the lines of constant v_{CE} and, mathematically,

$$h_{ie} = \left.\frac{\partial v_{BE}}{\partial i_B}\right|_{v_{ce} = 0} \tag{4–36}$$

From the same characteristics,

$$h_{re} = \left.\frac{\partial v_{BE}}{\partial v_{CE}}\right|_{i_b = 0} \tag{4–37}$$

4–7. Parameter Variations. Transistor parameters are dependent upon the physical characteristics of the materials used in manufacture, such as the conductivities of the various portions of the structure, and upon the important dimensions of the device, such as base width. Because junction temperature affects material properties, collector voltage influences the effective base width, and quiescent current determines the density of carriers in the base region, it is natural to expect that transistor parameters will be dependent upon T, V_{CE}, and I_C.

Variation of Parameters with Temperature. To some extent each of the parameters of any transistor equivalent circuit exhibits temperature sensitivity. When the internal or junction temperature varies over a considerable range, definite steps must be taken to compensate a circuit for changes in parameter values.

A family of curves showing typical variations in the T parameters is shown in Fig. 4–9. The major reduction that occurs in r_c can be extremely unwelcome. Likewise, variations in the other parameters present problems of gain stability and tend to alter input and output impedances. To overcome the effects of temperature variations on parameters, feedback networks and compensating circuitry are often employed. As can be seen from examination of Fig. 4–10, as much as a 4:1 variation in some of the parameters of a typical

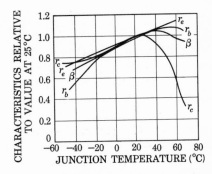

Fig. 4–9. Variation of the T parameters of a germanium transistor with junction temperature.

silicon transistor is possible if one considers operation over the wide temperature range indicated.

Variation of Parameters with Operating Point.   The parameters of the transistor are sensitive to biasing conditions. The quiescent collector-to-base voltage and the quiescent emitter current each account for specific factors that alter the nominal values of the parameters. Nominal parameter values for low-power transistors are most often given for operation at $I_C = 1$ mA and V_{CE} of 5 or 6 V;

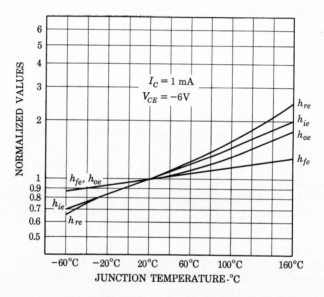

Fig. 4–10.   Variation of the *h* parameters of a silicon transistor with junction temperature.

should the application require operation at a different point (as it most often does), the nominal parameter values should be multiplied by the correction factors supplied by the manufacturer or determined by test. Typical correction information is shown in Figs. 4–11 and 4–12.

Example.   It is desired to operate a particular transistor at $I_C = 5$mA, $V_{CE} = 2$ V. The parameter-correction information of Figs. 4–11 and 4–12 applies. Consider the nominal parameters to be as follows: $h_{ie} = 3000\ \Omega$, $h_{fe} = 100, h_{re} = 10^{-3}, h_{oe} = 10^{-5}$ mho.

The corrected values of the parameters are

$$h_{ie} = (3000)(0.6)(0.92) = 1655\ \Omega,$$
$$h_{fe} = (100)(1.2)(0.92) \ = 110,$$
$$h_{re} = (10^{-3})(2.8)(1.7) \ = 4.75 \times 10^{-3},$$
$$h_{oe} = (10^{-5})(4.0)(2.0) \ = 8 \times 10^{-5}\ \text{mho}.$$

Effect of Manufacturing Tolerances. A most troublesome variation in parameters occurs because of production tolerances. The spread in possible values for the parameters of a single transistor type when it leaves the manufacturers is illustrated by the typical numbers quoted below:

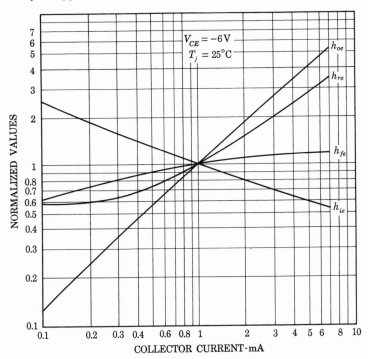

Fig. 4–11. Typical variation of h parameters with I_C.

Parameter	Minimum	Design Center	Maximum
h_{ib} in ohms	30	40	90
h_{ob} in micromhos	0.1	0.4	1.5
h_{rb}	$50(10^{-6})$	$500(10^{-6})$	$1500(10^{-6})$
h_{fb}	-0.97	-0.98	-1.0

While for any particular sample it is unlikely that all parameters will be at their maximum or at their minimum values, nevertheless the circuit designer must be cognizant of the expected variations and compensate his circuits for the effects of these variations upon performance.

4–8. High-Frequency Parameters. The parameters of some transistor types begin to take on complex form at the upper end of the audio-frequency spectrum, and to calculate circuit performance successfully corrections must be made to the low-frequency equivalent circuits.

Collector Capacitance. One of the important considerations is junction capacitance. The collector-to-base capacitance in the common-base equivalent, C_{ob}, parallels the aforementioned conductive h_{ob}, and has a nominal value in the range from 1 to 50 pF. To maintain a consistent set of symbols, C_{oe} will be used to designate collector-to-emitter capacitance in the common-emitter configuration.

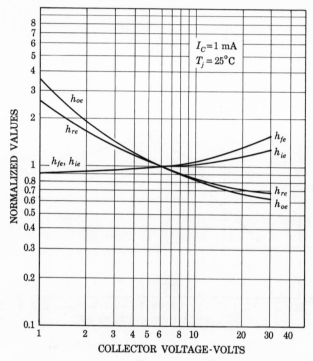

Fig. 4–12. Typical variation of h parameters with V_{CE}.

C_o is not a constant, but is subject to variations due to the same factors that caused the T and h parameters to vary, namely, temperature, emitter current, collector potential, frequency, and manufacturing techniques. Typical variations of this parameter are given in Fig. 4–13(a). It is customary to specify C_o at a high frequency, usually not that at which the other parameters are specified.

To include the effects of collector capacitance in the hybrid equivalent circuit, one needs only to add an admittance of $j\omega C_{ob}$ in parallel with the conductive h_{ob} element.

Alpha Variation. C_o is not the only factor that results in operational differences at high frequencies. Because of the diffusion capacitance, the magnitude of h_{fb} varies with frequency according to the approximate relation

$$h_{fb} = h_{fbo}/[1 + j(f/f_{hfb})],$$

$$(4\text{--}38)$$

where $h_{f_{bo}}$ indicates the reference or low-frequency value of the parameter, and $f_{h_{fb}}$ symbolizes the "alpha-cutoff frequency," the frequency at which the magnitude of the current-amplification factor has decreased to 0.707 of its low-frequency value. The symbols f_{ab} and f_{α} are also used for this quantity. To represent the "beta-cutoff frequency," $f_{h_{fe}}$ will be used. This parameter is also symbolized by $f_{\alpha e}$ and by f_{β}.

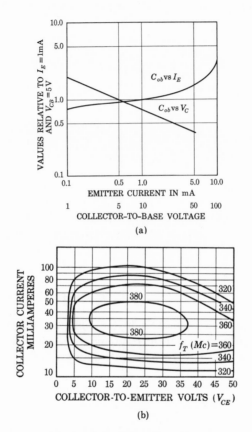

Fig. 4–13.   (a) Variation of collector capacitance with operating point; (b) contours of constant f_T for silicon planar transistor.

The common-emitter short-circuit current-amplification factor h_{fe} varies according to

$$h_{fe} = h_{feo}/[1 + j(f/f_{h_{fe}})],\tag{4-39}$$

but h_{fe} is a function of h_{fb}

$$h_{fe} = -h_{fb}/(1 + h_{fb}).\tag{4-40}$$

Therefore

$$h_{fe} = \frac{-h_{fbo}/[1 + j(f/f_{hfb})]}{1 + h_{fbo}/[1 + j(f/f_{hfb})]}.$$ (4–41a)

Simplifying,

$$h_{fe} = \frac{-h_{fbo}}{1 + h_{fbo} + j(f/f_{hfb})}$$ (4–41b)

h_{fe} in Eq. (4–41(b)) will be down by 3 dB when real and imaginary parts of its denominator are equal:

$$1 + h_{fbo} = f/f_{hfb},$$ (4–42)

or at

$$f = (1 + h_{fbo})f_{hfb}.$$ (4–43)

Hence

$$f_{hfe} = (1 + h_{fbo})f_{hfb}.$$ (4–44a)

The $(1 + h_{fbo})$ term has a nominal value of less than 0.1. It may be concluded that the common-emitter configuration is inferior to common-base circuitry when high-frequency operation is considered, for the former configuration experiences a decline in its current-amplification parameter at a much lower frequency. Nevertheless because it is basically a higher-gain configuration, common-emitter stages are used in most high-frequency applications.

Test data taken on transistors manufactured by various methods are not in complete agreement with Eq. (4–44a), and suggest that equation be modified to the form

$$f_{hfe} = K_{\theta}(1 + h_{fbo})f_{hfb}.$$ (4–44b)

The value of K_{θ} is never greater than unity and ranges as low as 0.6 with certain transistor types.

A parameter especially applicable to the common-emitter stage is f_T, the *current-gain bandwidth product* or the *transition frequency*. This parameter is the frequency at which $|h_{fe}|$ equals unity. Obviously f_T is very much higher in the spectrum than f_{hfe}.

If Eq. (4–39) is employed with $|h_{fe}| = 1$ at $f = f_T$, the following relation may be easily obtained by using the fact that $f_T \gg f_{hfe}$:

$$f_T = h_{feo}f_{hfe}.$$ (4–45)

Upon insertion of Eq. (4–45) for f_{hfe} into Eq. (4–44a), we conclude that the value of f_T is slightly smaller than f_{hfb}.

The variation of f_T with operating-point coordinates for a typical silicon planar transistor is shown in Fig. 4–13(b). From the figure it is evident that an optimum operating point exists, at least in regard to attaining a maximum value of f_T.

4–9. The Hybrid-π Model. When studying transistor-circuit operation at higher frequencies it is sometimes inconvenient to work with the set of h parameters that are complex functions of frequency. It would be desirable to represent the transistor by a model that separates the frequency variant parameters from the purely resistive elements. In addition it is sometimes of value to examine the device by representing it in terms of a set of parameters that are directly related to the physical processes present in normal operation, related to operating-point coordinates in a known manner, and related to one another if possible. The *hybrid-π* equivalent circuit developed by Giacoletto is a valuable representation of certain transistor types, for its parameters may be considered to be frequency invariant up to the vicinity of alpha cutoff.[4]

To develop the hybrid-π circuit for common-emitter applications from physical considerations, we start by making the assumption that I_c and I_b are linearly related. If signal size is sufficiently limited, I_c and V_{be} will also be linearly related. The proportionality constant is g_m, the *transconductance*. Therefore

$$I_c = g_m V_{be} \qquad (4\text{--}46)$$

An expression for the diode-like static transfer characteristics is

$$i_C \cong K(e^{qv_{BE}/kT} - 1). \qquad (4\text{--}47)$$

Because g_m is the slope of the transfer characteristics, it may be obtained from Eq. (4–47) by differentiation:

$$g_m \equiv \partial i_C/\partial v_{BE}. \qquad (4\text{--}48)$$

It follows that

$$g_m \cong (q/kT)I_C = \Lambda I_C. \qquad (4\text{--}49)$$

Λ will symbolize q/kT in the remainder of this chapter. The magnitude of the direct collector current is apparent in Eq. (4–49). Note that g_m *is independent of the transistor type being considered.*

Between base and emitter, the transistor can be simulated by three elements, the low-frequency input resistance $r_{b'e}$, the diffusion capacitance C_d, and the space-charge capacitance C_{ej}, as discussed in Sec. 2–6.

The collector and base may be joined by space-charge capacitance C_{cj}, and by $r_{b'c}$ and C_m elements representing the mechanism of *base-width modulation*, wherein the effective width of the transistor base is dependent upon collector voltage.

In addition to the aforementioned parameters, the collector is joined to the emitter by the parameter r_{ce}, also representing the base-width modulation effect. All of these elements are depicted in Fig. 4–14(a). The bulk resistance of the lightly doped base material is called the *base-spreading resistance* $r_{bb'}$, and joins the internal or intrinsic base terminal b' to the actual available base terminal b.

Collecting parallel capacitances simplifies the circuit of Fig. 4–14(a) to the complete hybrid π form of Fig. 4–14(b).

Because the hybrid π needs five low-frequency parameters, while only four are used in the T circuit and the matrix h circuit, it is necessary to know an additional parameter for the latter two networks in order to convert to the hybrid π. This

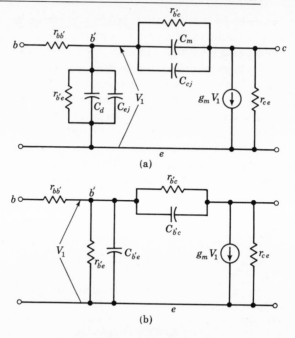

Fig. 4–14. Hybrid-π models.

extra parameter is the base-spreading resistance. Using the normal tools of circuit theory, the relations may be derived; Table 4–3 lists some of the possible equalities.

TABLE 4–3. APPROXIMATE RELATIONS AMONG PARAMETERS.*

$$r_{b'e} = h_{ie} - r_{bb'} \qquad\qquad \alpha = \frac{g_m r_{b'e}}{1 + g_m r_{b'e}}$$

$$r_{b'c} = \frac{h_{ie} - r_{bb'}}{h_{re}} \qquad r_b = r_{bb'} + \frac{r_{b'e}}{1 + (r_{ce}/r_{b'c})(1 + g_m r_{b'e})}$$

$$g_m = \frac{h_{fe}}{h_{ie} - r_{bb'}} \qquad \frac{1}{r_c} = \frac{1}{r_{b'c}} + \frac{1}{r_{ce}(1 + g_m r_{b'e})}$$

$$\frac{1}{r_{ce}} = h_{oe} - \frac{h_{fe} h_{re}}{h_{ie} - r_{bb'}} \qquad r_e = r_{b'e}/[(1 + g_m r_{b'e}) + r_{b'c}/r_{ce}]$$

* Low-frequency relations.

4–10. Parameters of the Hybrid π. It is of value to briefly investigate the behavior of the hybrid-π parameters with operating-point coordinates, and with

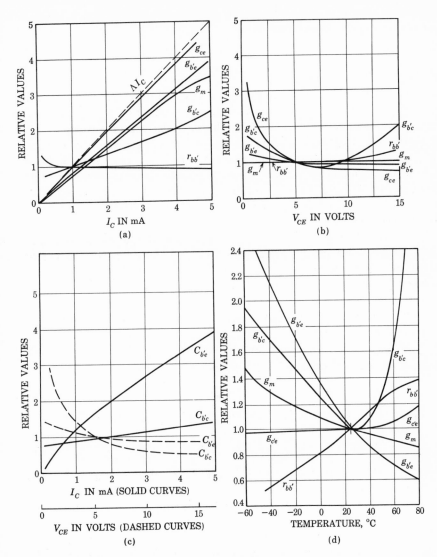

Fig. 4–15.   Typical measured behavior of hybrid-π parameters with I_C, V_{CE} and T.[2,4,5,15]

temperature. Derivations of some of the equations given in this section are not reproduced here; they are available in the literature.[4,15] Measured data relating the parameters of a sample alloy-junction germanium transistor to I_C, V_{CE}, and T are shown in Fig. 4–15.

Base-Spreading Resistance ($r_{bb'}$).   Analytical expressions for this parameter for simple transistor geometries show inverse linear dependence upon base conductivity σ_b and W the base width.[3]

$$r_{bb'} = K/\sigma_b W. \tag{4-50}$$

From this information we may predict the behavior of $r_{bb'}$ with changes in operating-point coordinates, temperature, frequency, and the correlation of the value of $r_{bb'}$ with that of the short-circuit current-amplification factor. One would expect that with increased collector voltage, which causes a widening of the depletion layer within the base region, $r_{bb'}$ should also increase. An increase in the level of emitter current should result in reduced $r_{bb'}$ because recombination will occur after a shorter distance of travel for majority carriers in the base region. It is also to be expected that $r_{bb'}$ will decrease somewhat with frequency although not predicted by Eq. (4-50), because a portion of this parameter is of a distributed nature in certain transistor types.

Measurements of alloy-junction-transistor parameters, as made by Giacoletto using bridge techniques,[5] generally confirm the predictions of the preceding paragraph. Typical behavior of $r_{bb'}$ with I_C, V_{CE}, and T is shown in Fig. 4-15.

The value of the $r_{b'c}$ element of the complete hybrid π is very large and often may be considered to be an open circuit. Under this assumption, at low frequencies, the input-resistance parameter h_{ie} of the circuit of Fig. 4-14(b) is

$$h_{ie} = r_{bb'} + r_{b'e}. \tag{4-51}$$

Because the model must exhibit a current gain of h_{fe}, it follows that

$$h_{fe} = g_m r_{b'e}. \tag{4-52}$$

Equation (4-51) may be solved for $r_{bb'}$, and $r_{b'e}$ removed by the use of Eq. (4-52). The result is

$$r_{bb'} = h_{ie} - h_{fe}/g_m. \tag{4-53}$$

When it is valid to use the theoretical value for g_m given by Eq. (4-49), simple measurements of h_{ie} and h_{fe} may be used to determine an apparent $r_{bb'}$. (The validity of this technique is discussed under the transconductance heading that follows).

While the current-amplification factor h_{fe} is not a basic parameter of the hybrid π, it is implied in $r_{b'e}$ as noted in Eq. (4-52). A high value of h_{fe} is associated with a narrow base and low base conductivity; both of these physical characteristics result in $r_{bb'}$ of large value. We would expect, therefore, that units with large h_{fe} tend to have large $r_{bb'}$.

Base–Emitter Resistance $(r_{b'e})$.   An expression that may be used for describing the reciprocal of $r_{b'e}$ is

$$g_{b'e} \cong \Lambda C I_E \tag{4-54}$$

with

$$C \equiv \sigma_b A_e W / \sigma_e A_b L_e.$$

σ_b and σ_e are conductivities of the base and emitter regions, respectively, and A_b and A_e the effective areas of those regions; W is base width and L_e the diffusion length for majority carriers in the emitter. From Eq. (4–54) we expect direct increase in $g_{b'e}$ with quiescent emitter current, and a slight decrease with increased collector voltage. Test results substantiate these predictions,[4] but the rate of increase with I_E is always less than the theoretical behavior predicted by Eq. (4–54). In order to account for this discrepancy, a further analysis of the effect of high-level carrier injection upon minority-carrier transport shows that the transistor operates as though the diffusion constant had almost doubled.

If it is recognized that $L_e = (\mu\tau/\Lambda)^{\frac{1}{2}}$, where τ is carrier lifetime in the base region, then the temperature variation of $g_{b'e}$ can be predicted. Ideally, $g_{b'e}$ should vary as $1/T^{3.2}$ because of the T in the denominator of Λ, and because of the dependence of L_e upon mobility, which may be considered to vary as $1/T^{1.6}$, and upon carrier lifetime, which varies as T^5.

Transconductance (g_m).   This parameter has already been described:

$$g_m = \Lambda I_C. \tag{4–55}$$

Measurements find g_m to be smaller than its theoretical value—down by as much as 15% from the value predicted by Eq. (4–55) at 1 mA. The effects of high-level injection are again considered to be the cause of the deviation from theoretical. A slight V_{CE} dependence has been noted, and Eschelman has reported that the measured temperature dependence of g_m agrees well with the theoretical $1/T$ function.[2]

The reciprocal of g_m is referred to in the literature as $r_{e'}$, the Shockley emitter resistance. In this study, g_m will be used exclusively.

Intrinsic Base-To-Emitter Capacitance $(C_{b'e})$.   An approximate expression for $C_{b'e}$ is

$$C_{b'e} \cong \Lambda I_C(W^2/2D). \tag{4–56}$$

D is the diffusion constant for minority carriers in the base region. Equation (4–56) implies that the transition capacitance is negligible compared with the diffusion capcitance, and assumes that I_B is small compared with I_E. It is identical with the expression for diffusion capacitance given in Eq. (2–8). Tests by Giacoletto show a large departure from the theoretical dependence upon I_C for current levels above 1 mA. At currents above 3 mA he finds a rise in $C_{b'e}$ with I_C of about one-half that predicted by Eq. (4–56). The electric field existing in the base region when the minority-carrier density is comparable with the majority-carrier density seems to be the cause of the complex behavior of this parameter.

The value of $C_{b'e}$ shows a slight decline with increased voltage because of narrowing basewidth, and exhibits essentially no change with temperature.

A form of Eq. (4–56) most useful for circuit analysis is

$$C_{b'e} \cong g_m/\omega_T. \tag{4–57}$$

The product of $C_{b'e}$ and $r_{b'e}$ describes the β-cutoff frequency $f_{h_{fe}}$, according to the relation

$$C_{b'e}r_{b'e} = h_{feo}/2\pi f_T = h_{feo}/2\pi f_{h_{fe}}h_{feo} = 1/2\pi f_{h_{fe}}. \qquad (4-58)$$

The low-frequency value of h_{fe} is h_{feo}. Proof of Eq. (4–57) is given later in this section.

Intrinsic Base-to-Collector Capacitance $(C_{b'c})$. This parameter can be theoretically described by a complicated function of physical quantities and circuit currents and potentials. It is most convenient to consider that $C_{b'c}$ will increase with increasing I_C and fall off as V_{CE} increases according to an inverse square-root relation, as given by Eq. (2–13) for barrier capacitance.

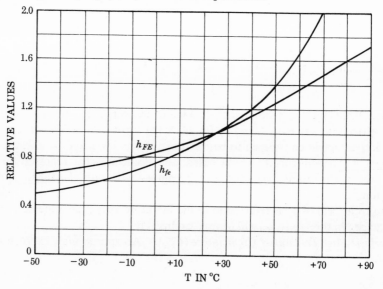

Fig. 4–16. h_{FE} and h_{fe} vs temperature.

Collector Resistive Parameters $(r_{ce}$ and $r_{b'c})$. Theoretically, these low-valued conductances should behave according to

$$g \cong KI_C(V_{CE})^{-\frac{1}{2}}. \qquad (4-59)$$

Measured values of g_{ce} do, in fact, agree well with values predicted by Eq. (4–59). The mutual element $g_{b'c}$ does not agree well with theoretically predicted behavior when an additional parameter—junction leakage—is present; its effect is not included in Eq. (4–59).

Short-Circuit Current-Amplification Factor (h_{fe}). According to the preceding theoretical treatment of $r_{b'e}$ and g_m, we might expect h_{fe} to increase as $T^{2.2}$, and to be unaffected by I_C and V_{CE}. A typical temperature variation is shown in Fig. 4–16. It is also universally found that h_{fe} increases somewhat with I_C, reaches a peak, and then declines at high current densities because of reduced emitter efficiency. The variation of h_{fe} with increasing V_{CE} generally shows a steady rise as shown in Fig. 4-12 because of reduction in base width.

Fundamental and Significant Parameters. Several of the parameters previously discussed will be considered as fundamental: they are g_m, h_{fe}, $r_{bb'}$, $C_{b'e}$, and $C_{b'c}$. Of these five parameters, h_{fe} is undoubtedly the most significant one, for the effects of production tolerances, operating point, and temperature upon h_{fe} are exceedingly important in the determination of the performance characteristics of even the simplest stage.

Typical values of the hybrid-π parameters for a type 2N2614 transistor are

$$r_{bb'} = 300 \ \Omega, \qquad\qquad g_m = 0.0385 \text{ mho},$$

$$r_{b'e} = 4000 \ \Omega, \qquad\qquad C_{b'e} = 750 \text{ pF},$$

$$r_{b'c} = 3 \times 10^6 \ \Omega, \qquad\qquad C_{b'c} = 9 \text{ pF}.$$

$$r_{ce} = 167,000 \ \Omega,$$

These values pertain at $I_C = 1$ mA, $V_{CE} = 6$ V.

Determination of the Hybrid-π Parameters. Because the hybrid-π parameters represent physical processes within the transistor that are generally inseparable, it is rather difficult to precisely measure the seven elements of the model. The special bridge techniques noted by Giacoletto provide good data on these quantities.[5] Simpler techniques will briefly be described here that provide approximate parameter values adquate for some problems. It must be remembered that these parameters are highly dependent upon bias conditions and temperature; the static conditions must be completely known before any measurements are taken.

Instead of measuring g_m, it is generally adequate to calculate this parameter from the relation given in Eq. (4-55); $g_m \cong 0.04 \times (I_C$ in mA). A measurement of h_{fe} yields $r_{b'e}$, for $r_{b'e} = h_{fe}/g_m$ according to Eq. (4-52). A low-frequency value for $r_{bb'}$ can be obtained after a measurement of h_{ie} is made, by substitution into $r_{bb'} = h_{ie} - r_{b'e}$.

At higher frequencies, $r_{bb'}$ may contain distributed effects that cause it to differ considerably from the value obtained by the method cited above. Usually a high-frequency value of $r_{bb'}$ is obtained by measuring h_{ie} at a frequency where $C_{b'e}$ and $C_{b'c}$ may be considered to be short-circuits, then $h_{ie} = r_{bb'}$.

With a signal potential source applied to the output terminals, and the input open to ac, h_{re} and h_{oe} may be determined. It follows from the hybrid-π low-frequency equivalent (neglecting capacitances) that

$$h_{re} = r_{b'e}/(r_{b'e} + r_{b'c}) \cong r_{b'e}/r_{b'c}. \tag{4-60}$$

Therefore

$$r_{b'c} \cong r_{b'e}/h_{re}. \tag{4-61}$$

To find the other resistive parameter, r_{ce}, we note that the output admittance is made up of three parts,

$$h_{oe} = 1/r_{ce} + g_m [r_{b'e}/(r_{b'e} + r_{b'c})] + 1/(r_{b'e} + r_{b'c}).   (4\text{–}62)$$

The third term is much smaller than either of the other two and will be omitted. From Eq. (4–61) and a rearrangement of Eq. (4–62), one obtains

$$r_{ce} \cong 1/(h_{oe} - g_m h_{re}).   (4\text{–}63)$$

It is possible to determine $C_{b'c}$ by use of a standard capacitance bridge. With emitter open, C_{ob}, the collector–base capacitance, can be measured. This quantity is essentially $C_{b'c}$.

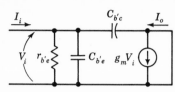

With output shorted and $r_{b'c}$ omitted, the admittance of the transistor at its intrinsic base is given by

Fig. 4–17. Simplified hybrid π with load short-circuited.

$$I_i/V_i = g_{b'e} + j\omega(C_{b'e} + C_{b'c}).   (4\text{–}64)$$

Refer to Fig. 4–17. At any frequency

$$h_{fe} = I_o/I_i \cong g_m(V_i/I_i) = g_m/[g_{b'e} + j\omega(C_{b'e} + C_{b'c})].   (4\text{–}65)$$

The short-circuit current amplification factor will be down by 3 dB from its low-frequency value when

$$f = f_{hfe} = 1/[2\pi r_{b'e}(C_{b'e} + C_{b'c})].   (4\text{–}66)$$

If we consider that $C_{b'e} \gg C_{b'c}$ and solve Eq. (4–66) for $C_{b'e}$, we obtain

$$C_{b'e} \cong 1/\omega_{hfe} r_{b'e}.   (4\text{–}67)$$

Recognizing that $h_{feo}\omega_{hfe} \cong \omega_T$, Eq. (4–67) can be written

$$C_{b'e} \cong g_m/\omega_T.   (4\text{–}68)$$

This equation was previously given as Eq. (4–57).

4–11. Junction FET Equivalent Circuit. To develop a small-signal circuit for the junction FET, we make use of the information available from the characteristics given in Chapter 1 and from the discussion of physical principles available in Chapter 2. An equivalent circuit is shown in Fig. 4–18. The input is a reverse-biased junction and so leakage-resistance and depletion-layer capacitance elements linking the gate to each of the other terminals are appropriate. A constant-current generator of transconductance g_m is dependent upon V_1, and is paralleled by the incremental resistance of the bar, r_d. The bulk resistance of the channel is of much smaller value than values of the leakage elements r_a and r_b and has been omitted from consideration; r_d, essentially the output resistance of the device, is of intermediate value. It is immediately obvious that this equivalent bears a high degree of similarity to the complete hybrid π discussed earlier. The element $r_{bb'}$ is not present in Fig. 4–18, for no such parameter is important to FET operation.

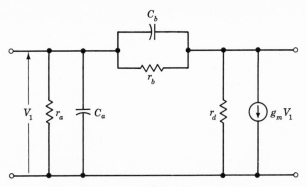

Fig. 4–18.   Simple FET equivalent circuit.

The parameters of the y matrix are often available for the FET, and it is convenient to relate them to the π circuit of Fig. 4–18. The standard form of the y equivalent is shown in Fig. 4–19(a). This model may be converted to the *normal* π form shown in Fig. 4–19(b), by equating terms of the y matrix of each network. For the circuit of Fig. 4–19(b),

$$I_1 = AV_1 + B(V_1 - V_2),$$

$$I_2 = B(V_2 - V_1) + CV_1 + DV_2.$$

$$(4\text{-}69)$$

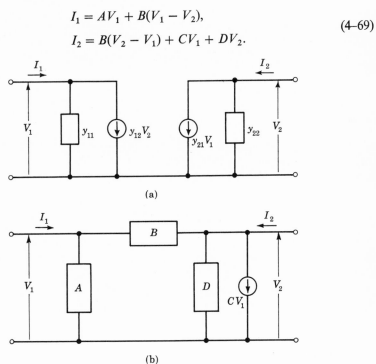

(a)

(b)

Fig. 4–19. y-parameter model and normal-π network.

Therefore the relations among parameters are

$$A = y_{11} + y_{12}, \qquad C = y_{21} - y_{12},$$
$$B = -y_{12}, \qquad D = y_{12} + y_{22}.$$

(4–70a)

These relations are complete but can be simplified through knowledge of typical values of the parameters. Since generally $y_{21} \gg y_{12}$ and $y_{22} \gg y_{12}$ in the usable frequency spectrum of the device, the revised relationships are

$$A = y_{11} + y_{12} = y_{gs}, \qquad C \cong y_{21} = g_m,$$
$$B = -y_{12} = y_{gd}, \qquad D = y_{22} = y_{ds}.$$

(4–70b)

In terms of the specific orientation being studied, the common-source connection, the general y parameters may be renamed as follows:

$$y_{11} = y_{is}, \qquad y_{21} = y_{fs},$$
$$y_{12} = y_{rs}, \qquad y_{22} = y_{os}.$$

An equivalent circuit for certain junction FET's that includes the elements of importance is shown in Fig. 4–20(a). Some difficulty may be encountered in the

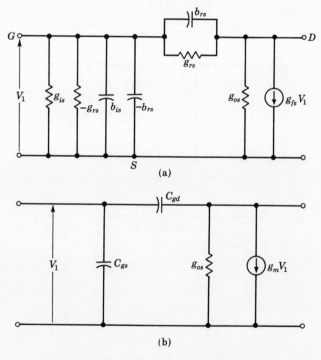

(a)

(b)

Fig. 4–20.   FET equivalent circuits.

interpretation of algebraic signs. In the measurement of y_{rs}, I_1 is found to flow away from the device, i.e., opposite to the conventional positive direction used in general network. theory. Therefore, y_{rs} as measured contains negative conductance and susceptance. The mutual element B in the normal-π network of Fig. 4–19(b) is, according to the relation in Eq. (4–70b), equal to the negative of y_{rs}, or $+ g_{rs} + jb_{rs}$. Element A is obtained by actually substracting the magnitudes of the conductances and capacitances. Neglecting the mutual elements for the moment, one sees an input conductance smaller than g_{is} alone, and input capacitance larger than that resulting from b_{is} alone. The suggested subtractions do not result in negative C_{gs} and g_{gs} parameters.

Because the input is a reverse-biased silicon diode, it is usually possible to consider the real part of the input impedance of the device as infinite. The effect of g_{rs} is found to be negligible when compared with b_{rs}. When these modifications are made to the equivalent circuit of Fig. 4–20(a), one obtains the modified form shown in Fig. 4–20(b).

At low frequencies, the FET is best characterized by the single parameter g_m. At higher frequencies the effects of C_{gs} and C_{gd} upon circuit operation is determined primarily by the frequency of the signal and the value of signal source resistance R_G. With an extremely low value of R_G it is possible for the output capacitance to be the most significant in limiting the bandwidth of a stage. Output capacitance may be approximated by the value of C_{gd}.

4–12. Parameters of the Modified Normal-π Model. A brief discussion of the parameters of the FET model of Fig. 4–20(b) follows.

Transconductance (g_m). Richer and Middlebrook have reported that the FET transfer characteristics in the pinched-off region can be described faithfully by the power-law relation[12]

$$I_D = I_{DSS}(1 - |V_{GS}/V_P|)^n. \tag{4-71}$$

Sevin has shown that when the exponent $n = 2$, the resulting parabola fits well with experimental evidence obtained on diffused devices.[16] The transconductance may be mathematically determined by taking the derivative of Eq. (4–71); with $n = 2$, one obtains

$$g_m = \partial I_D/\partial(-V_{GS}) = (2I_{DSS}/V_P)[1 - |V_{GS}/V_P|]. \tag{4-72}$$

Equation (4–72) gives g_m as a function of static parameters of the device. A decrease in g_m is to be expected with increased V_{GS} according to that equation. We note, from static characteristics curves, a decrease in g_m with decreasing I_D; a slight increase in g_m with increasing V_{DS} is also observable.

A physical analysis by Bockemuehl shows g_m to be directly proportional to μ, the mobility of carriers in the bar.[1] Prince has shown that

$$\mu = \mu_0(T/T_0)^{-n} \tag{4-73}$$

with

$$\mu_o = \text{mobility at reference temperature } T_o.$$

In Eq. (4–73) the constant n is taken as 2.3 for holes in silicon and 1.5 for electrons in silicon.[10] The behavior of g_m with frequency is not a significant factor in the spectrum of interest here.

Gate-to-Source Capacitance (C_{gs}) *and Gate-to-Drain Capacitance* (C_{gd}). For an increment of charge dQ flowing into the FET gate terminal in the circuit of Fig. 4–20(b), the nodal relation of interest is

$$dQ = C_{gs}\,dV_{GS} + C_{gd}\,d(V_{GS} - V_{DS})$$

$$= (C_{gs} + C_{gd})dV_{GS} - C_{gd}\,dV_{DS}. \qquad (4\text{–}74)$$

Because dQ is dependent, in the general case, upon both voltages, it follows that

$$C_{gd} = -\partial Q/\partial V_{DS} \qquad (4\text{–}75a)$$

and

$$C_{gs} + C_{gd} = \partial Q/\partial V_{GS}. \qquad (4\text{–}75b)$$

In the pinched-off region, $\partial Q/\partial V_{DS}$ is very small (typically below 5 pF).

An analytical expression has been derived for the incremental short-circuit input capacitance by Richer.[13] His evaluation of Eq. (14–75b) is

$$C(v) = 12kW(L/a)\{(1 + v^{\frac{1}{2}})/[(1 + 2v^{\frac{1}{2}})^2]\} \qquad (4\text{–}76)$$

with

$v = |V_{GS}/V_P|,$
$k = $ dielectric constant of the channel material,
$W = $ geometrical channel width,
$L/a = $ ratio of geometrical channel length to one-half the channel thickness.

The capacitance predicted by Eq. (4–76) is in the range below 30 pF when typical values for the physical dimensions are used. The decrease in capacitance with increasing V_{GS} is noted experimentally. It is also found that FET capacitances are reduced by operation at higher drain voltages.

4–13. MOS Equivalent Circuit and Parameters. The model shown in Fig. 4–21(a) is an accurate lumped representation of an MOS device useful over a wide frequency range when the device is operated beyond pinch-off.[6] A brief discussion of the parameters of this model follows.

D1 and D2 are diodes representing the p–n junctions between the substrate and drain and source. The drain–substrate diode is normally reversed biased; consequently this element will add little parallel conductance to the output terminal pair. The capacitances associated with $D1$ and $D2$ can be lumped into C_{ds}.

C_{gd}, C_{gs} *and* C_{ds} represent interlead capacitances. Typical values for these elements are 0.1, 0.9 and 2.0 pF, respectively.

r_{gs} and r_{gd} symbolize the resistance of leakage paths through the insulating oxide and around its edges. Generally these resistances are greater than 10^{15} Ω.

C_c and r_c represent the distributed network associated with the metal gate and the active channel. The voltage across C_c performs the charge control, and r_c represents the resistance of the channel between C_c and source and may be several hundred ohms in value. C_c may be 5 pF, for example.

g_{fs} or g_m, the transconductance, relates drain current to charge control voltage. Because V_c is the important control voltage, the generator is $g_m V_c$. For low-frequency analysis, $g_m V_{gs} \cong g_m V_c$.

$r_{d's}$ or r_d, the active channel resistance, is the output resistance of the device, and may be determined from the slope of the output characteristics. The value of this parameter is highly dependent upon the operating point.

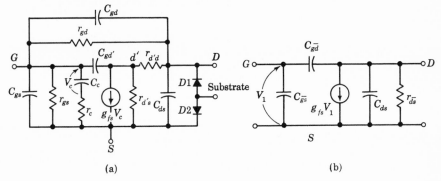

(a)   (b)

Fig. 4–21. MOS equivalent circuits: (a) complete; (b) approximate for general low-frequency use.

$r_{d'd}$ is the resistance of that portion of the channel which is not modulated by the voltage V_c. In a unit designed with a partial or offset gate so that the gate electrode does not fully cover the entire channel, $r_{d'd}$ may be several hundred ohms. In a full-gate unit this parameter is negligible.

$C_{gd'}$ in partial gate units may have a value such as 0.1 pF, an order of magnitude smaller than $C_{gd'}$ of full-gate types.

For low-frequency analysis, the equivalent of Fig. 4–21(b) is valuable. $C_{\overline{gs}} = C_{gs} + C_c$, $C_{\overline{gd}} = C_{gd} + C_{gd'}$, and $r_{\overline{ds}}$ is the parallel equivalent of $r_{d's}$ and diode resistance.

PROBLEMS

4–1. Write Eqs. (4–4), (4–5), (4–6), (4–7), and (4–8) in matrix form.

4–2. Draw an equivalent circuit for: (a) Eqs. (4–6); (b) Eqs. (4–7); (c) Eqs. (4–8).

4–3. Draw a practical circuit and specify all test equipment, switches, batteries, etc., for the laboratory measurement of the common-base h parameters of a low-power transistor at 400 cps. Show how to compute the parameters from meter readings.

4–4. Evaluate the *small-signal* hybrid parameters for the device whose characteristics are shown in the accompanying figures.

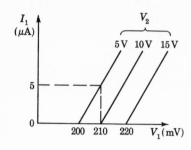 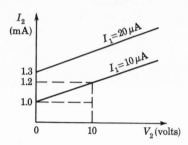

Problem 4–4.

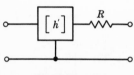

Problem 4–5.

4–5. Determine the over-all hybrid parameters of the network shown in the accompanying figure. The device in the box is represented by $[h']$ parameters, h_{11}', etc.

4–6. Draw a Tee model for common-collector studies. Use a dependent current generator βI_b in the collector branch.

4–7. Prove the relationships between h_{re} and h_{oe} and the common-base h parameters.

4–8. Prove the relationships between the common-collector and common-base h parameters.

4–9. Prove the relationships listed in Table 4–2 that include the T parameters expressed as functions of common-base h parameters.

4–10. Convert the following set of common-base h parameters to common-emitter and common-collector h parameters, and to T parameters: $h_{fb} = -0.99$, $h_{ib} = 50$, $h_{rb} = 10^{-4}$, $h_{ob} = 10^{-6}$.

4–11. For the transistor whose parameter variations are shown in Figs. 4–11 and 4–12, determine all common-emitter parameters at $I_C = 7$ mA and $V_{CB} = 20$ V. Nominal values are $h_{ib} = 40$ Ω, $h_{fb} = -0.95$, $h_{rb} = 5 \times 10^{-4}$ and $h_{ob} = 10^{-6}$ mho.

4–12. A transistor exhibits $f_{\alpha b}$ of 10 Mc and h_{fbo} of -0.985. Determine nominal $f_{\alpha e}$, h_{feo} and f_T and the magnitude of h_{fe} at 1 Mc.

4–13. If h_{fe} at 2 Mc has a value of 4, and f_{hfe} is 100 kc, calculate h_{fbo} and the 2-Mc value of h_{fb}.

4–14. A transistor with $f_{\alpha b} = 0.5$ Mc has the following low-frequency h parameters: $h_{ib} = 50$ Ω, $h_{rb} = 10^{-4}$, $h_{fbo} = -0.98$, $h_{ob} = 2 \times 10^{-6}$ mho. Express the common-emitter h parameters in complex form at 10,000 cps. $h_{fb} = h_{fbo}/(1 + jf/f_{\alpha b})$, with h_{fbo} the low-frequency or reference value of that parameter.

4–15. Derive expressions for the common-emitter h parameters in terms of low-frequency hybrid-π parameters.

4–16. Measurements on a junction transistor yield the following low-frequency parameters: $h_{fe} = 200$, $h_{ie} = 4000$, $h_{re} = 10^{-3}$, $h_{oe} = 10^{-4}$, $C_{ob} = 1$ pF. The operating point is at 1.5 mA, and $f_T = 50$ Mc. Determine approximate values for all seven of the hybrid-π parameters at room temperature.

4–17. A junction FET that obeys the square-law relation, Eq. (4–71), is characterized by $I_{DSS} = 10$ mA, $V_P = 5$ V. Find I_D and g_m at $V_{GS} = 0, 1, 2, 3, 4,$ and 5 V.

4–18. Convert the 1-kc y-parameters given below for the 2N2498 FET into elements of the circuit of Fig. 4–20. Consider y_{is} and y_{rs} to be capacitive admittances.

$$|y_{is}| = 0.2 \ \mu\text{mho}, \qquad |y_{fs}| = 4000 \ \mu\text{mho},$$
$$|y_{rs}| = 0.1 \ \mu\text{mho}, \qquad |y_{os}| = 100 \ \mu\text{mho}.$$

REFERENCES

1. Bockemuehl, R. R., "Analysis of the Field Effect Transistors with Arbitrary Charge Distribution," *IEEE Trans. Electron Devices* (January, 1963).
2. Eschelman, C. R., "Variation of Transistor Parameters with Temperature," *Semiconductor Products*, **1**, No. 1 (January, 1958).
3. Gaertner, W. W., *Transistors: Principles, Design and Applications* (D. Van Nostrand, Co., Inc., Princeton, New Jersey, 1960).
4. Giacoletto, L. J., "Study of P–N–P Alloy Junction Transistor from D-C through Medium Frequencies," *RCA Rev.*, **15**, No. 4 (December, 1954).
5. Giacoletto, L. J., "Equipments for Measuring Junction Transistor Admittance Parameters for a Wide Range of Frequencies," *RCA Rev.*, **14**, No. 2 (June, 1953).
6. Griswold, G. M. and Olmstead, J. A., "The MOS Transistor," Publication No. ST-2651, Radio Corporation of America, Somerville, New Jersey, 1964.
7. Hurley, R. B., *Junction Transistor Electronics* (John Wiley & Sons, Inc., New York, 1958).
8. Mattson, R. H., *Basic Junction Devices and Circuits* (John Wiley & Sons, Inc., New York, 1963).
9. Phillips, A. B., *Transistor Engineering* (McGraw-Hill Book Co., Inc., New York, 1962).
10. Prince, M. B., "Drift Mobilities in Semiconductors, II. Silicon," *Phys. Rev.* **93** (March 15, 1954).
11. Reddi, V. G. K., "Applying Transistor 'y' Parameters," *Electronic Industries* (January, 1960).
12. Richer, I., and Middlebrook, R. D., "Power-Law Nature of Field-Effect Transistor Experimental Characteristics," *Proc. IEEE*, **51** (August, 1963).
13. Richer, I., "Input Capacitance of Field Effect Transistors," *Proc. IEEE*, **51** (September, 1963).
14. Riddle, R. L., and Ristenbatt, M. P., *Transistor Physics and Circuits* (Prentice-Hall, Inc., Englewood Cliffs, New Jersey, 1958).
15. Searle, C. L., Boothroyd, A. R., Angelo, E. J., Gray, P. E. and Pederson, D. O., *Elementary Circuit Properties of Transistors* (John Wiley & Sons, Inc., New York, 1963).
16. Sevin, L. J., "A Simple Expression for the Transfer Characteristic of FETs," *Electronic Equipment Engineering*, **11**, No. 8 (August, 1963).
17. Shea, R. F., *Principles of Transistor Circuits* (John Wiley & Sons, Inc., New York, 1953).
18. Shea, R. F., *Transistor Audio Amplifiers* (John Wiley & Sons, Inc., New York, 1955).
19. Thornton, R. D., De Witt, D., Chenette, E. R., Lin, H. C., *Characteristics and Limitations of Transistors* (John Wiley & Sons. Inc., New York, 1963).

Chapter 5

ANALYSIS

This chapter introduces the reader to the standard methods for derivation of mathematical-performance relations that are useful in the analysis of simple circuits employing conventional transistors and field-effect transistors. Chapter 4 provided electrical equivalent circuits to describe these devices when biased for Class-A operation. This chapter continues with the assumption that signal levels are sufficiently small so that the assumptions of linearity made in the development of those models are not invalidated.

We now consider that the active device is fed from a signal source and feeds an electrical load. It is desired that formulas be derived for the prediction of the voltage, current, and power amplification provided by the network, and for the terminal impedance levels presented to the signal source and to the circuit load by the transistor's input and output ports or terminal pairs. In the analysis of these simple transistor and FET circuits, it is necessary to represent the terminations in terms of equivalent electrical parameters; it is technically unnecessary to know the exact physical makeup of the source and of the load. Thus a 500 Ω resistive load may physically represent a small motor, or a light bulb, or the input resistance of another stage; as far as the transistor being studied is concerned, these terminations are equivalent.

The frequency characteristics of simple circuits will be studied. In addition, a comparison will be made of the properties of the various circuit configurations. Finally, several examples of the analysis of complete networks will be presented.

5–1. The Terminated h-Parameter Network. The circuit shown in Fig. 5–1 is the general h-parameter network terminated in a resistive load R_L and fed from a signal source V_g of internal resistance R_G. This is a special case of the more general circuit with impedance terminations Z_L and Z_G. It can be seen from the figure that network parameters h_i and h_o are also being considered as resistive elements. Additionally, we may assume elements h_f and h_r to be described by real, rather than complex, numbers. The equations to be derived using Fig. 5–1 pertain to the conventional transistor over a rather wide frequency spectrum. For the more general complex case, refer to Appendix II.

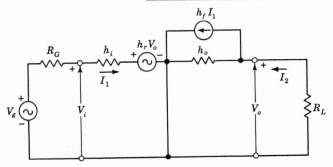

Fig. 5-1. Equivalent circuit for the general configuration with source and load terminations.

To describe this circuit, we use the general h-parameter equations given in Chapter 4:

$$V_i = h_i I_1 + h_r V_o,$$
$$I_2 = h_f I_1 + h_o V_o. \tag{5-1}$$

Note that V_o can be eliminated from Eqs. (5-1) by making the substitution

$$V_o = -I_2 R_L.$$

Thus

$$V_i = h_i I_1 - h_r R_L I_2,$$
$$0 = h_f I_1 - (1 + h_r R_L) I_2$$

The currents are considered to be unknown. The determinant of coefficients is

$$D = -h_i(1 + h_o R_L) + h_r h_f R_L.$$

Then

$$I_1 = \frac{\begin{vmatrix} V_i & -h_r R_L \\ 0 & -(1 + h_o R_L) \end{vmatrix}}{D} = \frac{-V_i(1 + h_o R_L)}{D},$$

$$I_2 = \frac{\begin{vmatrix} h_i & V_i \\ h_f & 0 \end{vmatrix}}{D} = \frac{-V_i h_f}{D}.$$

The *voltage gain* of this circuit is

$$A_v = \frac{V_o}{V_i} = \frac{-I_2 R_L}{V_i} = \left(\frac{V_i h_f R_L / D}{V_i} \right) = \frac{-h_f R_L}{h_i + R_L \Delta^h}, \tag{5-2}$$

where

$$\Delta^h = h_i h_o - h_r h_f.$$

Note the definition of voltage gain used here is V_o/V_i. If V_o/V_g is of interest, add R_G to h_i. The phase reversal present in common-emitter stages appears algebraically in Eq. (5–2). When h_f is positive, as is h_{fe}, A_v retains its negative sign. This indicates that a positive-going V_o results from a negative-going V_i. The absence of phase reversal in common-base and common-collector stages is apparent, for h_{fb} and h_{fc} are negative quantities. It is valuable for the reader to remember that *only the common-emitter connection provides phase reversal.*

Current Gain

$$A_i = \frac{I_2}{I_1} = \frac{V_i h_f/D}{V_i(1 + h_o R_L)/D} = \frac{h_f}{1 + h_o R_L}. \tag{5–3}$$

*Power Gain**

$$G = A_i \cdot A_v = h_f{}^2 R_L/[(1 + h_o R_L)(h_i + R_L \Delta^h)]. \tag{5–4}$$

Input Resistance

$$R_i = \frac{V_i}{I_1} = \frac{V_i}{-V_i(1 + h_o R_L)/D} = \frac{h_i + R_L \Delta^h}{1 + h_o R_L}. \tag{5–5}$$

Output Resistance

To find the output resistance of the network, V_g is short-circuited and a signal source V_o connected at the load terminals in place of R_L. The equations describing this situation are

$$0 = (h_i + R_G)I_1 + h_r V_o,$$
$$I_2 = h_f I_1 + h_o V_o. \tag{5–6}$$

Current directions and voltage polarities are as shown in Fig. 5–1. The ratio V_o/I_2 is the output resistance of the network. From Eqs. (5–6) we obtain

$$I_2 = h_f[-h_r V_o/(h_i + R_G)] + h_o V_o$$

and thus

$$R_o = V_o/I_2 = (h_i + R_G)/(R_G h_o + \Delta^h). \tag{5–7}$$

Although V_g is short-circulated in obtaining the expression for R_o, the "dependent" generators $h_r V_o$ and $h_f I_1$ must be retained.

With the preceding equations it is possible to calculate the performance of a common-base stage by simply inserting h_{ib}, h_{rb}, h_{fb}, and h_{ob}, whereas to predict the circuit operation of a common-emitter connected transistor we should use h_{ie}, h_{re}, h_{fe}, and h_{oe}. The common-collector configuration would be treated accordingly. Table 5–1 is a convenient summary of the formulas derived.

The relations of this section could be derived using other methods. Source interchanges and loop equations could be written, and the resulting two equations solved for the unknown currents. Alternately, Eqs. (5–1) could be solved by matrix methods (Problem 5–2).

*The product of A_i and A_v is the power gain of the network when all parameters are real.

TABLE 5–1. FORMULAS FOR THE HYBRID EQUIVALENT.

Voltage gain, A_v	$\dfrac{-h_f R_L}{h_i + R_L \Delta^h}$	(5–2)
Current gain, A_i,	$\dfrac{h_f}{1 + h_o R_L}$	(5–3)
Power gain, G	$\dfrac{h_f{}^2 R_L}{(1 + h_o R_L)[h_i + R_L \Delta^h]}$	(5–4)
Input resistance, R_i	$\dfrac{h_i + R_L \Delta^h}{1 + h_o R_L}$	(5–5)
Output resistance, R_o	$\dfrac{h_i + R_G}{\Delta^h + R_G h_o}$	(5–7)

$\Delta^h = h_i h_o - h_r h_f$

The values used for R_L and R_G in the equations given in this chapter must include any biasing elements that may be connected across the output and input ports. Examples are given in Sec. 5–9.

Feedback Elements. Eqs. (5–2) through (5–7) are useful for the analysis of simple common-emitter circuits if common-emitter parameters are used. However, *for inclusion of local feedback in the stage by connecting resistances in series with the emitter lead and/or from collector-to-base, it is more advantageous to study the common-emitter connection with common-base parameters.* If the base terminal of the common-base h-equivalent is connected to the signal source and the emitter terminal inserted into the common-branch, we obtain the circuit of Fig. 5–2. After making a source interchange in the collector branch, the expression for V_{cb} is:

$$V_{cb} = (I_1 h_{fb}/h_{ob}) + [I_2(1 + h_{fb})]/h_{ob}$$

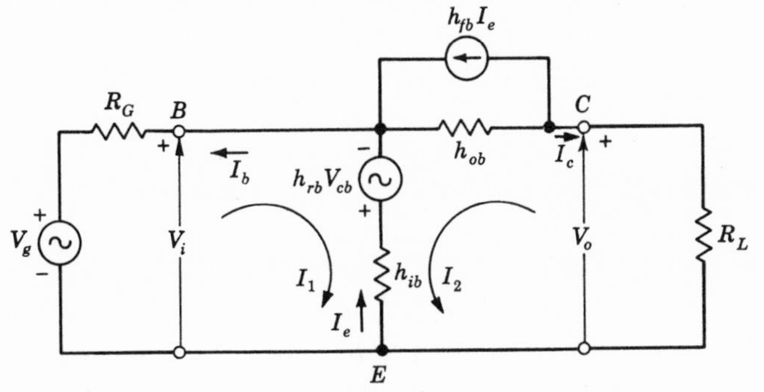

Fig. 5–2. Equivalent circuit for the common-emitter configuration with source and load terminations, common-base parameters.

The loop equations are:

$$V_i = I_1\left[h_{ib} - \frac{h_{fb}h_{rb}}{h_{ob}}\right] + I_2\left[h_{ib} - \frac{(1 + h_{fb})h_{rb}}{h_{ob}}\right];$$

$$0 = I_1\left[h_{ib} + \frac{(1 - h_{rb})h_{fb}}{h_{ob}}\right] + I_2\left[h_{ib} + R_L + (1 - h_{rb})\left(\frac{1 + h_{fb}}{h_{ob}}\right)\right]. \tag{5-8}$$

Solutions of these equations yield the expressions presented in Table 5–2. An alternate method for deriving these equations would involve the parameter interrelations of Table 4–1.

TABLE 5–2.   COMMON-EMITTER FORMULAS FOR THE HYBRID EQUIVALENT.

	Complete formulas*	Approximate formulas†
Voltage gain, A_v‡	$\dfrac{R_L(h_{ib}h_{ob} + h_{fb})}{h_{ib}(1 + R_L h_{ob}) - h_{rb}h_{fb}R_L}$ $\hspace{2em}$ (5–9)	$\dfrac{h_{fb}R_L}{h_{ib}(1 + R_L h_{ob})}$ $\hspace{2em}$ (5–9A)
Current gain, A_i	$\dfrac{-(h_{ib}h_{ob} + h_{fb})}{h_{ob}(h_{ib} + R_L) + (1 + h_{fb})}$ $\hspace{2em}$ (5–10)	$\dfrac{-h_{fb}}{h_{ob}R_L + (1 + h_{fb})}$ $\hspace{2em}$ (5–10A)
Power gain, G	$\dfrac{R_L(h_{ib}h_{ob} + h_{fb})^2}{\left\{\begin{matrix}[h_{ob}(h_{ib} + R_L) + (1 + h_{fb})] \\ \times\ [h_{ib}(1 + R_L h_{ob}) - h_{rb}h_{fb}R_L]\end{matrix}\right\}}$ $\hspace{2em}$ (5–11)	$\dfrac{h_{fb}{}^2 R_L}{\left\{\begin{matrix}h_{ib}(1 + R_L h_{ob}) \\ \times\ [R_L h_{ob} + (1 + h_{fb})]\end{matrix}\right\}}$ $\hspace{2em}$ (5–11A)
Input resistance, R_i	$\dfrac{h_{ib}(1 + R_L h_{ob}) - h_{rb}h_{fb}R_L}{h_{ob}(h_{ib} + R_L) + (1 + h_{fb})}$ $\hspace{2em}$ (5–12)	$\dfrac{h_{ib}(1 + R_L h_{ob})}{R_L h_{ob} + (1 + h_{fb})}$ $\hspace{2em}$ (5–12A)
Output resistance, R_o	$\dfrac{h_{ib} + R_G[h_{ib}h_{ob} + (1 + h_{fb})]}{h_{ob}(h_{ib} + R_G) - h_{rb}h_{fb}}$ $\hspace{2em}$ (5–13)	$\dfrac{h_{ib} + R_G(1 + h_{fb})}{h_{ob}(h_{ib} + R_G) - h_{rb}h_{fb}}$ $\hspace{2em}$ (5–13A)

*$(1 - h_{rb})$ factors omitted.
†$(1 + h_{fb}) \gg h_{ib}h_{ob}$, $R_L \gg h_{ib}$, $h_{ib} \gg h_{rb}h_{fb}R_L$.
‡Ratio of V_o to V_i in Fig. 5–2.

Equations (5–9) through (5–13) allow us to include an element R_e connected from emitter to ground by *addition of R_e to h_{ib}* in each of the formulas. Likewise a conductance G_c connected between collector and base may be included by *addition of G_c to h_{ob}*. Because these feedback elements are often used in transistor stages, these equations are particularly valuable.

5–2. The Terminated y-Parameter Network. The y-parameter network is connected to a load Y_L and signal source I_g paralleled by Y_G in Fig. 5–3. Admittances are used at the terminations because the resulting network then contains

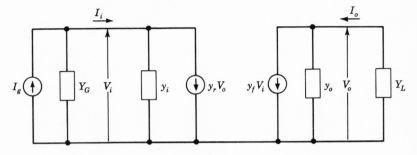

Fig. 5–3. The terminated y-parameter network.

only two nodes, and therefore may be simply analyzed. The nodal equations for the transistor are:

$$I_i = y_i V_i + y_r V_o,$$
$$I_o = y_f V_i + y_o V_o. \tag{5–14}$$

If the substitution $V_o = -I_o Z_L$ is used, the equations for gains and impedances presented in Table 5–3 may be derived.

TABLE 5–3.   FORMULAS FOR THE y EQUIVALENT.

Voltage gain, A_v*	$\dfrac{-y_f Z_L}{1 + y_o Z_L}$	(5–15)
Current gain, A_i†	$\dfrac{y_f}{y_i + \Delta^y Z_L}$	(5–16)
Input impedance, Z_i	$\dfrac{1 + y_o Z_L}{y_i + \Delta^y Z_L}$	(5–17)
Output impedance, Z_o	$\dfrac{1 + y_i Z_G}{y_o + \Delta^y Z_G}$	(5–18)

*Ratio of V_o to V_i in Fig. 5–3.
†Ratio of I_o to I_i in Fig. 5–3.

5–3. The Terminated T-Equivalent Circuit. Low-frequency T-models were given in Sec. 4–5 for the common-emitter and common-base orientations. In Fig. 5–4 these networks, along with the common-collector representation, are shown with resistive load and source terminations.

Common-Emitter. After the collector-branch current source is replaced by an equivalent voltage source, the applicable equations are:

$$V_i = I_1(r_b + r_e) - I_2(r_e),$$

$$0 = -I_1[r_e - \beta r_c(1 - \alpha)] + I_2[r_e + r_c(1 - \alpha) + R_L]. \qquad (5-19)$$

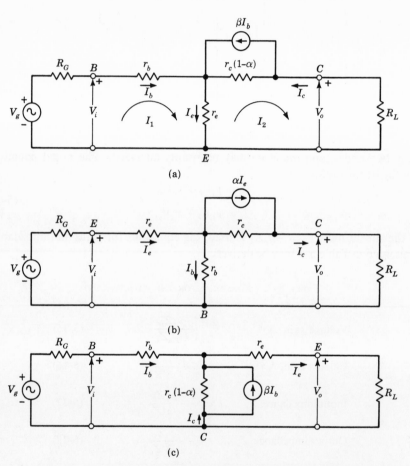

Fig. 5–4. Small-signal equivalent circuits: (a) common emitter; (b) common base; (c) common collector.

Solutions of these equations for the gain and resistance-level properties of this network are given in Table 5–4.

Study of the current-gain expression, Eq. (5–21), may suggest that a curve ball has been thrown. β was defined as the short-circuit current amplification

TABLE 5–4. COMMON-EMITTER FORMULAS FOR THE T EQUIVALENT.

	Complete formulas	Approximate formulas†
Voltage gain, A_v*†	$$\dfrac{R_L(\alpha r_c - r_e)}{r_b[r_e + r_c(1 - \alpha) + R_L] + r_e(r_c + R_L)}$$ (5–20)	$$\dfrac{\alpha R_L}{r_e + r_b(1 - \alpha)}$$ (5–20A)
Current gain, A_i*	$$\dfrac{\alpha r_c - r_e}{r_e + r_c(1 - \alpha) + R_L}$$ (5–21)	$$\dfrac{\alpha}{1 - \alpha} = \beta$$ (5–21A)
Power gain, G	$$\dfrac{R_L(\alpha r_c - r_e)^2}{\{[r_e + r_c(1 - \alpha) + R_L]\{r_b[r_e + r_c(1 - \alpha) + R_L] + r_e(r_c + R_L)\}\}}$$ (5–22)	$$\dfrac{\alpha^2 R_L}{(1 - \alpha)[r_e + r_b(1 - \alpha)]}$$ (5–22A)
Input resistance, R_i	$$r_b + \dfrac{r_e(r_c + R_L)}{r_e + r_c(1 - \alpha) + R_L}$$ (5–23)	$$\dfrac{r_b(1 - \alpha) + r_e}{1 - \alpha}$$ (5–23A)
Output resistance, R_o	$$r_c(1 - \alpha) + \dfrac{r_e(R_G + r_b + r_c)}{R_G + r_b + r_e}$$ (5–24)	$$\dfrac{R_G r_c(1 - \alpha) + r_e r_c}{R_G + r_b + r_e}$$ (5–24A)

*Phase reversal.
†$r_c \gg r_e$, $r_c(1 - \alpha) \gg (R_L + r_e)$, $R_G \gg r_b$, $r_c \gg (R_G + r_b)$.
‡Add R_G to r_b if V_0/V_g is needed.

factor for this configuration, yet from Eq. (5–21), when $R_L = 0$, which clearly represents a short circuit,

$$A_i = (\alpha r_c - r_e)/[r_e + r_c(1 - \alpha)],$$

instead of

$$A_i = \beta = \alpha/(1 - \alpha).$$

The discrepancy that exists can be clarified by stating that the βI_b current generator technically is in error, and to be more exact that generator should have some new nomenclature such as $\beta' I_b$. We can then define

$$\alpha' = \beta'/(\beta' + 1).$$

Equation (5–21) can be correctly written as

$$A_i = (\alpha' r_c - r_e)/[r_e + r_c(1 - \alpha')].$$

To find the value of α', equate this expression to β:

$$(\alpha' r_c - r_e)/[r_e + r_c(1 - \alpha')] = \alpha/(1 - \alpha),$$

and then

$$\alpha' = (\alpha r_c + r_e)/r_c. \tag{5–35}$$

When normal values for the parameters are inserted, Eq. (5–35) describes a difference between α and α' that amounts to less than 0.01%. It therefore seems logical to call the current generator α, or β, rather than assign another symbol, for the accuracy of the equivalent circuit itself and the accuracy of measurement of the parameters each result in errors of considerably greater magnitude that the difference between the short-circuit current-amplification factor and the factor we have called α'.

Common-Base. Derivation of the formulas for the common-base configuration proceeds from the circuit with the transistor connected to a source and a load given in Fig. 5–4(b). The derived expressions are available in Table 5–5 and the reader is invited to verify them (see Problems 5–9 and 5–10). *This connection does not provide phase reversal between input and output quantities.*

TABLE 5–5.   COMMON-BASE FORMULAS FOR THE T EQUIVALENT.

	Complete formulas	Approximate formulas†
Voltage gain, A_v*	$$\dfrac{(r_b + \alpha r_c)R_L}{r_b[R_L + r_c(1 - \alpha)] + r_e(r_b + r_c + R_L)}$$ (5–25)	$$\dfrac{\alpha R_L}{r_e + r_b(1 - \alpha)}$$ (5–25A)
Current gain, A_i	$$\dfrac{r_b + \alpha r_c}{r_b + r_c + R_L}$$ (5–26)	α (5–26A)
Power gain, G	$$\dfrac{(r_b + \alpha r_c)^2 R_L}{\{(r_b + r_c + R_L)\{r_b[R_L + r_c(1 - \alpha)] + r_e(r_b + r_c + R_L)\}}$$ (5–27)	$$\dfrac{\alpha^2 R_L}{r_e + r_b(1 - \alpha)}$$ (5–27A)
Input resistance, R_i	$$r_e + \dfrac{r_b[R_L + r_c(1 - \alpha)]}{r_b + r_c + R_L}$$ (5–28)	$r_e + r_b(1 - \alpha)$ (5–28A)
Output resistance, R_o	$$r_c + \dfrac{r_b(R_G + r_e - \alpha r_c)}{R_G + r_b + r_e}$$ (5–29)	$$\dfrac{r_c[R_G + r_b(1 - \alpha) + r_e]}{R_G + r_b + r_e}$$ (5–29A)

*Add R_G to r_e if V_o/V_g is needed.
†$r_c \gg r_b, r_c(1 - \alpha) \gg R_L, r_c \gg (R_G + r_e)$.

Common-Collector. The circuit of Fig. 5–4(c) may be used to derive performance equations for the common-collector configuration. Formulas for the prediction of transistor operation in this orientation are listed in Table 5–6. *The common-collector orientation does not provide phase reversal between input and output quantities.*

TABLE 5–6. COMMON-COLLECTOR FORMULAS FOR THE T EQUIVALENT.

	Complete formulas	Approximate formulas†
Voltage gain, A_v*	$$\dfrac{r_c R_L}{r_b(r_e + R_L) + r_c[r_e + R_L + r_b(1 - \alpha)]}$$ (5–30)	1 (5–30A)
Current gain, A_i	$$\dfrac{r_c}{r_c(1 - \alpha) + r_e + R_L}$$ (5–31)	$\dfrac{1}{1 - \alpha}$ (5–31A)
Power gain, G	$$\dfrac{r_c^2 R_L}{\left\{ \begin{array}{l} [r_c(1 - \alpha) + r_e + R_L]\{r_b(r_e + R_L)\} \\ \quad + r_c[r_e + R_L + r_b(1 - \alpha)]\} \end{array} \right\}}$$ (5–32)	$\dfrac{1}{1 - \alpha}$ (5–32A)
Input resistance, R_i	$$r_b + \dfrac{r_c(r_e + R_L)}{r_c(1 - \alpha) + r_e + R_L}$$ (5–33)	$\dfrac{R_L}{1 - \alpha}$ (5–33A)
Output resistance, R_o	$$r_e + \dfrac{r_c(1 - \alpha)(R_G + r_b)}{R_G + r_b + r_c}$$ (5–34)	$r_e + (1 - \alpha)(R_G + r_b)$ (5–34A)

*Add R_G to r_b if V_o/V_g is needed.

†$r_c(1 - \alpha) \gg R_L$, $R_L \gg [r_e + r_b(1 - \alpha)]$, $r_c \gg (R_G + r_b)$.

Approximate Formulas. Tables 5–4, 5–5, and 5–6 are listings of the formulas derived for the three configurations. The so-called "complete" formulas, which themselves are based upon assumptions and approximations, are presented along with more "approximate" formulas, which are useful to gain a rapid insight into the circuit under consideration, without performing the more laborious task of solving the complete expression.

In deriving the approximate formulas, the following considerations are among those of importance: $r_c \gg r_b$, $r_c \gg r_e$, $r_c \gg R_L$, $r_c(1 - \alpha) \gg R_L$, $R_L \gg r_e$. These assumptions stem from knowledge of typical values for the parameters; one might expect to encounter values such as

$$r_b = 500 \ \Omega,$$
$$r_e = 30 \ \Omega,$$
$$r_c = 1,500,000 \ \Omega,$$
$$\alpha = 0.975.$$

Many other approximate relationships may be derived, some of which may more satisfactorily describe the operation of a particular transistor type or circuit.

It must be borne in mind that all equations presented herein pertain only to the circuits for which the formulas were derived. If series resistance were inserted into the emitter lead of the common-emitter configuration, for example, then r_e would have to be increased by the amount of that additional resistance, and certain approximate formulas might not hold; or, more specifically, the results of the use of the approximate formulas might be in error by an additional amount.

5-4. The Terminated Hybrid-π Network. The complete hybrid π is an all-frequency model; however, it is too complex to use in its complete form. If we restrict our interest to low frequencies, we may eliminate the capacitances from the complete network—the resulting modified network contains five resistive elements. A further reduction is in order because the equations for an entire stage with source, load, and local feedback are still unwieldy. For many purposes r_{ce} and $r_{b'c}$ can be omitted. These two elements represent rather high values of resistance; their elimination makes the model unilateral at low frequencies. The final low-frequency modified hybrid-π network is shown in Fig. 5-5 connected to source and load and including local feedback element R_e.

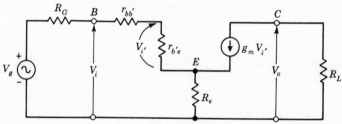

Fig. 5-5. Modified hybrid-π network, with load R_L, local feedback R_e, and source resistance R_G.

In order to justify numerically the use of the modified equivalent circuit, the following example is of assistance. The modifications suggested in the preceding paragraph result in the elimination of the h_{re} and h_{oe} hybrid parameters at low frequencies. Consequently, the matrix determinent $\Delta^h e$ becomes zero in the voltage-gain expression for a stage fed from an ideal voltage source, Eq. (5-2). The applicable expression is then

$$A_v = h_{fe} R_L / h_{ie}. \tag{5-36}$$

Let us consider the 1 kc parameters of the type 2N2614 germanium-alloy-junction transistor at $V_{CE} = 12$ V, $I_C = 1$ mA, to be as quoted by the manufacturer:

$$h_{ie} = 4300\ \Omega, \qquad h_{fe} = 160,$$
$$h_{re} = 0.0014, \qquad h_{oe} = 60 \times 10^{-6}\ \text{mho}.$$

Calculations yield $\Delta^{he} = 0.034$. With R_L equal to 1000 Ω, A_v from Eq. (5-36) differs by less than 1 % from the value obtained by the use of Eq. (5-2), and when the transistor feeds a 10,000 Ω load, the error has increased to only 7.3 %.

Gain and impedance formulas can be easily derived for the circuit of Fig. 5–5. Because it is often necessary to include local feedback in order to gain stabilize a transistor circuit, the circuit of the figure includes R_e, an unbypassed resistance connected between emitter terminal and ground.

Other means for degenerative local feedback are possible, most significant of which is the connection of a resistance from collector to base, a scheme that reduces input resistance and works well with constant-current signal sources. The use of the emitter-leg external element will be the only feedback method considered here; discussion of other methods is reserved for Chapter 10.

The voltage amplification of the circuit of Fig. 5–5 is

$$A_v = |V_o/V_i| = h_{fe}R_L/[r_{bb'} + r_{b'e} + R_e(1 + h_{fe})]. \tag{5-37a}$$

To include the source resistance for a study of $|V_o/V_g|$, it is simply necessary to add R_G to $r_{bb'}$. By letting R_L equal the parallel combination of the external load and r_{ce}, the effect of that parameter may be included. If we note that $r_{b'e} = h_{fe}/g_m$ as mentioned in Sec. 4–10, an alternate form of Eq. (5–37a) is

$$A_v = g_m h_{fe}R_L/[h_{fe} + g_m r_{bb'} + g_m R_e(1 + h_{fe})]. \tag{5-37b}$$

The assumption of unilateralization mentioned previously shows up in Eq. (5–37), for the equation predicts that A_v rises monotonically with R_L. It must be borne in mind that the results of any studies based upon Eq. (5–37) are increasingly in error as R_L approaches the output resistance of the active device.

Equation (5–37) is valid at low frequencies and may serve as a reference for amplifier analysis. It is simply a version of the general expression

$$A_v = A_i R_L/R_i. \tag{5-38}$$

Current amplification of the modified model is simply h_{fe}, an approximation valid over a wide range of load values. Input resistance is

$$R_i = V_i/I_i = r_{bb'} + r_{b'e} + R_e(1 + h_{fe}). \tag{5-39}$$

The assumption of unilateralization evident in Eq. (5–39) is also valid over a wide range of load values. Interesting to note is the effect of the local feedback upon input resistance—it does not improve voltage gain even when the circuit is being fed from a source of high internal resistance. This conclusion can be seen by manipulation of Eq. (5–37). Thus

$$\frac{A_v(\text{without feedback})}{A_v(\text{with feedback})} = 1 + \frac{R_e(h_{fe} + 1)}{r_{b'e} + r_{bb'}}. \tag{5-40}$$

Examination of Eq. (5–40) indicates that it is not possible, by addition of R_e, to increase the voltage gain above that of a stage without feedback.

5–5. Comparison of Configurations. It was stated earlier that the common-emitter configuration is the most widely accepted and that emphasis would be placed upon that type of connection; this emphasis was apparent in the chapter devoted to biasing. It is natural to question the reasons behind the popularity of common-emitter circuity, so a comparison of the configurations is in order.

The three configurations have been compared and the results depicted in Figs. 5–6 through 5–10. Typical parameter values of

$$h_{ib} = 50 \ \Omega$$

$$h_{rb} = 5 \times 10^{-4},$$

$$h_{fb} = -0.98,$$

$$h_{ob} = 1 \ \mu\text{mho}$$

were used in the equations previously derived for A_v, A_i, G, R_i, and R_o, and expected performance calculated. Load resistance was considered to be the independent variable except for the calculation of transistor output resistance. Output resistance depends upon the source and is not a function of load.

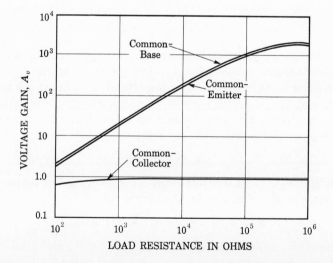

Fig. 5–6. Typical variation of voltage gain with load resistance.

Voltage Gain. The common-emitter and the common-base configurations provide essentially the same voltage gain, as evidenced by the curves of Fig. 5–6. A common-collector stage will never exhibit voltage gain greater than unity. It remains near unity for most high values of load resistance.

Current Gain. The common-emitter and common-collector configurations exhibit similar current-gain curves; they generally drop off for higher values of load resistance. These variations are depicted in Fig. 5–7. The common-base configuration is incapable of current amplification above the value of h_{fb} ($-\alpha$).

Power Gain. Multiplication of the current gain and the voltage gain for each

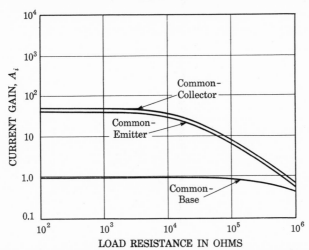

Fig. 5-7. Typical variation of current gain with load resistance.

connection results in the power-gain curves of Fig. 5-8. Since the common-emitter stage shows the greatest power gain for all values of load resistance, it is most frequently used.

Input Resistance. The curves of Fig. 5-9 depict input resistance for the various configurations. The highest resistance is presented by the common-collector circuit although the common-emitter circuit with unbypassed resistance between

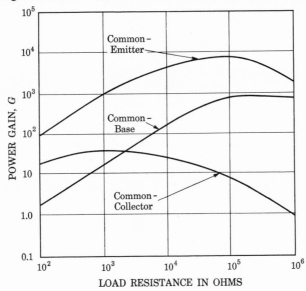

Fig. 5-8. Typical variation of power gain with load resistance.

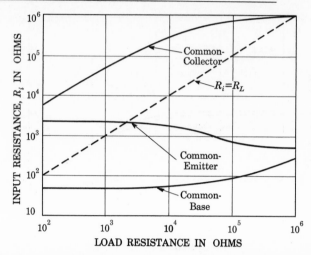

Fig. 5–9. Typical variation of input resistance with load resistance.

emitter terminal and ground would present higher input resistances than shown in the figure. The curves, it must be remembered, apply only to the transistor under consideration; alteration of the circuit by feedback or otherwise will alter the values of gain and resistance presented in the curves.

Output Resistance. Output resistance is not a function of R_L, but rather depends upon R_G; consequently Fig. 5–10 presents R_o vs R_G. The common-emitter connection yields intermediate values of output resistance and its variations are not too extreme for most applications.

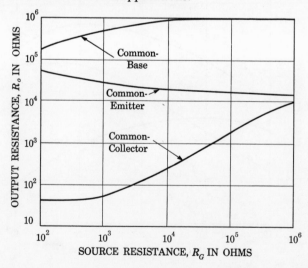

Fig. 5–10. Typical variation of output resistance with source resistance.

5–6. High-Frequency Considerations. *If the appropriate parameters are available in complex form*, either the h or y equivalent circuits may be used to analyze the performance of a transistor stage at a particular frequency by using the equations presented earlier in this chapter. With the help of the hybrid-π model, additional study will be made of the common-emitter connection in this Section.

The preceding chapter defined the beta-cutoff frequency f_{hfe} as the frequency at which the short-circuit current amplification factor has declined to 0.707 of its low-frequency reference value. With most practical values of load resistance A_i and β are synonymous. Therefore, with many transistor types one finds current gain falloff at a relatively low frequency. However, *the upper-cutoff frequency for voltage gain may extend far beyond* f_{hfe}. We may appreciate this statement by writing the general expression for voltage gain:

$$A_v = A_i R_L / Z_i.$$

If Z_i and A_i behave similarly with frequency, we expect little change in A_v. This is precisely what happens with the junction transistor; Z_i and A_i decline with increased frequency because of input capacitance.

To assist in the understanding of the frequency behavior of A_v, consider the circuit of Fig. 5–11 to represent the quantities of interest in the input circuit of a junction transistor stage. The element R_G' can represent the sum of source resistance R_G and base-spreading resistance $r_{bb'}$. The elements C_i and R_i

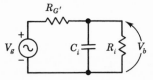

Fig. 5–11. Input circuit of junction transistor.

are the remaining input quantities. An expression for the voltage transfer function of this simple network is

$$V_b / V_g = R_G' / (R_i + R_G' + j\omega C_i R_G' R_i). \tag{5-41}$$

The voltage available at the base V_b has decreased by 3 dB when the real and imaginary portions of the denominator of this expression are equal. The frequency at which this reduction occurs is the upper cut-off frequency, f_{3dB}. For this circuit,

$$f_{3dB} = 1/2\pi C_i R_T, \tag{5-42}$$

where R_T is the parallel equivalent of all resistive elements. Here $R_T = R_i \| R_G'$. Equation (5–42) also describes the frequency at which the current through R_i will be down by 3 dB from its low-frequency reference value.

An important conclusion obtainable from Eq. (5–42) is that *the upper cutoff frequency is determined to a large extent by source resistance and base-spreading resistance.*

Equation (5–41) as well as the variation of alpha with frequency, Eq. (4–38), and the variation of beta with frequency, Eq. (4–41), are of the same form and when graphed can be represented by the same curve. Figure 5–12 depicts the change in the magnitude of the amplification, expressed as a ratio and measured in decibels, versus the denominator term, f/f_{hf} or f/f_{3dB}, common to each of the equations cited. When the absissa has a value of unity, the corresponding ordinate is -3 dB. A 3-dB loss indicates that current gain or voltage gain has diminished to 0.707 of its reference value.

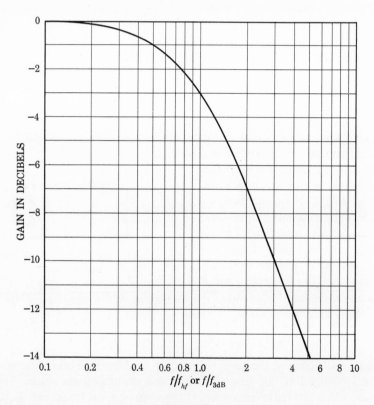

Fig. 5–12.

Miller effect. The element R_i in Fig. 5–11 is $r_{b'e}$ for a junction transistor, but C_i is not simply the $C_{b'e}$ element of the hybrid-π representation. In circuits using conventional transistors, FET's, or vacuum tubes, additional input capacitance is apparent and is referred to as the *Miller effect*. The Miller effect is significantly increased input capacitance caused by a mutual capacitance element linking the output to input portions of an amplifying circuit. To show this effect, let us find the input admittance of the "boxed" portion of Fig. 5–13. We write

$$I_i = I_m + I_s.$$

Now
$$I_s = j\omega C_{b'e} V_i$$

and
$$I_m = -j\omega C_{b'c}(V_o - V_i).$$

Z_L is generally a small impedance compared with the other parallel paths. Consequently,

$$V_o \cong -g_m V_i Z_L.$$

A combination of the foregoing equations yields

$$I_i/V_i = Y_i = j\omega[C_{b'e} + C_{b'c}(1 + g_m Z_L)]. \tag{5--43}$$

Notice that $C_{b'c}$ has effectively been multiplied by a term $(1 + g_m Z_L)$ considerably greater than unity. This, then, is the Miller effect; the total input capacitance is much greater than $C_{b'e}$. Typical parameter values are given in an example to follow.

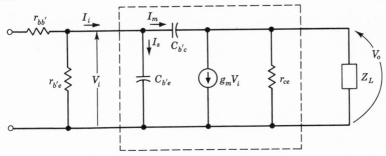

Fig. 5–13. Hybrid-π circuit analyzed for input capacitance. $r_{b'c}$ has been omitted from the diagram.

Should the load impedance Z_L be inductive, it is easy to prove that Y_i will have a negative real part; a negative resistance physically means that power is being fed back from the output circuit through $C_{b'c}$, and under certain conditions oscillation may occur. Neutralization, discussed later, can be used to minimize this internal feedback.

Example. A numerical example is in order. It is desired to find the voltage gain upper cutoff frequency for a stage coupling a 500 Ω source to a 1000 Ω load. Assume the transistor parameters to be:

$$f_T = 6 \text{ Mc}, \qquad g_m = 0.04 \text{ mho},$$
$$h_{fe} = 50, \qquad r_{bb'} = 100 \text{ ohms},$$
$$C_{b'c} = 10 \text{ pF},$$

Calculations yield

$$r_{b'e} = h_{fe}/g_m = 1250 \ \Omega,$$
$$C_{b'e} = g_m/\omega_T = 1060 \text{ pF},$$
$$C_i = C_{b'e} + C_{b'c}(1 + g_m Z_L) = 1460 \text{ pF}.$$

The upper cutoff frequency, as given by Eq. (5–42), is 300,000 cps. A lower value of load resistance will reduce C_i and raise the cutoff frequency. Also a smaller source resistance will allow operation to higher frequencies. The limiting effects of source resistance and base-spreading resistance are evident.

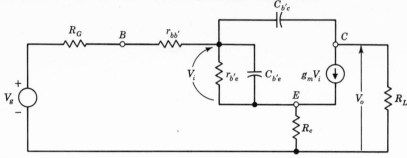

Fig. 5–14.   Terminated hybrid π useful for bandwidth studies.

Bandwidth extension.   Local feedback element R_e is included with the modified hybrid-π transistor representation in Fig. 5–14. The element R_e extends the voltage-gain bandwidth as is noted from the following derivation:

$$A_v(\omega) \equiv \left| \frac{V_o}{V_g} \right| = A_i(\omega) \frac{R_L}{Z_i(\omega)}$$

$$= \frac{g_m V_i}{V_i/Z} \frac{R_L}{R_G + r_{bb'} + Z + R_e(1 + A_i(\omega))}. \tag{5–44a}$$

Z represents the impedance of the parallel combination of $r_{b'e}$ and C_T. The sum of $C_{b'e}$ and reflected $C_{b'c}$ including Miller effect is C_T. For simplicity, let $R_x \equiv R_G + r_{bb'}$. Then manipulations of Eq. (5–44a) yield

$$A_v(\omega) = \frac{g_m h_{fe} R_L}{h_{fe} + g_m R_x + g_m R_e(1 + h_{fe}) + j\omega r_{b'e} C_T(R_e + R_x)}. \tag{5–44b}$$

The voltage gain will be down by 3 dB when the real and reactive portions of the denominator have equal magnitudes. Thus

$$\omega_{3dB} = \frac{h_{fe} + g_m R_x + g_m R_e(1 + h_{fe})}{h_{fe}(R_e + R_x)\{C_{b'e} + C_{b'c}[1 + g_m(R_e + R_L)]\}}. \tag{5–45}$$

Analysis of this expression for bandwidth indicates that, in most circuits, the bandwidth will be increased by the addition of R_e. For

$$g_m R_x < 1,$$

the bandwidth will not be increased by R_e but rather declines with increased local feedback. This condition is not often encountered; consequently, when concerned with bandwidth requirements, one can consider that bandwidth generally will be increased by the negative feedback.

5–7. The Terminated FET. A single FET stage, fed from a source of internal resistance R_G and feeding a load resistance R_L, may be described by relatively simple relations for voltage gain and bandwidth.

Common Source. The assumption previously made that the input impedance is infinite at low frequencies results in the simplified expression for common-source voltage gain first noted in Chapter 1:

$$|A_v| = g_m Z_L.$$

Ideally Z_L includes any drain-to-source internal impedance as well as the external load. The common-source orientation provides phase reversal not present in other FET connections.

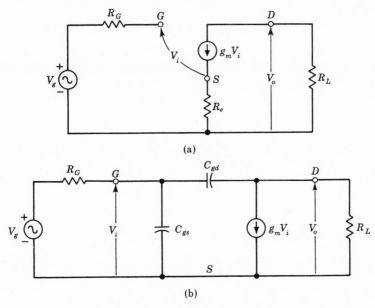

(a)

(b)

Fig. 5–15. FET circuits: (a) simple low-frequency equivalent with feedback element R_e; (b) equivalent useful for bandwidth studies.

Occasionally it is advantageous to provide negative feedback in the form of unbypassed resistance between source terminal and ground as shown in Fig. 5–15(a). The voltage amplification for this case is

$$A_v = |V_o/V_g| = g_m R_L/(1 + g_m R_e). \tag{5-46}$$

The influence of R_e upon A_v is not serious until $g_m R_e$ becomes comparable to unity. The unbypassed source-lead resistance increases the output resistance of the stage. Let r_o be the output resistance of the FET alone. With R_e in the circuit, it is easily shown that the total output resistance is

$$R_o = r_o + (1 + g_m r_o)R_e. \tag{5-47}$$

We include interelemental capacitances in Fig. 5–15(b). A Miller effect will be present because of C_{gd}. Consequently,

$$C_{in} = C_{gs} + C_{gd}(1 + g_m Z_L), \tag{5-48}$$

with

$$C_{gs} = C_{is} - C_{rs} \quad \text{and} \quad C_{gd} = C_{rs}.$$

When it is advantageous to study the gate–source conductance, the value of that parameter is

$$g_{gs} = g_{is} - g_{rs}.$$

The total input conductance of an amplifying stage is also dependent upon the Miller effect:

$$g_{in} = g_{gs} + g_{gd}(1 + g_m Z_L). \tag{5-49}$$

Common Drain. When the FET is connected in the common-drain orientation, voltage gain is less than unity, no phase reversal between input and output is apparent, the effective input capacitance is reduced, and the output impedance is lowered. The low-frequency voltage gain of this connection is

$$A_v = g_m r_o R_L / [r_o + R_L(1 + g_m r_o)]. \tag{5-50a}$$

The product $g_m r_o$ is often referred to as μ, the open-circuit voltage gain parameter. For $\mu \gg 1$, Eq. (5–50a) becomes

$$A_v = g_m R_L / (1 + g_m R_L). \tag{5-50b}$$

In Eqs. (5–50) R_L is the load resistance connected between source terminal and ground.

Common Gate. This connection can be used when a low input impedance and a high output impedance are desired. No phase reversal exists in common-gate circuits. The voltage gain is given by

$$A_v = R_L(1 + g_m r_o) / [R_L + r_o + R_G(1 + g_m r_o)]. \tag{5-51}$$

The internal resistance of the signal source is R_G, and R_L is the circuit load connected between drain terminal and ground.

Frequency Response. A study of the frequency response of the common-source FET stage is considerably simplified if the problem is broken into two parts. For the range of values of R_G that results in significant signal attenuation of gate signal, the bandwidth is

$$\omega_{3dB} = 1 / \{R_G[C_{gs} + C_{gd}(1 + g_m R_L)]\}. \tag{5-52}$$

When the signal-source resistance is low, frequency cutoff occurs because of output capacitance which steals $g_m V_i$ current from R_L. Then

$$\omega_{3dB} = 1 / C_o R_L. \tag{5-53}$$

C_o is the effective output capacitance of the device. Included in C_o is any inherent C_{ds} paralleled by capacitance of approximate value C_{gd}.

Test data taken on a low-frequency junction FET type feeding $R_L = 8.2\,\text{k}\Omega$, with $I_D = 1$ mA, $V_{DS} = 12$ V, result in the curve of Fig. 5–16. The effect of C_o upon the curve is evident at frequencies above 1 Mc.

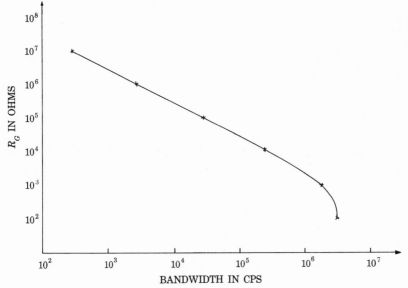

Fig. 5–16.   Bandwidth vs R_G for simple FET stage.

When considering MOS units that behave according to the model given in Fig. 4–21(a), it is obvious that gain falloff will be affected by an additional factor, namely, the reduction in V_c caused by reduced reactance of C_c. The primary cause for gain reduction ultimately depends upon the signal source and circuit load resistance values.

5–8. Gain Considerations. Thus far in the chapter the voltage amplification of a simple transistor stage usually has been defined by the ratio of the voltage at the collector terminal to the voltage at the base terminal. This definition gives a valid picture of the contribution of the transistor to over-all voltage gain, but the circuit designer is sometimes more concerned with the ratio of load voltage to source voltage. In a like manner, concern may be centered about the ratio of load current to source current rather than gain as given by the preceding gain expressions, which involve collector current and base current.

If a transistor is being fed from a source with high internal resistance compared to its input resistance, as is true in the circuit of Fig. 5–17(a), the voltage available at its base, based upon the numbers indicated in the diagram, is

$$[R_i/(R_G + R_i)]V_g = V_g/11.$$

A considerable attenuation is evident. In the figure all of the current leaving the source enters the transistor base (base-biasing resistance is assumed large compared with R_i).

If the method of base bias is as shown in Fig. 5–17(b), a greater signal loss is evident. The signal voltage at the base is

$$\frac{R_i R_2/(R_i + R_2)}{R_G + R_i R_2/(R_i + R_2)} V_g = \frac{V_g}{16}$$

and the base current is

$$[R_2/(R_i + R_2)]I_s = \tfrac{2}{3}I_s.$$

In a like fashion loss of signal can occur in the collector-load circuit, and in the next section examples are given. Certainly from this brief discussion it can be seen that the amplification required from a circuit must be clearly defined, and that the loss of gain due to passive circuit elements warrants attention.

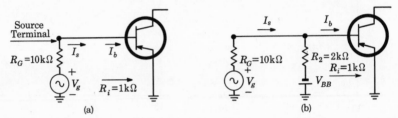

Fig. 5–17. Diagrams for sample gain calculations.

We have previously defined power gain as simply the product of A_v and A_i. Other power-gain expressions have evolved and are used in the literature to measure how efficiently a transistor stage fits into a network containing a specific signal source and a specific load.

The ratio of actual power delivered to a load to power available from the signal generator is known as *transducer gain*. Available power, or the maximum power the source is capable of supplying, depends upon impedance matching. Under conditions where the source (V_g) sees a load equal to its internal resistance (R_G), then

$$P_{\text{avail}} = V_g^2/4R_G \tag{5–54}$$

and the transducer gain (G_t) is

$$G_t = P_o/P_{\text{avail}} = P_o/(V_g^2/4R_G). \tag{5–55}$$

With the substitutions that $P_o = I_o^2 R_L$ and $V_g = I_g(R_G + R_i)$,

$$G_t = 4I_o^2 R_L R_G/[I_g^2(R_G + R_i)^2] \tag{5–56}$$

or

$$G_t = 4A_i^2 R_L R_G/[(R_G + R_i)^2]. \tag{5–57}$$

Equation (5–57) may be useful when comparing several amplifiers in a circuit with fixed generator resistance.

Available power gain (G_a) is defined as the ratio of power available from the transistor to power available from the signal source. Available power depends upon output matching, and

$$G_a = (V_{co}^2/4R_o)/(V_g^2/4R_G) = V_{co}^2 R_G/V_g^2 R_o, \qquad (5\text{–}58)$$

where V_{co} is the open-circuit or no-load output voltage and R_o is the output resistance.

If both the input and output of the transistor are matched, *maximum available gain* (MAG) will result. Under these conditions, for a specific transistor, no greater power amplification can occur.

$$\text{MAG} = I_o^2 R_o/I_g^2 R_i = A_i^2(R_o/R_i) = A_i^2(R_L/R_G) \qquad (5\text{–}59)$$

for $R_L = R_o$ and $R_G = R_i$. To achieve this optimum of operation, impedance-matching devices may have to be employed. This is generally not done at audio frequencies, for the cost of such devices (transformers) may prohibit the achievement of optimum performance in certain applications, and the low cost of transistors may dictate that an additional stage is less costly. Every transistor type has an MAG; this gain is independent of the actual load or source, although matching is assumed.

Other expressions for the power gains discussed here are given in Problems 5–34, 5–35, and 5–36.

Example. A source with an open-circuit voltage of 1 mV and an internal resistance of 1000 Ω supplies a transistor with input resistance of 500 Ω and $G = 10,000$. Find G_t.

$$P_i = \frac{V_g^2 R_i}{(R_G + R_i)^2} = \frac{(10^{-3})^2(500)}{(1000 + 500)^2} = 0.222 \times 10^{-9} \text{ W},$$

$$P_o = P_i G = (0.222 \times 10^{-9})(10^4) = 2.22 \times 10^{-6} \text{ W},$$

$$P_{avail} = \frac{V_g^2}{4R_G} = \frac{(10^{-3})^2}{4(1000)} = 0.250 \times 10^{-9} \text{ W}.$$

Then

$$G_t = \frac{P_o}{P_{avail}} = \frac{2.22 \times 10^{-6}}{0.25 \times 10^{-9}} = 8880.$$

The transducer gain and the power gain are nearly equal, indicating a fairly efficient input circuit. If $R_i = R_G$, then $G = G_t$.

5–9. Examples of Circuit Analysis.

Example 1. It is desired to analyze the circuit of Fig. 5–18 to determine the A_v and A_i provided by the circuit.

A good starting point is investigation of the operating point; this means solving the dc circuit. The base terminal is essentially at ground potential because $I_B R_G$ will be small. The emitter-to-base potential drop will be considered

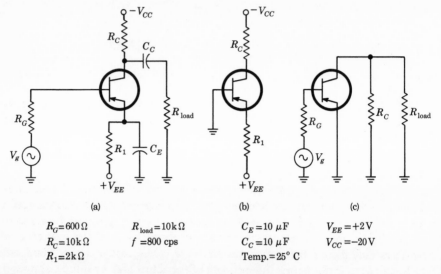

(a)   (b)   (c)

$R_G = 600\,\Omega$	$R_{load} = 10\text{k}\,\Omega$	$C_E = 10\,\mu\text{F}$	$V_{EE} = +2\,\text{V}$
$R_C = 10\text{k}\,\Omega$	$f = 800\,\text{cps}$	$C_C = 10\,\mu\text{F}$	$V_{CC} = -20\,\text{V}$
$R_1 = 2\text{k}\,\Omega$		Temp. $= 25°\,\text{C}$	

Fig. 5–18.   Analysis of single-stage amplifier, Example 1: (a) complete circuit; (b) dc portion; (c) ac portion.

negligible, so it can be concluded that the emitter terminal is also near dc ground, and

$$I_E \cong V_{EE}/R_1 = 2/(2\text{ k}) = 1\text{ mA}.$$

$I_C \cong I_E$; therefore, $I_C = 1$ mA, and the drop across R_C is

$$I_C R_C = (1 \times 10^{-3})(10 \times 10^3) = 10\text{ V}.$$

Therefore

$$V_{CE} = -V_{CC} + I_C R_C = -20 + 10 = -10\text{ V}.$$

Thus the operating point is completely defined.

To obtain the ac parameters, we can make use of the design-center values supplied by the manufacturer for this transistor type. Assume the parameter values, corrected for the 1 mA, 10 V Q-point, to be

$$h_{ib} = 29\,\Omega, \qquad\qquad h_{fe} = 46,$$

$$h_{rb} = 3.75 \times 10^{-4}, \qquad h_{ob} = 0.6\,\mu\text{mho},$$

$$h_{fb} = -0.979.$$

The ac load (R_L) upon the stage is R_C in parallel with R_{load} (when C_C is large enough for its reactance to be negligible). Thus $R_L = 5\text{ k}\Omega$. Operation of the circuit is calculated from the approximate formulas of Table 5–2:

$$A_v = h_{fb}R_L/[h_{ib}(1 + h_{ob}R_L)] = 169,$$

$$A_i = h_{fb}/[h_{ob}R_L + (1 + h_{fb})] = 40.8,$$

$$G = A_vA_i = 6900, \text{ or } 38.4 \text{ dB.}$$

The gain calculations pertain only to the transistor; to include the entire circuit we observe that not all of the alternating collector current flows to R_{load}; in fact only one-half of I_c gets to the required resistor. All of the alternating collector voltage is available at R_{load}; therefore the actual figures are

$$A_v = 169$$

$$A_i = 20.4$$

$$G = 3450, \text{ or } 35.4 \text{ dB.}$$

Further information concerning this circuit may be obtained if desired. The ratio of load voltage to source voltage V_g may be found as follows:

$$R_i = [h_{ib}(1 + R_Lh_{ob})]/[R_Lh_{ob} + (1 + h_{fb})] = 1208 \ \Omega.$$

The signal voltage at the base terminal is

$$[R_i/(R_i + R_G)]V_g = 0.67 \ V_g.$$

Therefore the load-voltage to source-voltage ratio or voltage gain is (0.67)(169) = 113.

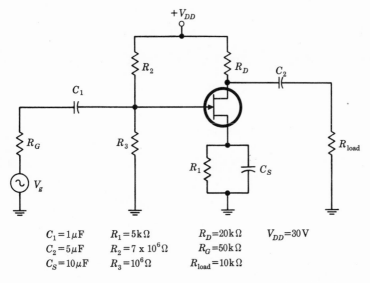

$C_1 = 1\mu\text{F}$	$R_1 = 5\text{k}\Omega$	$R_D = 20\text{k}\Omega$	$V_{DD} = 30\text{V}$
$C_2 = 5\mu\text{F}$	$R_2 = 7 \times 10^6 \Omega$	$R_G = 50\text{k}\Omega$	
$C_S = 10\mu\text{F}$	$R_3 = 10^6 \Omega$	$R_{\text{load}} = 10\text{k}\Omega$	

Fig. 5–19.   Circuit for Example 2.

Example 2.   Find the voltage gain provided by the circuit of Fig. 5–19.

Consider that the following information is known about the *n*-channel FET of the figure:

$$I_{DSS} = 10 \text{ mA}, \qquad V_P = 2 \text{ V}.$$

The device behaves according to the square law relation, Eq. (4–71),

$$I_D = I_{DSS}(1 - |V_{GS}/V_P|)^2.$$

Both I_D and V_{GS} are unknown, so we seek a second relation involving those quantities. Considering gate current to be negligible, the following applies:

$$(30)\left(\frac{10^6}{10^6 + 7 \times 10^6}\right) = I_D(5 \text{ k}) + V_{GS}.$$

From these two relations we find that $I_D \cong 1 \text{ mA}$, $V_{GS} \cong -1.4 \text{ V}$. Therefore

$$V_{DS} = 30 - I_D(25 \text{ k}) = 5V.$$

The parameter g_m is given by Eq. (4–72):

$$g_m = \frac{2I_{DSS}}{V_P}\left(1 - \left|\frac{V_{GS}}{V_P}\right|\right) = 0.003 \text{ mho}.$$

Because the stage load is $20 \text{ k}\Omega \| 10 \text{ k}\Omega$, the voltage gain provided by the FET is

$$A_v = 20.$$

For all practical purposes, the input resistance of the stage at low frequencies is 875 kΩ. If we assume that $C_{gs} = 2 \text{ pF}$, $C_{gd} = 1 \text{ pF}$, then

$$C_{in} = 2 + 1(21) = 23 \text{ pF}.$$

The upper cutoff frequency of this circuit would be in the neighborhood of

$$f_{3dB} = 1/[2\pi(50 \text{ k}\Omega)(23 \text{ pF})] = 138 \text{ kc}$$

Additional information concerning the allowable signal-size capabilities of the circuits considered in these examples is best studied after the subject of dynamic load lines is treated in Chapter 6.

5–10. Instantaneous Analysis.   Often it is desirable to analyze circuit operation by assuming that instantaneous signals of certain polarities are introduced at a circuit input for the purpose of determining the resulting changes in voltages and currents at some other place in a composite circuit. Consider the *p–n–p* transistor shown in Fig. 5–20(a). The directions of normal dc currents and potentials are shown on the diagram. Collector characteristics for the transistor, Fig. 5–20(b), include the load line and the operating point. The load line is determined by R_1 and R_L in series, and applies to both dc and ac analyses. R_1 is included in the diagram for completeness.

Let us now introduce an ac source at the input terminals of the network, and assume that terminal A of that source is, at the moment of inspection, more positive than terminal B [Fig. 5–20(c)]. The source will thus attempt to cause a current i_s to flow *into* the transistor base, or in other words, the source will reduce the instantaneous value of base current. Turning our attention back to (b) of the figure we may note that a reduction in base current causes a corresponding reduction in the magnitude of collector current and a corresponding increase in the magnitude of the collector–emitter voltage. Emitter current likewise will be reduced.

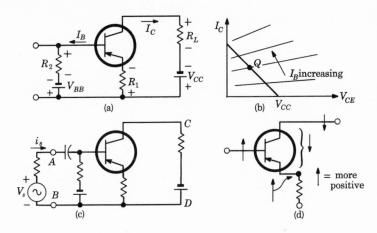

Fig. 5–20. Instantaneous analysis.

Now examine the altered circuit potentials. The voltage at C of Fig. 5–20(c) was, in the absence of signal, equal to $(-V_{CC} + I_C R_L)$. The positive-going base signal has, as described above, reduced collector current. Therefore the point C potential is now more negative because of that reduction. It can easily be seen that a phase reversal has occurred, because a positive-going input has resulted in a more negative-going output.

A corresponding reduction in emitter current will result when conditions are as described above, and this, for a circuit with resistance in the emitter lead, will cause the drop across R_1 to decrease, and the emitter terminal will become more positive.

Now suppose that we adopt a shorthand notation to specify the operation discussed here. Using an arrow pointed upward to indicate a potential that is instantaneously becoming more positive, it is possible to draw Fig. 5–20(d). This figure shows that when the base is subjected to a positive-going signal, the collector potential becomes more negative. The emitter potential is now more positive than previously if an emitter resistance is included in the circuit. The effects of an unbypassed emitter resistance such as R_1 in the diagram may be clearly understood. The assumed input signal has increased the emitter potential, allowing a reduced signal from base-to-emitter, an indication of negative feedback.

Some may prefer analyzing transistor circuits by current. Base current instantaneously flowing toward the base (reducing the normal bias current) causes a reduced collector current, or one that is instantaneously flowing toward the collector, and an emitter current away from the emitter terminal. Of course in all cases these ac excursions are superimposed upon the normal direct currents. It is possible to extend this type of reasoning to other configurations and naturally to the n–p–n unit. It is suggested that the reader work out a system of analysis that he finds most satisfactory to explain the operation.

5-11. Matrix Analysis of Interconnected Networks. Performance relations for networks considered earlier in this chapter were generally derived by simultaneously solving the mesh and nodal equations written according to Kirchhoff's Laws. It is possible and sometimes convenient to derive relations for pairs of interconnected two-port networks by using matrix algebra.

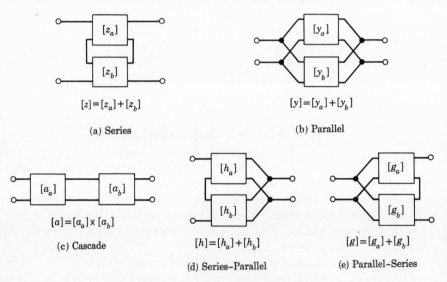

Fig. 5-21. Two-port network connections.

Consider Fig. 5-21 which shows various network pairs. To interpret the diagram of (a) of that figure, we note that the z-matrix equivalent of the two networks in "series" is obtained by adding the z matrices; thus

$$[z] = [z_a] + [z_b].$$

The other equivalencies are noted in the figure. They may easily be proven (Problem 5-40).

Let us take as an example the case of a common-emitter-connected transistor, with an unbypassed resistance R connected between emitter and ground (see Fig. 5–22). The transistor may be described by

$$[z_a] = \begin{bmatrix} z_{11a} & z_{12a} \\ z_{21a} & z_{22a} \end{bmatrix}.$$

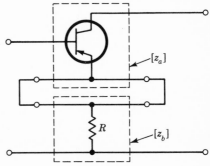

If necessary the transistor's z parameters may be obtained by using parameter interrelations given in Appendix II.

The resistance R must also be represented by a z matrix:

$$[z_b] = \begin{bmatrix} R & R \\ R & R \end{bmatrix}.$$

Fig. 5–22. Unbypassed emitter-lead resistance added to common-emitter stage.

Because the transistor and the resistance are connected as in Fig. 5–21(a), the z matrix of the entire network, transistor plus R, is

$$[z] = [z_a] + [z_b] = \begin{bmatrix} z_{11a} + R & z_{12a} + R \\ z_{21a} + R & z_{22a} + R \end{bmatrix}.$$

To find the gains and impedance levels of this network, we may utilize the formulas of Appendix II for the terminated $[z]$. Naturally when using those formulas, $z_{11} = z_{11a} + R$, etc.

PROBLEMS

5–1. Prove that the power gain of a transistor stage can be expressed as

$$G = A_i{}^2 R_L / R_i,$$

or as

$$G = A_v{}^2 R_i / R_L$$

5–2. Solve Eqs. (5–1) for $\begin{bmatrix} I_1 \\ V_0 \end{bmatrix}$ by using matrix manipulations.

5–3. Verify Eqs. (5–8).

5–4. Verify Eqs. (5–9), (5–10), (5–11), and (5–12) of Table 5–2.

5–5. Verify Eq. (5–13) of Table 5–2.

5–6. Verify Eqs. (5–15), (5–16), (5–17), and (5–18) of Table 5–3.

5–7. Verify Eqs. (5–20), (5–21), (5–22), and (5–23) of Table 5–4.

5–8. Verify Eq. (5–24) of Table 5–4.

5–9. Verify Eqs. (5–25, (5–26), (5–27), and (5–28) of Table 5–5.

5–10. Verify Eq. (5–29) of Table 5–5.

5–11. A common-base stage couples a low-resistance source to a load of 50,000 Ω. If $h_{ib} = 32\ \Omega$, $h_{fb} = -0.96$, $h_{rb} = 2 \times 10^{-4}$, and $h_{ob} = 10^{-6}$ mho, find the input and output resistance and the voltage gain provided by the circuit.

5–12. Analyze the common-collector circuit with common-base parameters shown in the accompanying diagram in order to confirm the gain and resistance equations which are presented in the table.

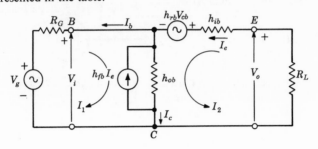

Problem 5–12.

COMMON-COLLECTOR FORMULAS FOR THE h EQUIVALENT*

Voltage gain, A_v	$R_L/(h_{ib} + R_L)$
Current gain, A_i	$[h_{ob}(h_{ib} + R_L) + (1 + h_{fb})]^{-1}$
Power gain, G	$\dfrac{R_L}{(h_{ib} + R_L)[h_{ob}(h_{ib} + R_L) + (1 + h_{fb})]}$
Input resistance, R_i	$\dfrac{h_{ib} + R_L}{h_{ob}(h_{ib} + R_L) + (1 + h_{fb})}$
Output resistance, R_o	$\dfrac{h_{ib}(1 + R_G h_{ob}) + R_G(1 + h_{fb})}{1 + R_G h_{ob}}$

*$(1 - h_{rb})$ factors omitted.

5–13. Confirm the formulas given in Problem 5–12 by using the formulas of Table 5–1 and the parameter relations of Table 4–1.

5–14. It is desired to investigate the common-collector configuration with local feedback from output (emitter) to input (base). Use the h-matrix equivalent circuit of Fig. 4–7(b) and derive an expression for current gain in terms of the common-base h-parameters and the feedback resistance R_x.

5–15. What is the power gain of a 2N3242 with typical parameters and $R_L = 2000$ Ω? Calculate the voltage and current gains of this common-emitter circuit.

5–16. Consider a 2N2614 to be operated common-emitter at the recommended point. Convert the hybrid-π parameters to h parameters, and calculate the voltage gain provided by the circuit when it feeds a 5000 Ω load.

5–17. Use the typical values of T parameters listed in Sec. 5–3 to calculate the voltage gain, current gain, and input resistance of a common-emitter stage feeding a 2000 Ω load. Compare the answers obtained from using the complete equations with those obtained from the approximate equations of Table 5–4.

5–18. A transistor being operated common-emitter and feeding a 5000 Ω load has $\alpha = 0.99$, $r_b = 100$ Ω, $r_c = 2 \times 10^6$ Ω, and $r_e = 40$ Ω. What is the input resistance and voltage amplification at low frequencies?

5–19. Calculate the current amplification and input and output resistance of a simple transistor circuit feeding a 1000 Ω load from a 1000 Ω source. $\beta = 50$, $r_b = 500$ Ω, $r_e = 30$ Ω, and $r_c = 10^6$ Ω. Consider the three practical configurations.

5–20. The curves representing power gain vs load resistance each reach a maximum at a particular value of load resistance. This value of load resistance may be determined by differentiating the appropriate gain formulas with respect to R_L. Impedance matching thus could describe this effect. Derive an expression for R_L for maximum power gain for the common-emitter configuration in terms of the h parameters.

5–21. Repeat Problem 5–20 for the common-base configuration.

5–22. Repeat Problem 5–20 for the common-collector configuration.

5–23. A particular transistor has the following low-frequency parameters: $h_{ie} = 2500$ Ω, $h_{re} = 2 \times 10^{-3}$, $h_{fe} = 50$, $h_{oe} = 5 \times 10^{-5}$ mho, $r_{bb'} = 60$ Ω.

(a) Draw a hybrid-π network and calculate the values of the parameters.

(b) Draw a current-generator equivalent tee and calculate the values of the parameters.

5–24. Consider a transistor with the parameters given in Problem 5–23 and, in addition, $C_c = 10$ pF, $f_{\alpha b} = 10$ Mc, $R_L = 2000$ Ω, and $R_G = 100$ Ω.

(a) Calculate the input capacitance including the Miller effect.

(b) At what frequency will $|V_o/V_g|$ be $1/\sqrt{2}$ of its mid-frequency value.

5–25. Measurements of the input impedance of a particular common-emitter stage indicate that the 1000-cycle value is 800 Ω and at 90,000 cycles the magnitude has diminished to 566 Ω. From this data determine the effective input resistance and input capacitance.

5–26. If it is known that the transistor of Problem 5–25 is feeding a 1000 Ω load from a 1000 Ω source, and that $C_{b'c} = 20$ pF and $g_m = 30$ mA/V, calculate:

(a) The emitter diffusion capacitance.

(b) The alpha cutoff frequency.

(c) The upper voltage-gain cutoff frequency.

5–27. Confirm the following formulas that have been derived for the hybrid-π circuit of the figure.

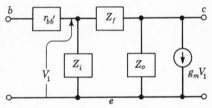

Problem 5–27.

$$A_i = \frac{Z_i Z_o [1 - g_m Z_f]}{Z_o [Z_i + Z_f] + Z_L [Z_i + Z_f + Z_o + g_m Z_i Z_o]},$$

$$A_v = \frac{Z_i Z_o Z_L r_{bb'} [1 - g_m Z_f]}{[Z_o + Z_L][r_{bb'}(Z_i + Z_f) + Z_i Z_f + Z_o Z_L (r_{bb'} + Z_i + g_m r_{bb'} Z_i)]},$$

$$R_i = \frac{Z_o [r_{bb'}(Z_i + Z_f) + Z_i Z_f] + Z_L [r_{bb'}(Z_i + Z_f + Z_o + g_m Z_o Z_i) + Z_i(Z_f + Z_o)]}{Z_o(Z_i + Z_f) + Z_L(Z_i + Z_f + Z_o + g_m Z_o Z_i)},$$

$$R_o = \frac{Z_o [(Z_i + Z_f)(Z_G + r_{bb'}) + Z_i Z_f]}{[Z_G + r_{bb'}][Z_i + Z_f + Z_o + g_m Z_i Z_o] + Z_i [Z_f + Z_o]}.$$

5–28. It is desired to study the complete hybrid-π equivalent, with the omission of the capacitances and r_{ce}. The loading effect of $g_{b'c}$ upon the b' and c nodes will also be neglected, but the mutual effect of that parameter is to be retained. Show that, under these conditions,

$$A_v \cong \frac{g_m R_L}{(1 + r_{bb'}/r_{b'e}) + g_m R_L r_{bb'}/r_{b'c}}.$$

and, if $g_{b'c} \ll g_{bb'} + g_{b'e}/g_m R_L$, this expression reduces to that of the text, namely,

$$A_v = g_m R_L r_{b'e}/(r_{bb'} + r_{b'e}).$$

5–29. Find the output impedance of the modified hybrid-π model of Fig. 5–5 including R_e, r_{ce}, $C_{b'e}$, and $C_{b'c}$ as $\omega \to 0$ and as $\omega \to \infty$.

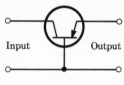

Input   Output

Problem 5–30.

5–30. Very occasionally a transistor is employed in the reverse common-base configuration. Power gain of less than unity is thereby achieved, so this connection is not useful for amplification. Although no applications are treated here as an exercise, derive the formulas for A_v, A_i, R_i, and R_o from the T-equivalent circuit.

5–31. The curves of Figs. 5–6 through 5–10 can be approximated by straight lines intersecting at "break" values of R_L. Each of the complete A_v, A_i, G, and R_i equations can be put in the form

$$(a + bR_L)/(c + dR_L).$$

Breaks in the straight-line approximations will occur at $R_L = a/b$ and $R_L = c/d$.
  (a) From Table 5–2 determine formulas that will predict the breaks in the common-emitter performance vs R_L curves.
  (b) Repeat part (a) for the common-base curves.

5–32. Compare the current-gain frequency response of a particular transistor operating common-emitter with the response of that same transistor operating common-base. Consider alpha reduction as the only source of gain falloff, and assume that the transistor is feeding a low-resistance load. Which orientation provides the greater gain at $f_{\alpha e}$ and at $f_{\alpha b}$?

5–33. A high-fidelity amplifier with a current-gain bandwidth of 12 cps to 40,000 cps is to be incorporated into a measuring circuit. Find the frequency range over which the amplifier's current gain does not change by more than 1 dB. If the specification were 10% rather than 1 dB would it be tighter?

5–34. Prove that, for any configuration, transducer gain may be given by

$$G_t = \frac{4R_L R_G h_f^2}{[R_G R_L h_o + R_G + (h_i h_o - h_r h_f)R_L + h_i]^2}.$$

5–35. Prove, that, for any configuration, available gain may be given by

$$G_a = \frac{h_f^2 R_G}{[(h_i h_o - h_r h_f) + R_G h_o][R_G + h_i]}.$$

5–36. Prove that, for any configuration, maximum available gain may be given by

$$\text{MAG} = \frac{h_f^2}{[(h_i h_o - h_r h_f)^{1/2} + (h_i h_o)^{1/2}]^2}.$$

5–37. For the transistor of Problem 5–15, by how much will the circuit gains change if an unbypassed emitter resistance of 100 Ω is used?

5–38. In the calculation of the gains of the circuit of Fig. 5–18, approximate formulas were used. Using complete equations, determine the error resulting from the use of the approximate relations.

5–39. When a transistor feeds a load consisting of C_L' and G_L' in parallel, the input circuit of the device can be represented by the elements shown in the figure. Show that $C_1 = C_{b'e} + C_{b'c}$, $C = C_{b'c}g_m/G_L'$, $R = C_L'/C_{b'c}g_m$.

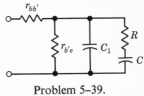

5–40. Prove the matrix equations for the five interconnected networks shown in Fig. 5–21.

5–41. Using matrix algebra, determine the y parameters for a network consisting of a common-emitter transistor and a feedback resistance connected between collector and base.

Problem 5–39.

REFERENCES

1. Early, J. M., "Design Theory of Junction Transistors," *Bell System Tech. J.*, **32** November 1953.
2. Greiner, R. A., *Semiconductor Devices and Applications* (McGraw-Hill Book Co., Inc., New York, 1961).
3. Hurley, R. B., *Junction Transistor Electronics* (John Wiley & Sons, Inc., New York, 1958).
4. Lo, A. W., *et al.*, *Transistor Electronics* (Prentice-Hall, Inc., Englewood Cliffs, New Jersey, 1955).
5. Shea, R. F., *Principles of Transistor Circuits* (John Wiley & Sons, Inc., New York, 1953).
6. Shea, R. F., *Transistor Audio Amplifiers* (John Wiley & Sons, Inc., New York, 1955).
7. Shea, R. F., *Transistor Applications* (John Wiley and Sons, Inc., New York, 1964).
8. von Weiss, A., *Matrix Analysis for Electrical Engineers* (D. Van Nostrand, Co., Inc., Princeton, New Jersey, 1964).

Chapter 6

DESIGN

The designer of a transistor circuit must have a working knowledge of the information presented in Chapters 1 through 5—the basic definitions, transistor-operation theory, biasing techniques, parameter variations, and the methods of predicting gain and circuit impedance levels. In addition, he must know the specifications for the particular circuit to be designed; those specifications may take on various forms. For practical designs, information of the following types is necessary:

1. Desired gain (voltage, current, or power)
2. Input and output signal levels
3. Carrier frequency and phase shift, or frequency response, or transient response
4. Input and output impedance levels
5. Load and signal-source characteristics
6. Available power-supply potentials
7. Allowable current drain from power supplies
8. Noise and distortion
9. Sensitivity to parameter and supply-voltage variations
10. Operating and storage temperature range
11. Other environmental conditions, i.e., shock, humidity, etc.
12. Cost, weight, and size requirements
13. Life expectancy

After collection of the pertinent requirements, the design can be initiated.

The primary emphasis in this chapter is on the design of low-power, single-stage amplifiers suitable for audio, control, and measuring circuits. Additional topics pertinent to the design of linear amplifying circuits are included in later chapters.

To design even the simplest of transistor circuits requires that the designer use all available information, *including test data taken especially for the purpose*, to create a circuit that satisfies the given specifications. For many design problems an infinite number of solutions are possible; for others, no solution can be attained. For example, let it be required that a single transistor stage provide a voltage gain of 10 when feeding a 10,000 Ω load from a 1000 Ω source. If no additional requirements on power-supply voltage, current drain, impedance levels, etc., are forthcoming, an infinite number of circuits could do this job. The solutions would differ in operating-point coordinates, transistor type, etc. Now if the voltage-gain requirement were changed to 10^6, and a single stage were still to be used, we could not solve the problem. In this instance it may be said that the specifications are nonrealizable.

In the process of circuit design, one makes repeated use of analysis. While a few step-by-step procedures are available in the literature for certain specialized design procedures, the vast number of problems encountered are unique, and require that the designer have a good command of network analysis. It is of value to study examples of circuit designs. Such examples are liberally sprinkled throughout this text.

6–1. Choosing the Transistor Type. What transistor type should be used for a hi-fi preamplifier, a motor-driving stage, an aircraft installation, a computer, a radio-frequency amplifier, etc.? These questions arise daily. The answers to them are available from manufacturers' literature and from tests performed by the interested circuit designer.

All transistor types are classified by the manufacturer to the intended application, i.e., audio, high-frequency, switching, high-power, general-purpose, etc. To narrow the field, we can choose all those transistors that pertain to our application. Then a study of circuit specifications will allow a choice of semiconductor material and finally the particular transistor can be chosen for the job.

Silicon vs *Germanium.* The transistor-circuit designer must choose between silicon and germanium units for most of his applications. Study of the peculiarities of each will usually result in certain advantages of one material over the other— in general, the choice is obvious for a particular application.

A major difference between the two materials is the width of their respective energy gaps. The larger gap for silicon results in a much lower leakage current (I_{co}), and lower sensitivity to temperature extremes. A brief operational comparison is given here:

1. Temperature—Silicon units operate satisfactorily at temperatures of 175° C or higher, whereas operation with germanium is impossible above a junction temperature of about 90° to 100° C. Both types can be operated at the low temperatures, $-55°$ C, for example.

2. Cutoff currents—Silicon transistors have leakage currents 100 or more times lower than the I_{co} of comparable germanium units.

3. Collector voltage—Higher maximum collector-voltage ratings are available in present silicon units.

4. Saturation resistance (R_{CS})—Silicon devices may exhibit several hundred ohms of collector-to-emitter resistance when in the full ON or saturated condition. R_{CS} for germanium units is generally lower.

The Particular Transistor. Hundreds of transistor types are available to the circuit designer, just as hundreds of vacuum-tube types are available, and a choice must be made; usually this choice must come near the beginning of each circuit design.

Choosing the correct transistor involves familiarization with available products; knowledge of the relative advantages of silicon and germanium must result in a material decision. After the material has been selected, the following items should be considered:

1. Current-amplification factor—High-, medium-, and low-beta types are available.

2. Maximum collector-operating voltage—Ratings range from 3 to 400 V. This rating is sometimes called BV_{CE}, minimum collector-to-emitter breakdown voltage at a specific collector current.

3. Maximum collector-power dissipation—This limitation is usually specified at 25° C (77° F).

4. Maximum junction temperature—When the transistor is operated with junction temperature at the specified maximum, the allowable collector-power dissipation is zero. Between the limiting junction temperature and 25° C a linear relationship often exists between maximum power dissipation and operating temperature.

5. Maximum collector current.

6. Gain–bandwidth product (f_T).

7. Physical size, mounting dimensions.

8. Cost.

9. Noise factor—Low-noise transistors are available for special applications.

10. Leakage current—Low-leakage units may be selected during manufacture.

11. Variation of parameters—Types can be compared according to the extent of parameter variations due to production tolerances and ambient-temperature excursions.

6–2. Transformer Coupling. As has been stated, the transistor is capable of voltage and current amplification. Should an application require primarily voltage amplification (or power amplification), then, from study of the gain equations and the sample graphs of the preceding chapter, the stage must be terminated in a high-resistance load. On the other hand, if current amplification is of primary concern, a low value of load resistance is mandatory. In the majority of circuits, the general requirement is to raise the signal power level. It is generally desirable to work into high-resistance loads to achieve maximum power transfer, but often this is impossible because of other considerations, which will be apparent from the discussion of coupling circuitry.

The joining of a low-frequency stage to its signal source or load can be accomplished for both vacuum tube and transistor with transformers or resistance-capacitance circuitry. The advantages and disadvantages of each method are discussed in the paragraphs that follow.

It was shown in Chapter 3 that a high level of operation-point stability is achieved with transformer coupling. This is by no means the only advantage of transformers; *their ability to transform impedances is of particular importance.* If we consider an *ideal* transformer, the power levels of primary and secondary will be equal, and thus

$$P_1 = P_2 \tag{6-1a}$$

or

$$V_1{}^2/R_1 = V_2{}^2/R_2. \tag{6-1b}$$

The load on the secondary is R_2 and R_1 is the effective load at the primary terminals (not the dc resistance of the transformer winding, for that resistance is assumed negligible when we state that the device is ideal). Let N_1 and N_2 denote the number of primary and secondary turns, respectively. Then

$$V_2 = (N_2/N_1)V_1. \tag{6-2}$$

Substitution of Eq. (6–2) into Eq. (6–1b) yields

$$R_1 = (N_1/N_2)^2 R_2. \tag{6-3}$$

Since R_1 is the reflected value of R_2 at the primary terminals, it follows that *the circuit designer may achieve any desired ac load on a given stage by choosing the proper turns ratio of the transformer used in coupling a given load to the transistor.*

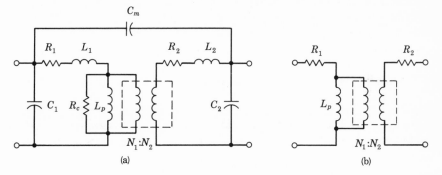

Fig. 6–1.   Transformer equivalent circuits: (a) complete circuit for iron-core transformer; (b) approximation useful at low frequencies.

It is true, however, that coupling transformers are by no means ideal. Figure 6–1(a) presents the transformer as a complex circuit configuration of resistance, inductance, and capacitance. C_1 and C_2 represent distributed winding capacitances; L_1 and L_2 are leakage inductances; R_1 and R_2 are winding resistances; R_c is representative of core losses. The capacitance C_m exists between primary and secondary winding. L_p is a measure of primary inductance and is of interest when the magnetizing current is studied. The only ideal portion of an actual transformer is shown by the windings N_1 and N_2.

For low-frequency use, the equivalent circuit of Fig. 6–1(a) can be approximated by the circuit of Fig. 6–1(b). Considering each component separately, the following observations may be made:

1. The winding resistances R_1 and R_2 must generally be kept low to minimize losses. The slope of the dc load line is directly determined by R_1 because transistor collector potential is usually fed through this transformer winding. Resistances of typical interstage transformers range from 200 to 1000 Ω per winding.

2. L_p should generally be large. If $2\pi f L_p$ is more than twice the reflected load resistance $(N_1/N_2)^2 R_L$, the ac load line will approach the desired straight line. Should L_p be small or should R_L be removed, the transistor works into a reactive load; operation on the resulting elliptical load line will often damage the transistor by causing its ratings to be exceeded.

Low-frequency response falls off because of decreasing ωL_p; at the high end of the usable frequency spectrum, resonances within a transformer may cause a response "hump"; a general decrease in response is apparent for frequencies beyond the "hump" because of lowered shunt capacitive reactances and increased leakage reactance.

To specify an interstage transformer, it is common to supply information of the following types:

1. Impedance ratio (or turns ratio)
2. Maximum ac power delivered to the primary
3. Maximum unbalanced direct current in the windings
4. Minimum primary inductance (at a specified voltage level, frequency, and dc unbalance)
5. Maximum permissible power loss (or efficiency)
6. Frequency response

An efficiency percentage can describe power loss; an insertion-loss factor in decibels may be supplied, or voltage regulation can be used as a figure of merit.

$$\text{Regulation} = (V_{SO} - V_{SF})/V_{SF}. \tag{6–4}$$

V_{SO} and V_{SF} stand for no-load and full-load secondary voltages, respectively. V_{SO} can also be used to signify the secondary voltage at full load if no losses are experienced. Since

$$V = (PR)^{1/2}, \tag{6–5}$$

then

$$\text{Regulation} = [(P'_{SO}R)^{1/2} - (P_{SF}R)^{1/2}]/(P_{SF}R)^{1/2}$$

$$= [(P_{SO})^{1/2} - (P_{SF})^{1/2}]/(P_{SF})^{1/2} \tag{6–6}$$

P_{SO} is the no-loss full-load secondary power and P_{SF} is the actual secondary power at full load. If a 3-dB loss is to be considered, then $P_{SO} = 2P_{SF}$, for one-half of the input power is lost, and

$$\text{Regulation (3-dB loss)} = [(2P_{SF})^{1/2} - (P_{SF})^{1/2}]/(P_{SF})^{1/2} \qquad (6\text{--}7)$$

$$= 0.414, \text{ or } 41.4\%.$$

Similarly,

$$\text{Regulation (2-dB loss)} = 26\%.$$

$$\text{Regulation (1-dB loss)} = 12\%.$$

Interstage transformers are useful for coupling transistor circuits. A high level of circuit efficiency is attainable, and the few components simplify circuit design, although transformer disadvantages such as weight, physical size, cost, and availability may rule them out in some designs. A 2- to 3-dB loss can be expected for the average miniature coupling transformer.

6–3. Capacitance Coupling and Bypassing. Because input resistance of common-emitter stages is low (generally below 5000 Ω), large coupling capacitors must be employed if acceptable frequency response is necessary, and if phase shift is not to be excessive at the lower frequencies. Advances in the art of capacitor manufacture have resulted in high-capacitance, low-voltage electrolytics that have become widely adopted by circuit designers. It is commonplace to find 5 μF capacitors joining stages of a transistor amplifier.

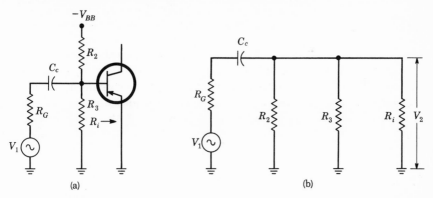

Fig. 6–2.   Typical input circuit: (a) actual schematic; (b) low-frequency ac equivalent for (a).

The circuit shown in Fig. 6–2(a) and its equivalent can form the basis for several sample calculations. Should a voltage source V_1 of internal resistance R_G be driving the stage shown, the phase shift in the signal voltage between V_1 and base can be calculated utilizing conventional circuit theory. If we assume $R_2 \gg R_3$, we obtain the voltage transfer ratio:

$$V_2/V_1 = R_3 R_i/[R_3 R_i + R_G R_3 + R_G R_i - jX_c(R_3 + R_i)]. \qquad (6\text{--}8)$$

Phase shift is determined by the complex denominator, and is

$$\theta = \tan^{-1}\left[X_c(R_3 + R_i)\right]/(R_3 R_i + R_G R_3 + R_G R_i). \tag{6-9}$$

θ is a positive angle, or, stated otherwise, the coupling network provides a phase lead in its output voltage with respect to the source. The lower cutoff frequency where voltage transfer is 3 dB down from its mid-frequency or reference value occurs when $\theta = 45°$. Thus

$$f_{3dB} = (R_3 + R_i)/[2\pi C_c(R_3 R_i + R_G R_3 + R_G R_i)]. \tag{6-10}$$

When the transistor is fed from another common-emitter stage, as in Fig. 6–3, R_G can be represented by R_o, the output resistance of the first stage. This element is paralleled by R_C and by a signal current generator I_o. Let us consider R_o to be much greater than R_C (or include it in the value used for R_C); we then conclude that *Eqs.* (6–8), (6–9), *and* (6–10) *apply to this case provided the substitution $R_C = R_G$ is made.*

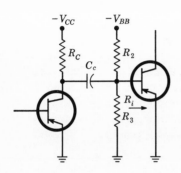

Fig. 6–3. Typical R-C coupled circuit.

For accuracy in calculations one must be aware of any assumptions used. In the preceding work R_o and R_2 were not to affect the resulting equations; however, there are some practical circuits where these parameters are important and should be thoroughly investigated.

In the preceding work the transistor's input impedance was assumed to be resistive (R_i). When bypassed-emitter resistance is used, input impedance will be sensitive to frequency, and low-frequency response thus limited. This condition warrants study.

Consider that the emitter of the second transistor in the circuit of Fig. 6–3 is connected to ground through R_1 bypassed by C_1 as shown in Fig. 6–4(a). The load on the coupling network is no longer R_i alone—it must also include R_1 and C_1. Let Z_1 represent the net impedance of the parallel connection of R_1 and C_1. Because *emitter current flows through this impedance, its effect is approximately* $(\beta + 1)$ *times that of any element in the base circuit.* Therefore the impedance of transistor and Z_1 in series is

$$Z_i \cong R_i + (\beta + 1)Z_1 = R_i + [(\beta + 1)R_1]/(1 + j\omega C_1 R_1). \tag{6-11}$$

We are interested in signal transfer to R_i from the signal source. For convenience, assume C_c to be a short circuit to the signal. The voltage drop across R_i is the following fraction of the signal source voltage:

$$\frac{R_i}{R_T + Z_i} = \frac{R_i(1 + j\omega C_1 R_1)}{(R_T + R_i)(1 + j\omega C_1 R_1) + (\beta + 1)R_1}. \tag{6-12}$$

R_T is the equivalent resistance of the parallel combination of R_C, R_o, R_2, and R_3. Upon equating the real and imaginary parts of the denominator of Eq. (6–12), we obtain the lower cutoff frequency:

$$f_{3dB} = \frac{(\beta + 1)R_1 + R_i + R_T}{2\pi C_1 R_1 (R_i + R_T)}. \qquad (6\text{–}13)$$

For Eq. (6–13) to accurately forecast f_{3dB}, it is necessary for the "break" frequencies of numerator and denominator of Eq. (6–12) to differ by 2 octaves or more. An octave is a doubling of frequency. The numerator break occurs at $f = 1/(2\pi R_1 C_1)$ and the denominator break is f_{3dB} from Eq. (6–13). A sketch of the voltage across R_i vs f is shown in Fig. 6–4(b).

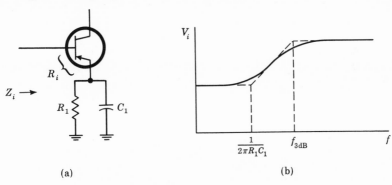

(a) (b)

Fig. 6–4. Effect of bypass capacitor upon frequency response.

Example. Consider a typical stage having the following characteristics:

$$R_i = 1500\ \Omega, \qquad R_G = 600\ \Omega,$$
$$R_C = 10{,}000\ \Omega, \qquad f = 400\ \text{cps}.$$
$$R_3 = 10{,}000\ \Omega,$$

It is desired to find a value for C_c that will result in a phase shift of 5° or less when the transistor is employed in the circuits of Fig. 6–2 and Fig. 6–3.

For the circuit of Fig. 6–2, Eq. (6–9) can be rearranged to the form

$$X_c = [\tan \theta (R_3 R_i + R_G R_3 + R_G R_i)]/(R_3 + R_i),$$

from which

$$C_c = 2.4\ \mu\text{F}.$$

For the circuit of Fig. 6–3, the same equation can be used, with $R_C = R_G$. Then

$$C_c = 0.4\ \mu\text{F}.$$

Any value of capacitance in excess of these values will result in less than a 5° phase shift.

If the low-frequency response of the Fig. 6–3 circuit is desired, and a 5-μF coupling capacitor used, then the frequency at which the response is 3 dB down from its mid-frequency value is given by Eq. (6–10):

$$f_{3dB} = 2.8 \text{ cps.}$$

Suppose that 20 μF is bypassing 1000 Ω in the emitter branch of the load transistor, and its current amplification factor is 50. The lower half-power frequency for this circuit is 70 cps according to Eq. (6–13).

From the numbers cited, emitter bypassing is obviously the limiting area in most low-frequency response studies.

6–4. The Dynamic Load Line. Rules were presented in Chapter 3 for drawing a static or dc load line on the output characteristics of the active device. Summation of all resistance in the emitter–collector path dictates the slope of the line; the line originates at $V_{CC} + V_{EE}$ and terminates at $(V_{CC} + V_{EE})/\Sigma R$. The quiescent or operating point is established by circuitry providing the desired base or collector current.

The dynamic path of operation or dynamic load line is the locus of all corresponding values of instantaneous collector current and voltage during a cycle of the signal. The ac load on a stage can be established by summing the impedance of all circuit elements in the emitter-to-collector circuit. This task is usually simplified by considering that all bypass and coupling capacitors are short circuits to an ac signal.

To illustrate the handling of loads and the drawing of load lines, consider the circuit of Fig. 6–5. The dc loading is comprised of the series combination of R_1, R_e, and R_C. The ac load is R_e plus the parallel combination of R_C, R_2, and R_i of the second stage.

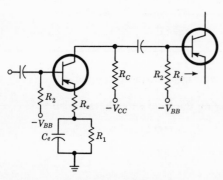

Fig. 6–5.   Circuit for text example.

If the parameters of the circuit of Fig. 6–5 are

$$R_e = 220 \ \Omega, \qquad R_C = 10 \ \text{k}\Omega, \qquad R_2 = 120 \ \text{k}\Omega,$$

$$R_1 = 2.2 \ \text{k}\Omega, \qquad R_i = 10 \ \text{k}\Omega,$$

the dc load line has a slope that is the negative reciprocal of $220 + 2.2 \text{ k} + 10 \text{ k}$, or 12,420 Ω, and the slope of the ac line is the negative reciprocal of

$$220 + [1/(1/10 \text{ k} + 1/120 \text{ k} + 1/10 \text{ k})]$$

or 4800 Ω. *AC load lines must pass through the Q point and are not established by axes intersections.*

In Fig. 6–6, dc and ac load lines are drawn on output characteristics. After the dc line linking V_{CC} and V_{CC}/R_{dc} is positioned and the Q point located, the ac line may be drawn through Q with the appropriate slope. With capacitance coupling, the dynamic line will always exhibit the greater slope because it is dependent upon the paralleling of two or more elements.

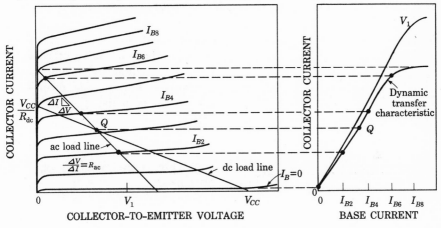

Fig. 6–6.   DC and ac load lines on output characteristics, and construction of dynamic transfer characteristic.

For some purposes a *dynamic transfer characteristic* is valuable. Projection of the points of intersection of the ac load line and lines of constant base current to an I_C–I_B curve is easily accomplished as noted in Fig. 6–6. Linearity of operation is easily studied from the transfer characteristic, and operating-point suitability therefore clearly established. The characteristic is said to be dynamic, for it is derived from the load line and does not assume a constant collector potential. A static characteristic at potential V_1 is also shown in the figure.

When transformer coupling is employed, as in Fig. 6–7, *the static line will have the greater slope.* The summation of resistance to direct current could

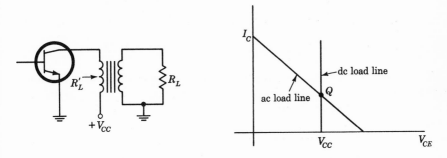

Fig. 6–7.   Transformer coupling.

ideally approach zero if the transformer primary has little resistance. The dynamic line, through Q, has a slope dictated by the reflection of R_L into the transformer primary.

Examination of Fig. 6–7 shows that the ac load line extends far beyond V_{CC}. This may seem to be a violation of Kirchhoff's voltage law, for the instantaneous total value of collector–emitter voltage is considerably larger than the available

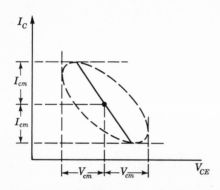

Fig. 6–8.   Elliptical dynamic load line.

voltage supply for the circuit, V_{CC}. It can be noted, however, that when v_{CE} is large, the total value of collector current i_C is quite small, and the instantaneous time-varying drop $i_c R_L'$ *opposes* the potential v_{ce}. The applicable equation is

$$V_{CC} = i_c R_L' + v_{CE} \qquad (6\text{–}14)$$

and there is no violation of basic principles.

When the dynamic load is not a pure resistance, the shape of the dynamic load line is elliptical (see Fig. 6–8). To prove this statement, assume that the instantaneous collector current is sinusoidal; then

$$i_c = I_{cm} \sin \omega t \qquad (6\text{–}15)$$

and

$$v_{ce} = -I_{cm}|Z_L| \sin (\omega t + \theta). \qquad (6\text{–}16)$$

The load impedance $Z_L = R_L + jX_L$ and

$$\theta = \tan^{-1}(X_L/R_L). \qquad (6\text{–}17)$$

Sin $(\omega t + \theta)$ can be expanded, and then Eq. (6–15) substituted in Eq. (6–16). This yields

$$-v_{ce} = i_c|Z_L| \cos \theta + |Z_L| (\sin \theta)(I_{cm}^2 - i_c^2)^{1/2}.$$

The sin and cos terms may be eliminated through use of Eq. (6–17). The result is

$$v_{ce}^2 + 2 v_{ce} i_c R_L + i_c^2|Z_L^2| = I_{cm}^2 X_L^2. \qquad (6\text{–}18)$$

Equation (6–18), the dynamic load line, is an ellipse with center at the operating point. The slope of the line through Q joining the points of tangency of the ellipse to the upper and lower horizontal extremes is equal to the reciprocal of the load *resistance*.

6–5. Effects of the Operating Point upon Gain.   The parameters of the transistor are sensitive to operating point, for, as evidenced by the curves and discussion of Chapter 4, corrections must be made to the nominal parameters when operating with collector voltage and emitter current differing from the manufacturer's recommended values. It is true for certain transistors that astute operation-point selection, when feasible, permits a maximization of gain, or provides a means for gain adjustment, and in certain instances may be useful in meeting the gain specifications for a particular circuit design.

Let us numerically investigate the variation in performance due to emitter quiescent-current selection. From the manufacturer's design-center parameters and his correction information, a listing has been made for the 2N43 transistor. A large variation in h_{ib} is evident from the numbers cited and it is to be suspected

EMITTER CURRENT IN MILLIAMPERES

	0.1	0.2	0.5	1.0	4.0	7.0	10.0
h_{ib}	230	120	55	29	9	5.8	4.6
$h_{rb} \times 10^{-4}$	3.8	4.2	4.6	5	6.5	7.5	8.0
h_{fb}	−0.966	−0.968	−0.974	−0.977	−0.986	−0.988	−0.988
$h_{ob} \times 10^{-6}$	0.32	0.36	0.55	0.80	2.4	3.6	5.0

that this will result in a substantial change in input impedance and voltage gain. Common-emitter current amplification will be affected by the changing $(1 + h_{fb})$ factor.

With a 1000 Ω load assumed, calculations based upon the parameters listed above serve to predict the performance of a single common-emitter stage. The results of such calculations and test results based upon a built-up stage are displayed as Fig. 6–9. (A_v is here used to signify the load-voltage to base-voltage ratio.) It is necessary in such a study to hold V_{CE} constant (5 V throughout), for this potential also has a strong effect upon gains and resistance levels. The collector supply voltage therefore differed at each investigated operating point according to

$$V_{CC} = V_{CE} + I_C R_L,$$

so

$$V_{CC} = 5 + I_E(1000).$$

The circuit designer has the gain and resistance levels of a transistor at his control. By using a large quiescent current he can achieve higher-gain circuitry, at the price of high standby current and lowered input resistance and possibly the need for a higher direct-voltage supply. One practical application of the material of this section is in the automatic gain control systems used in communications receivers and discussed in Chapter 10.

6–6. Gain Stability. A most troublesome variation in parameters occurs because of production tolerances. The spread in possible values for the parameters

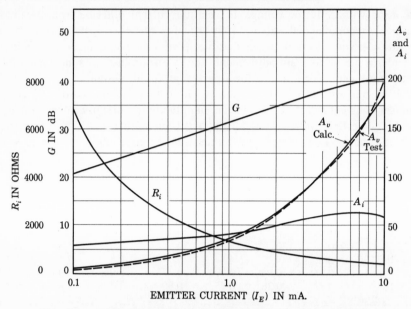

Fig. 6–9.   Performance vs emitter current for a typical transistor.

of a single transistor type when it leaves the manufacturers is illustrated by the typical numbers quoted below:

Parameter	Minimum	Design Center	Maximum
h_{ib} in ohms	30	40	90
h_{ob} in micromhos	0.1	0.4	1.5
h_{rb}	$50(10^{-6})$	$500(10^{-6})$	$1500(10^{-6})$
h_{fb}	-0.97	-0.98	-0.99

If this transistor type were to be used in the common-emitter mode and were to feed a load R_L of several thousand ohms, the current gain, approximated by h_{fe}, would vary from 32 to 99; a variation of more than 3:1 between minimum and maximum parameter values. The voltage amplification of the stage, on the other hand, would drop with maximum parameters to approximately 1/3 of its minimum-parameter value, and the input resistance with maximum parameters would be about 9 times greater than its value when a transistor having the minimum parameters were used. The problem noted here is compounded when temperature variations are taken into account.

Gain calculations for a multistage amplifier will tend to show an even greater degree of predictability. The problem is one of making the gain of constructed amplifiers similar to that calculated by the designer using nominal parameter values. Use of degenerative local feedback provides a partial solution to the repeatability problem. The gain of a stage is reduced when using feedback, but gain spread is also reduced.

For the common-emitter configuration, local feedback can take on two forms: an unbypassed resistor in series with the emitter terminal, or a resistor between collector and base terminals. Occasionally both are employed in the same circuit. Consider the circuit and equivalent shown in Fig. 6–10. The emitter resistance R_e can be thought of as swamping variations in h_{ib}; the collector-to-base admittance G_c is bypassing h_{ob} by providing a lower resistance path. (The capacitor C_b blocks dc to keep from altering the original biasing of the stage.)

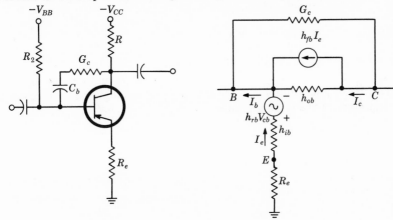

Fig. 6–10.   Local feedback for gain stabilization: (a) location of R_e and G_c in a physical circuit; (b) equivalent for (a) from Fig. 4–7.

Since R_e and G_c are respectively in series and parallel with h_{ib} and h_{ob}, these elements can be easily incorporated into the formulas for operation; here the approximate formulas of Table 5–2 are modified:

$$A_v = \frac{h_{fb}R_L}{(h_{ib} + R_e)[1 + R_L(h_{ob} + G_c)]}, \tag{6-19}$$

$$A_i = \frac{h_{fb}}{(h_{ob} + G_c)R_L + (1 + h_{fb})}, \tag{6-20}$$

$$G = \frac{h_{fb}{}^2 R_L}{(h_{ib} + R_e)[1 + R_L(h_{ob} + G_c)][R_L(h_{ob} + G_c) + (1 + h_{fb})]}, \tag{6-21}$$

$$R_i = \frac{(h_{ib} + R_e)[1 + R_L(h_{ob} + G_c)]}{R_L(h_{ob} + G_c) + (1 + h_{fb})}, \tag{6-22}$$

$$R_o = \frac{h_{ib} + R_e + R_G(1 + h_{fb})}{(h_{ob} + G_c)(h_{ib} + R_e + R_G) - h_{rb}h_{fb}}. \tag{6-23}$$

A more complete treatment of feedback theory is reserved for Chapters 9 and 10.

6-7. Input Resistance Considerations. It is often required that a particular transistor circuit provide a high level of input resistance in order not to load down the source of its signal, whether that source be a transducer or simply the preceding circuitry. Four methods for providing input-resistance levels higher than the several thousand ohms provided by a conventional transistor are at our disposal; they will be discussed in the paragraphs that follow.

Low-level operation. If the signal level is small so that we may operate at a low value of static collector current, the input resistance of a common-emitter stage is fairly large, as evident from Fig. 6–9. The transistor used should have a high h_{fe} because input resistance is

$$R_i \cong h_{fe}/g_m = h_{fe}/\Lambda I_C. \tag{6-24}$$

Values of R_i as high as 50,000 Ω are attainable in this manner.

Degenerated common-emitter. The connection of an unbypassed resistance between emitter and ground as discussed in the preceding section increases the input resistance of the stage according to

$$R_i \cong r_{bb'} + r_{b'e} + R_e(h_{fe} + 1). \tag{6-25}$$

This application of negative feedback reduces the voltage gain of the stage, but that is the price one must pay for the increased input resistance. A collector-to-base resistance actually reduces input impedance and thus does not apply to this discussion.

Emitter Follower. Although the emitter-follower or common-collector stage cannot provide a signal voltage gain of greater than unity, the circuit finds considerable application where a high level of input impedance or a low level of output impedance is required. As can be noted from Table 5–1, considerable current gain is possible with this connection.

The emitter-follower stage can be analyzed as a simple extension of the common-emitter circuit of Fig. 6–10 with G_c equal to zero, and the output signal taken from the emitter instead of the collector. An expression for the voltage gain of an emitter-follower stage is given in the Table of Problem 5–12 as

$$A_v = V_e/V_b = R_e/(h_{ib} + R_e). \tag{6-26}$$

The stage load is R_e, and V_e and V_b represent voltages at the emitter and base terminals, respectively. The applicable equation for the common-emitter stage is Eq. (5–9). Modified to include R_e, it becomes

$$A_v = \frac{V_c}{V_b} = \frac{-R_L((h_{ib} + R_e)h_{ob} + h_{fb}))}{(h_{ib} + R_e)(1 + R_L h_{ob}) - h_{rb}h_{fb}R_L}. \tag{6-27}$$

To convert this equation for use with its ouput across R_e, we must multiply by $R_e/h_{fb}R_L$. Equation (6–27) then becomes, for $R_L = 0$ and $(h_{ib} + R_e)h_{ob} \ll h_{fb}$, identical to Eq. (6–26).

From the table of Problem 5–12, we obtain

$$R_i = \frac{h_{ib} + R_e}{h_{ob}(h_{ib} + R_e) + (1 + h_{fb})}. \tag{6-28}$$

We see from this equation that the input resistance of an emitter-follower equals approximately $(h_{fe} + 1) R_e$ until $R_e h_{ob}$ becomes equal in importance to $(1 + h_{fb})$. For very large values of R_e, the input resistance is simply $1/h_{ob}$. Because h_{fe} and h_{ob} tend to vary considerably from unit-to-unit, and are sensitive to temperature excursions, it follows that input resistance will not be a highly stable quantity.

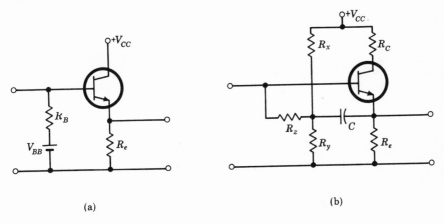

(a)   (b)

Fig. 6–11.   Biasing of the emitter-follower.

To bias an emitter-follower stage, one could provide for a constant base current as evident in Fig. 6–11(a). It is to be noted, however, that the base terminal is above ground potential by $V_{BE} + I_E R_e$. Therefore, if V_{BB} is not much larger than the base-to-ground potential difference, R_B may not take on as large a value as would be desirable for a high level of input resistance.

In order to elminate the paralleling effect of R_B upon the signal, the circuit of Fig. 6–11(b) is suggested. The operating point is determined by elements R_x, R_y, and R_z. The element C blocks the dc at the emitter from being fed back to the base circuit; however, the time-varying signal *is* fed back and available at the junction of the three resistances. Because the signal voltage across R_e is approximately of the same amplitude and phase as the incoming signal ($A_v \cong 1$), there exists across R_z essentially *zero signal-potential difference*. Therefore, the base-biasing elements look like an open circuit to the signal and the input impedance is essentially that given by Eq. (6–28). A slight modification must be made, for R_x and R_y appear in parallel with R_e. This may slightly reduce the input resistance of the stage.

The purpose of element R_C shown in Fig. 6–11(b) is to protect the collector-base diode. When an extremely large signal is applied to the base, the transistor saturates and that junction may become forward biased. In order to limit the forward diode current, R_C may be 100 Ω or so.

FET *stages.* Of course the FET provides an input resistance higher than any of the schemes preciously discussed. Nevertheless, it is necessary in some critical applications to cancel the paralleling effects of the gate biasing elements. Bootstrapping, as discussed in connection with the emitter follower, is helpful in this regard. The circuit shown in Fig. 6–12(a) includes feedback from the

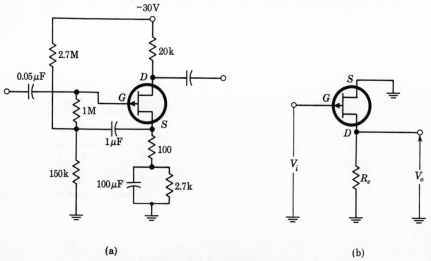

(a)   (b)

Fig. 6–12. FET circuits: (a) bootstrapped common-source circuit; (b) common-drain connection.

source to gate through the 1 μF capacitor. If the signal voltage across the 100 Ω unbypassed source-leg resistance is equal to the signal voltage at the gate, no signal current will flow through the 1-MΩ biasing resistance.

At a sacrifice in gain, higher input impedances can be obtained by using the common-drain or source-follower connection. If we consider that the circuit of Fig. 6–12(b) can be approximated by a three-element model consisting of gate-to-source resistance r_{gs}, current generator $g_m V_{gs}$, and load R_e, it is easy to show that

$$R_i = r_{gs} + R_e(1 + g_m r_{gs}). \tag{6–29}$$

The term $(1 + g_m r_{gs})$ represents the current gain of the connection. The voltage gain is always less than unity:

$$A_v = V_o/V_i = 1/[1 + (1/g_m R_e)]. \tag{6–30}$$

No phase reversal is provided by this connection.

Additional methods for obtaining high input impedances are treated in Chapter 10 and are available in the literature.

6-8. Design Examples.

High-Impedance Circuit Design Example.

Object. Design a low-power transistor stage with an input resistance of 100,000 Ω. The transistor to be used has parameter values of

$$h_{ib} = 50 \, \Omega, \qquad h_{ob} = 2 \times 10^{-6} \, \text{mho},$$

$$h_{rb} = 10 \times 10^{-4}, \qquad h_{fb} = -0.99.$$

The load to be fed is 10,000 Ω. Consider that corrections have been made to the parameters because of temperature and operating point. We shall use a common-emitter stage with emitter biasing. Base current may flow through the source, which is of fairly low dc resistance. Consider signal levels to be extremely small.

Solution. This problem has been simplified to the point where it is only necessary to calculate the required value of R_e and to determine the resulting gain. From the expression for input resistance, Eq. (5-12), modified to include R_e,

$$h_{ib} + R_e = \frac{R_i(h_{ob}R_L + 1 + h_{fb}) + h_{rb}h_{fb}R_L}{1 + h_{ob}(R_L - R_i)}$$

$$= 3300 \, \Omega.$$

Thus

$$R_e = 3250 \, \Omega.$$

The power gain to be expected is checked using the approximate formula

$$G = \frac{h_{fb}^2 R_L}{(h_{ib} + R_e)(1 + R_L h_{ob})(R_L h_{ob} + 1 + h_{fb})}$$

$$= 97,$$

which is very low, but it must be remembered that the primary concern in this design is to achieve a high input impedance.

R-C Amplifier Design Example.

Object. Design a transistor amplifying stage to meet the following requirements:

1. Frequency response: 40 to 20,000 cps
2. Load resistance: 1000 Ω
3. Input impedance: no requirement
4. Voltage gain: 10 minimum (load voltage to source voltage)

5. Source characteristics: impedance, 1000 Ω (resistive); maximum output, 10 mV

6. Temperature: 30 ± 5° C

7. DC potential available: −12 V

Solution. Since a good frequency response is a primary concern, let us employ *R-C* coupling and use the 2N2614 transistor, which behaves well throughout the audio range. A silicon unit is unnecessary since wide temperature variations are not expected.

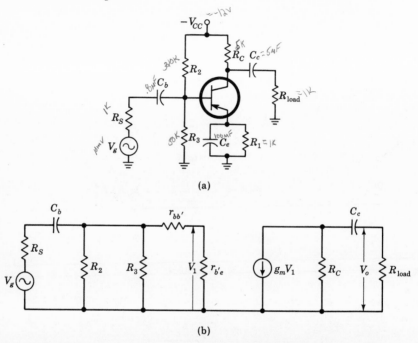

(a)

(b)

Fig. 6–13. Circuit design example: (a) schematic; (b) equivalent.

Single-battery bias will be used, and the circuit selected is shown in Fig. 6–13. We shall choose a tentative operating point at $V_{CE} = -6$ V and $I_C = -1$ mA. No corrections to the nominal parameters are necessary at that point. From the manufacturer

$$r_{bb'} = 300 \ \Omega, \qquad\qquad r_{ce} = 167{,}000 \ \Omega,$$

$$r_{b'e} = 4000 \ \Omega, \qquad\qquad C_{b'e} = 750 \ \text{pF},$$

$$g_m = 0.0385 \ \text{mho}, \qquad\qquad C_{b'c} = 9 \ \text{pF},$$

$$r_{b'c} = 2.85 \times 10^6 \ \Omega, \qquad\qquad f_{hfb} = 10 \ \text{Mc}.$$

If we choose $R_C = 5000\ \Omega$, then very little ac power will be lost in that resistor, and R_1 must then be $1000\ \Omega$ to satisfy the dc collector circuit equation

$$V_{CC} = I_C R_C + I_E R_1 + V_{CE}.$$

We can make $R_3 = 50{,}000\ \Omega$, and, since we wish I_C to be 1 mA, R_2 will be large enough so it will not affect calculations to any great extent.

A brief check on R_2 is in order. The voltage from base to ground will be $I_E R_1 + V_{BE}$ or approximately -1.2 V. The current through R_3 is $1.2/(50\text{ k})$ or 24 μA. If h_{FE} is assumed to be 100, base current is 10 μA. Therefore, the R_2 element is obtained from

$$R_2 = (12 - 1.2)/(34 \times 10^{-6}) = 320{,}000\ \Omega.$$

A few preliminary calculations are necessary in order to obtain the proper parameters for use in the various formulas:

$$R_L = \frac{R_C R_{\text{load}}}{R_C + R_{\text{load}}} = \frac{(5\text{ k})(1\text{ k})}{5\text{ k} + 1\text{ k}} = 833\ \Omega,$$

$$R_G \cong \frac{R_s R_3}{R_s + R_3} = \frac{(1\text{ k})(50\text{ k})}{1\text{ k} + 50\text{ k}} = 980\ \Omega,$$

$$f_{hfe} = (1 + h_{fb}) f_{hfb} = (0.01)(10^6) = 100\text{ kc}.$$

These figures enable us to calculate the operation of the transistor alone:

$$A_i \cong h_{fe} = g_m r_{b'e} = 154,$$

$$R_i \cong r_{bb'} + r_{b'e} = 4300\ \Omega,$$

$$A_v = A_i R_L / R_i = 35.1,$$

$$G = A_i A_v = 5400.$$

Total input capacitance C_T is given by

$$C_T = C_{b'e} + C_{b'c}(1 + g_m R_L) = 1100\text{ pF}.$$

To determine the upper voltage-gain cutoff frequency,

$$R_T = r_{b'e} \| (R_G + r_{bb'}) = 970\ \Omega.$$

Then

$$f_{3\text{dB}} = 1/(2\pi C_T R_T) = 150\text{ kc}.$$

At mid-frequencies, the current entering the transistor base may be approximated by the following fraction of that which leaves the signal source:

$$R_3/(R_i + R_3).$$

In this example 92% of the source output gets to the base. Load current is the following fraction of the ac collector current

$$R_C/(R_C + R_{load}).$$

Thus 83.3% of the collector current is available to the load.

All of the collector voltage is available across the load; however, the source output is split between R_s and the parallel combination of R_i and R_3 according to

$$\frac{R_3 R_i/(R_3 + R_i)}{R_s + [R_3 R_i/(R_3 + R_i)]}.$$

For this example, 80% is across the transistor input terminals.

Using the values previously cited, the over-all performance at mid-frequencies is

$$A_{iT} = (0.92)(0.833)(154) = 118.0,$$

$$A_{vT} = (0.80)(35.1) = 28.1,$$

$$G = (118.0)(28.1) = 3320.$$

A_{vT} is here defined as the ratio of collector voltage to source voltage V_g, and A_{iT} is the ratio of load current to source current.

The reduction in current gain due to beta variation at 20,000 cycles is read from Fig. 5–12 as less than 0.1 dB. Acceptable high-frequency performance could have been predicted from knowledge of the f_{hfb} and C_o of the transistor, and from the fact that low load and source resistances were employed.

When the real portion of the denominator of Eq. (6–8) is set equal to the imaginary portion, it will yield the 3-dB down point at the low-frequency (40 cps) end of the spectrum:

$$R_3 R_i + R_s R_3 + R_s R_i = X_c(R_3 + R_i).$$

Then

$$X_c = 4960 \ \Omega.$$

Therefore, if C_b is acting alone, its value is

$$C_b = 1/[2\pi 40(4960)] = 0.8 \ \mu F.$$

A 5-μF capacitor would be fine for this application. Similar calculations indicate that 5 μF would be acceptable for load coupling and 100 μF for emitter-resistance bypassing; it is to be remembered that all three are important at the low frequencies and will contribute to gain fall-off.

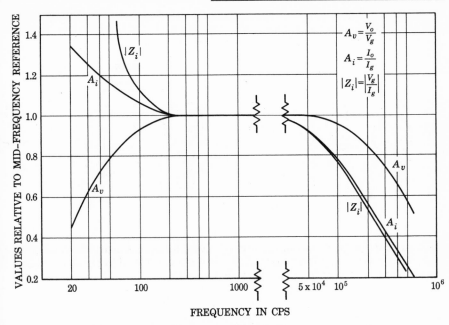

Fig. 6–14. Test data on amplifier similar to text example.

The measured frequency response for an amplifier very similar to this design is shown in Fig. 6–14.

PROBLEMS

6–1. Show that the use of a transformer for coupling between a transistor connected common-emitter and its load provides increased voltage amplification even though the transformer is connected so that there is a voltage step-down from primary to secondary.

6–2. A signal source has an internal resistance of 10,000 Ω and is feeding a transistor stage that presents an input resistance of 2000 Ω (including biasing resistors). Determine the size of the coupling capacitor necessary for the lower half-power frequency to be 25 cps.

6–3. A 1.0 μF coupling capacitance is joining two transistor stages. The driver may be characterized by a current generator I_o paralleled by $R_o = 25,000$ Ω and transistor and wiring capacitance of 400 pF. The load is $R_i = 2000$ Ω; $R_C = 10,000$ Ω. Determine
  (a) The mid-frequency current-transfer ratio between I_o and R_i.
  (b) The lower half-power frequency.
  (c) The upper half-power frequency.

6–4. For the accompanying circuit, draw the dc and ac load lines on a sketch of the collector characteristics of the 2N2614 and locate the Q point. With sinusoidal base current drive, what is the maximum amount of power that can be delivered to the load before clipping occurs?

6–5. Draw the dc and ac load lines for the circuit of the figure on a sketch of the 2N3242 transistor collector characteristics. Locate the Q point. How much can base current vary before clipping of the collector current will occur?

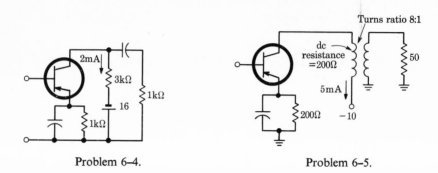

Problem 6–4.   Problem 6–5.

6–6. For the stage shown in the accompanying figure, calculate the value of C_e required for a lower cutoff frequency of 50 cps, if it is considered to be the sole source of gain falloff. Consider R_i to be 3000 Ω and $h_{fe} = 40$.

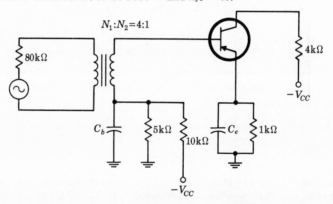

Problem 6–6.

6–7. To the input resistance of a transistor common-emitter stage must be added the approximate term $(\beta + 1)Z_e$ to include the effects of impedance in the emitter branch. If Z_e is the equivalent of R_1 paralleling C_1, derive Eq. (6–13) for the lower half-power frequency of the network of Fig. 6–4(a). For simplicity, neglect the effects of the coupling capacitor. The transistor itself may be considered to have a resistive input impedance R_i.

6–8. The h parameters of two circuit elements can be added if the elements are connected in series-shunt. To derive an expression for the input impedance of a common-collector stage in terms of common-emitter parameters, use the representation of the figure. Show that the composite h matrix is

$$\begin{bmatrix} h_{ie} & (1 - h_{re}) \\ -(h_{fe} + 1) & (h_{oe} + G_e) \end{bmatrix}$$

and thus prove that

$$R_i = h_{ie} + \frac{(h_{fe} + 1)(1 - h_{re})}{h_{oe} + G_e}.$$

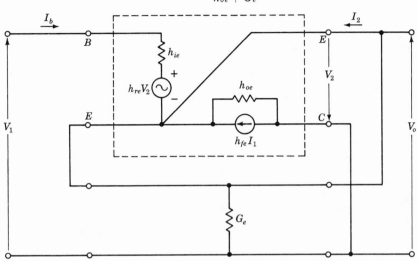

Problem 6–8.

6–9. It is impossible for the voltage gain of an emitter-follower stage to equal unity. If a gain of precisely unity were required, then a common-emitter stage with emitter leg local feedback could be used. How large must R_e be in order for $|A_v| = 1$?

6–10. Confirm Eqs. (6–29) and (6–30).

6–11. It is required that the active device in the circuit shown be chosen so that the maximum signal-voltage amplification be attained (ratio of V_o to V_g). Available devices are a conventional transistor characterized by h_{fe} and h_{ie}, and a triode vacuum tube with small signal parameters r_p and μ. Values of the parameters are $h_{fe} = \mu = 30$, and $r_p = h_{ie} = 2000$. $R_G = 500$ Ω, and $V_g = 1$ mV, 1000 cps. For what resistance range of R_L is the transistor superior to the tube?

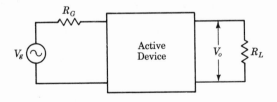

Problem 6–11.

Design Problems. In the problems that follow, perform the operations necessary in order to obtain a stage that will meet the listed requirements. Choose an appropriate biasing arrangement, and, for each solution, choose a transistor from those in Appendix I, and correct the nominal parameters for operating point. Itemize any assumptions made and clearly indicate the steps leading to your choice of each component.

A general specification applicable to the problems that follow is that dc is not permitted in the signal source and in the stage load. Do not consider production variations in parameter values unless directed to.

6–12. Requirements:
1. Frequency response: 30 to 20,000 cps (minimum)
2. Load resistance: 5000 Ω
3. Input impedance: no requirements
4. Voltage gain: 50 (minimum load-voltage to source-voltage ratio)
5. Source characteristics: impedance—100 Ω (resistive) in series with generator of 0 to 20 mV.
6. Temperature: $20° \pm 5°$ C
7. Power supply available: -8 V

6–13. Requirements:
1. Carrier frequency: 400 cps
2. Load resistance: 10,000 Ω
3. Input impedance: $50,000 \pm 10\%$ Ω
4. Power gain: 10 (minimum)
5. Source characteristics: impedance—50,000 Ω (resistive); 1 mV maximum open-circuit voltage.
6. Temperature: $25° \pm 5°$ C
7. Power supply available: -12 V

6–14. Requirements:
1. Frequency response: 50 to 50,000 cps (minimum)
2. Load resistance: 1000 Ω
3. Input impedance: no requirements
4. Current gain: 100 (minimum)
5. Source characteristics: impedance—10^6 Ω resistive; open-circuit voltage $= 100$ V, maximum.
6. Power supply available: $+9$ V
7. Transistor type: use 2N2614. Bias to accept $100 < h_{FE} < 300$.

REFERENCES

1. Lo, A. W., et al., *Transistor Electronics* (Prentice-Hall Inc., Englewood Cliffs, New Jersey, 1955).
2. Ryder, J. M., *Electronic Fundamentals and Applications* (Prentice-Hall, Inc., Englewood Cliffs, New Jersey, 1964), 3rd ed.
3. Shea, R. F., *Transistor Circuit Engineering* (John Wiley & Sons, Inc., New York, 1957).

View with cover removed of type 2N1936 silicon power transistor. This transistor is capable of 150 watts power dissipation at 100°C. (Photo Courtesy Texas Instruments, Incorporated).

Chapter 7

LARGE-SIGNAL AMPLIFIERS

Devices that perform the function of amplifying large signals are commonly called *power amplifiers*. Since it has been shown previously that all transistors are power amplifiers, this chapter will be devoted to those applications where the assumptions of linear operation are not valid, and where variations in collector voltage and current are a significant fraction of the total allowable range of operation.

The power stage is the final unit of a cascade amplifier and serves to drive the energy-conversion device that transforms electrical energy into some other form, such as sound or mechanical energy. The power stage is, in turn, dependent upon the "driver stage" for its signal.

The equations for circuit gains and impedances developed in Chapter 5 are not directly applicable to power stages because those relations were derived from equivalent circuits valid for small-signal excursions, and include small-signal parameters. When transistor operation swings over a large region of its characteristics, more accurate analysis is made using graphical procedures and dc parameters. The Chapter 5 equations may be useful in approximating actual operation provided the parameters are available (they are not normally published for power transistors), and the input and output signals are generally sinusoidal (no clipping of the waveforms).

We have previously discussed the drawing of both ac and dc load lines. Graphical techniques, when applied to small-signal amplifiers, permit study of the suitability of the operating point, determination of maximum allowable current and voltage swings, and calculation of overload capacity. In this chapter we shall rely upon graphical methods to determine gains and impedance levels, output power and overload capacity, and the distortion content of the output waveform. Large-signal analysis is often necessary for the driver stage of a multistage amplifier.

7–1. Limitations. One of the general problems associated with the design of power amplifiers is that of obtaining the maximum possible power output. Power output for a common-emitter stage is limited by the following:

1. The maximum allowable power dissipation
2. The maximum allowable collector current
3. Saturation
4. Cutoff
5. The maximum allowable collector-to-emitter operating potential

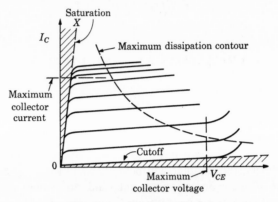

Fig. 7–1.   Operation limits.

Figure 7–1 depicts the limiting conditions. The maximum power dissipation line is a hyperbolic curve having the equation

$$V_C I_C = K \tag{7-1}$$

for a given junction temperature. If, in actual operation, the voltage–current product exceeds the design constant K, damage to the transistor will result. The resistive parameters of the device will cause internal power conversion. The heat generated, if unable to completely escape from the device, will raise the operating temperature, and with internal temperature rise comes breaking of covalent bonds. Transistor operation ceases when sufficient covalent bonds are broken.

A collector-current limit is set in part by the decrease in β at high current densities; the amount of reduction in current amplification can be used as a criterion to place a limit on maximum allowable current.

Saturation is of little consequence in germanium transistors, but must be taken into account when silicon units are used because of their higher R_{CS}. R_{CS} is the inverse of the slope of line O–X in Fig. 7–1 and can be thought of as the collector-to-emitter resistance of a transistor in the full ON condition.

The cutoff region, often erroneously considered to be below the $I_B = 0$ line, in reality lies below the I_{CO} line, because it is possible to operate with small positive values of base current (p–n–p). Because of nonlinearities at such levels, particularly in the input characteristics, some distortion may result just prior to complete cutoff.

Breakdown of the collector junction is shown in Fig. 7–1 by the upswing of the lines of constant base current. The Zener theory, that under the influence of a strong electric field, electrons are pulled from their valence bonds to become mobile carriers, may account for this increased current; more likely the cause is avalanche breakdown, a secondary-emission phenomenon. A high voltage may also widen the collector-depletion layer so that it contacts the emitter-depletion layer, resulting in a form of short-circuit. (A depletion layer, it is recalled, is the region near a semiconductor junction where a reduced number of mobile carriers are to be found.) A collector-voltage limit is also set by thermal runaway characteristics as discussed in the next section.

When the transistor is connected common-base, collector-base breakdown is caused by avalanche multiplication. The avalanche takes place in the depletion region and results from collisions between rapidly accelerating minority carriers and atoms in the crystal lattice. The avalanche multiplication factor M is generally considered to be the following:

$$M = 1/[1 - (V_{CB}/V_A)^n] \qquad (7\text{–}2)$$

where V_A is the avalanche breakdown voltage and n is the rate of breakdown. The collector current equation becomes

$$I_C = \alpha M I_E + M I_{CBO}. \qquad (7\text{–}3)$$

Both components of I_C are multiplied by M in Eq. (7–3) because they both cross the collector junction. At $V_{CB} = V_A$, $M \to \infty$, and Eq. (7–3) predicts that the lines of constant emitter current will curve upward and widen when approaching that potential.

At a voltage where $\alpha M = 1$, $\beta \to \infty$. This phenomenon occurs at a value of V_{CE} considerably lower than V_A, as shown in Fig. 7–2. For values of base current below the V_{CEO} line, operation is possible for values of collector voltage greater than $V_{\alpha M = 1}$. Eventually we encounter a negative slope to the characteristics in the low-current region. Before discussing this phenomenon, we first must note the system of nomenclature employed. The third subscript on a voltage indicates the state of the third terminal of the device. Thus V_{CES} means that the base is shorted, V_{CEO} means the base is open, and V_{CEX}, when used, indicates that the base is reverse-biased.

Consider the V_{CES} line; this is not a line of constant I_B. If we consider that the transistor is being driven from an ever-increasing collector current supply and V_{CE} is being measured, we eventually reach BV_{CES}. At this point the drop between base and emitter, namely $I_{B}r_{bb'}$, is sufficiently large so that it begins to turn-on the emitter junction. Carriers injected from the emitter precipitate avalanche multiplication in the collector depletion region, I_B increases, and the emitter junction becomes more strongly forward biased. The required V_{CE} to maintain a given level of collector current is reduced. The breakdown with additional resistance in the base lead, BV_{CER}, occurs at a lower collector voltage.

Another form of breakdown, called *secondary breakdown*, apparently caused by localized melting of the lattice, occurs in some transistor types when operated near $\alpha M = 1$. It is completely destructive. A typical secondary breakdown locus of trigger points is shown in the figure.

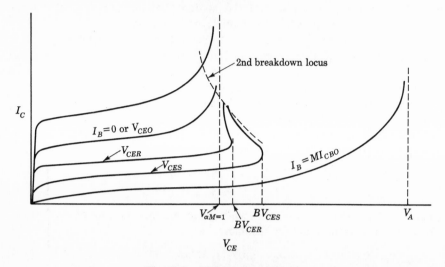

Fig. 7–2.   Voltage breakdown.

7–2. Thermal Considerations.   The removal of heat from the collector–base junction must be considered when employing all types of transistors, but it warrants considerable attention in high-power types. The cooling of low-power transistors (below 200 mW) is generally accomplished by radiation to the surroundings. For power transistors (500 mW and up), cooling fins are sometimes used, but more often the units are firmly attached to metallic heat sinks (chassis or separate plate). Mounting for the 2N539A is shown in Fig. 7–3. When feasible, the transistor case can make direct contact with the heat sink; more often a mica washer is employed for electrical insulation, as shown in the diagram, since the collector, in most power transistors, is directly attached to the case.

A maximum allowable collector-junction temperature is specified for all transistors. For germanium units this maximum temperature is between 85° and 100° C. A similar figure for silicon is 175° C. The temperature at which the junction is operating (T_j) depends upon the ambient temperature (T_a), the thermal resistance of the heat path from the junction to surroundings (θ_T), and the electrical power being converted into heat (P_T), according to the relation

$$T_j = T_a + \theta_T P_T \quad ^\circ \text{C.} \qquad (7\text{–}4)$$

Thermal resistance is measured in degrees Centigrade per watt (° C/W).

Internal power dissipation almost entirely occurs at the collector junction so

$$P_T = V_C I_C. \tag{7-5}$$

The maximum dissipation is

$$P_{T\max} = (V_C I_C)_{\max} = (1/\theta_T)(T_{j\max} - T_a), \tag{7-6}$$

which is the hyperbola of Eq. (7-1).

The over-all thermal resistance θ_T is determined by solving a thermal network, analogous to an electrical circuit. The network for a power transistor is shown in Fig. 7-4. A current source symbolizing the heat-power generating properties of the transistor is in series with three electrical resistances, each representing the

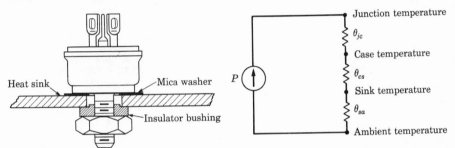

Fig. 7-3. Typical mounting of a power transistor.

Fig. 7-4. Transistor thermal network.

thermal resistance of a portion of the thermal circuit. θ_{jc} is the resistance from junction to transistor case, θ_{cs} represents resistance from case to heat sink, and θ_{sa} stands for sink-to-ambient resistance.

Solution of the thermal network by electrical series circuit theory gives

$$\theta_T = \theta_{jc} + \theta_{cs} + \theta_{sa} = \theta_{ja}. \tag{7-7}$$

For low-power transistors a single resistance from junction to ambient (θ_{ja}) is often specified, because heat sinks are generally not employed; a typical value for θ_{ja} is 250° C/W. For the larger power transistors, thermal resistances are smaller, and conduction is the primary method of heat transfer, so values of θ_{jc} are made available and range from 0.5° to 2.5° C/W. If the transistor case and the heat sink are separated by an electrical insulator such as a mica washer, θ_{cs} takes on values of 0.2° to 0.5° C/W.

Removal of heat from a power transistor is accomplished mainly by conduction to the heat sink and convection from the sink to the cooler surrounding air. Forced-air cooling reduces the size requirement for the sink, but most applications depend upon natural convection from both sides of an aluminum or copper plate. Vertical mounting of the sink is preferable, to make use of natural air movement.

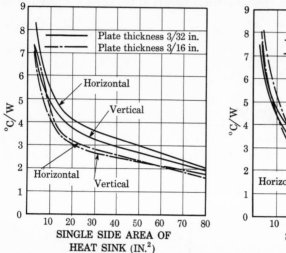

Fig. 7–5. Heat transfer characteristics of square aluminium heat sinks. (Courtesy Delco Divn., G.M. Corp.).

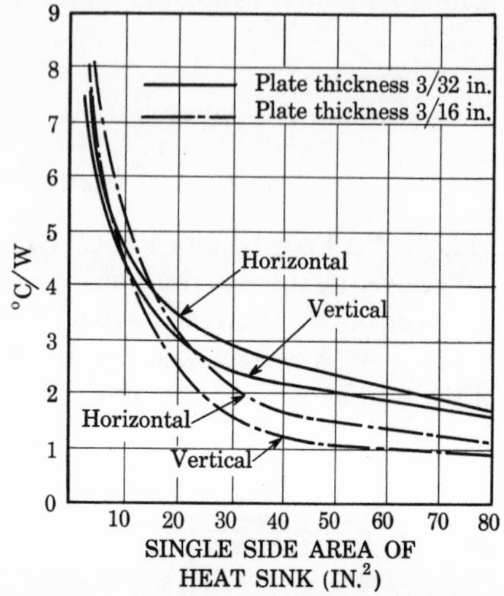

Fig. 7–6. Heat transfer characteristics of square copper heat sinks. (Courtesy Delco Divn., G.M. Corp.).

To estimate the total surface area required for a sink to adequately dissipate the heat developed in a power transistor, use can be made of Figs. 7–5 and 7–6, which give the thermal resistance of flat aluminum and copper plates for various surface areas and plate thicknesses. A numerical example may prove of assistance in understanding the cooling problem. Consider 10 W being converted to heat at a collector junction and a junction-to-case thermal resistance of 2.0° C/W, with mounting hardware accounting for an additional resistance of 0.5° C/W. The problem is to predict the dimensions of a mounting plate so junction temperature will not exceed 80° C in a 40° C ambient. Eq. (7–4) limits θ_T to 4.0° C/W, and since the transistor and the insulator represent 2.5° C/W, 1.5° C/W remains for the plate. In Fig. 7–6 this requirement corresponds to a $\frac{3}{16}$-in. copper plate of approximately 50 in.^{2} per side mounted horizontally; the dimensions could be 7.1 by 7.1 in. if both sides are utilized. An aluminum sink to do the same job must be $\frac{3}{16}$ inch or thicker and nearly 10 × 10 in. It is normal to include a safety factor.

A thermocouple fastened to the transistor case may be used to measure the temperature at that point, although it must be remembered that the temperature of importance is at the inaccessible junction.

Because the heat sink represents resistance in the thermal path, at first thought one may suggest doing away with the sink, and thereby removing a limitation upon allowable power-handling capacity. But after removing the sink from the circuit diagram, we should have to place in its stead another resistance, namely, that of the case-to-ambient convection and radiation. Such a resistance is considerably larger than that contributed by a flat metallic plate.

Associated with each thermal resistance of Fig. 7–4, but not shown on the diagram, is a parallel capacitance that is necessary to explain transient behavior. The thermal time constant, the product of thermal resistance and capacitance, is long for the external elements in the diagram (capacitance very large), but relatively short for the transistor itself (30 msec for the 2N539A). With a short time constant, junction temperature may consequently be governed by the peak instantaneous power dissipation rather than by the average collector dissipation. The circuit designer is concerned with thermal time constants when the transistor is operated *across* the maximum-dissipation hyperbola.

A condition known as *thermal runaway* can result if the rate of increase in collector power dissipation with junction temperature exceeds the ability of the thermal network to remove heat. The network can remove dissipated heat energy according to the relation

$$1/\theta_T = \partial P_T/\partial T_j. \tag{7–8}$$

Equation (7–8) is obtained by differentiation of Eq. (7–4) with respect to T_j. *To assure thermal stability, it is necessary for*

$$\partial(V_c I_c)/\partial T_j < 1/\theta_T. \tag{7–9a}$$

For a constant V_c, the condition for stability is

$$V_c(\partial I_c/\partial T_j) < 1/\theta_T. \tag{7–9b}$$

The change in collector current with temperature is caused by variations in the current amplification factor and in the leakage current of the transistor, and thus depends upon the biasing circuitry employed. If leakage current is considered to be the chief cause of collector current excursions, then Eq. (7–9b) can be written in the following form:

$$V_c(\partial I_c/\partial I_{CBO})(\partial I_{CBO}/\partial T_j)_{max} < 1/\theta_T. \tag{7–9c}$$

The static stability factor was defined in Chapter 3 by

$$S \equiv \partial I_C/\partial I_{CBO}. \tag{7–10}$$

For a thermally stable network, Eq. (7–9c) can be written as

$$(\partial I_{CBO}/\partial T_j)_{max} < 1/\theta_T V_c S. \tag{7–11}$$

To evaluate the maximum value of $\partial I_{CBO}/\partial T_j$, a graph such as Fig. 3–6 may be used or an analytical procedure may be employed. A germanium transistor may experience a doubling of I_{CBO} every 9° C; this may be represented mathematically by

$$I_{CBO} = I_{CBO}'(1.08)^{\Delta T_j} \tag{7–12}$$

with $T_j = T_j - T_{ref}$. I_{CBO}' is the leakage current at the reference temperature, usually 25° C. The derivative of interest is

$$\partial I_{CBO}/\partial T_j = I_{CBO}'(0.077)(1.08)^{\Delta T_J}. \qquad (7\text{--}13)$$

A knowledge of leakage-current behavior and of thermal resistance can be used to predict the maximum allowable collector voltage, or the upper limit on S, that need be considered in the design of power transistor stages.

7–3. **Large-signal Parameters.** Information supplied by manufacturers of power transistors differs from that made available concerning low-power devices. In most applications, the load resistance on a power stage will be low, to make use of the allowable collector current swing, and thus h_{22} and h_{12} will be of little consequence. The parameters of importance will thus be h_{11} and h_{21}. Occasionally the small-signal values of these parameters will be given; more often large-signal or dc values are available. The variations in large-signal values of h_{11} and h_{21} are normally obtainable.

DC beta, the static value of the common-emitter short-circuit forward current transfer ratio, is defined by the ratio of direct currents according to

$$h_{FE} \equiv \left.\frac{I_C}{I_B}\right|_{V_{CE}=\text{const.}} \qquad (7\text{--}14)$$

Since, when dealing with direct quantities, leakage current may be a considerable fraction of the total, Eq. (7–14) is often modified to

$$h_{FE}^* \equiv \left.\frac{I_C - I_{CEO}}{I_B}\right|_{V_{CE}=\text{const.}} \qquad (7\text{--}15)$$

The dc or large-signal value of input resistance is

$$h_{IE} = \left.\frac{V_{BE}}{I_B}\right|_{V_{CE}=\text{const.}} \qquad (7\text{--}16)$$

Of course the values of these parameters are very dependent upon the operating point chosen.

Other systems of large-signal parameters are employed. Transconductance

$$G_M = I_C/V_{BE} \qquad (7\text{--}17)$$

and power conductance

$$G_R = I_C^2/V_{BE}I_B \qquad (7\text{--}18)$$

are used occasionally (Appendix I).

7–4. **Modes and Configurations.** The operational modes originally defined for vacuum-tube circuits also apply to transistor work. Basically, in *Class-A* operation, the device conducts over the entire cycle, and the output waveform reasonably duplicates the input waveform. This is the mode of operation assumed in all preceding and succeeding discussions unless specified to the contrary. To satisfy the definition, no appreciable clipping is allowable, but distortion in the output waveshape due to nonlinearities of characteristics is tolerable.

In *Class-B* operation the device conducts over one half of the entire input-signal cycle, so in order to successfully amplify a sinusoidal signal two transistors are necessary, each working on successive alternations. Class-B operation is achieved by biasing transistors near cutoff. The use of a relatively small amount of forward biasing for the emitter–base diode is common and necessary to eliminate crossover distortion (described later). This type of operation has been referred to as *Class-AB*, but generally the simpler nomenclature (Class-B) is used.

Class-C performance results when the device conducts over less than one half of the cycle. Because relatively few applications for Class-C transistor circuits are available, no detailed discussion of this mode will be presented. The reader who desires more information is referred to the literature.[9]

Because the common-emitter configuration provides the highest power gain, the use of other configurations is limited to applications where they exhibit a distinct advantage over the common-emitter. Occasionally such an advantage arises. It may be that a very low input resistance is necessary, or the requirement may be for better frequency response; in either case a common-base circuit may be the solution to the problem. When one is concerned with distortion as in large-signal amplifiers, the extreme linearity of the common-base output characteristics may, for some applications, justify its use. Since the input circuit is a prime contributor to distortion, the following general rule may be helpful in providing grounds for the determination of the proper configuration for a particular job: *To minimize distortion, a common-emitter power stage should be fed from a low source resistance compared with its input resistance, while a common-base stage should be fed from a high source resistance compared with its input resistance.* From this statement we may conclude that the nonlinearities of the common-emitter input circuit are useful to compensate for those of the output; for common-base stages, since the output circuit is very linear, we wish to swamp the input circuit resistance with a high source resistance. *Exceptions to these rules exist.*

Our concern, in this chapter, is with the common-emitter large-signal amplifier. Study, analysis, and design of circuits in the other configurations will be left to the reader. Sufficient information is available in the literature.[1,4,5]

7–5. Distortion. When the transistor is operated over a significant range of its characteristics, the nonlinearities inherent in semiconducting devices are sources of distortion for signal waveforms. The input characteristics, which relate base-to-emitter voltage to base current, are exponential and therefore the input resistance of the device is not constant, but varies with signal amplitude. While the effect of this variation can be minimized by driving the transistor from a current source, it must be remembered that current sources are inefficient and cannot always be designed into a particular circuit. A typical variation to be expected in input resistance is shown in Fig. 7–7.

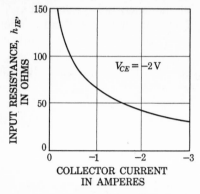

Fig. 7–7. Variation of input resistance with collector current for a typical power transistor.

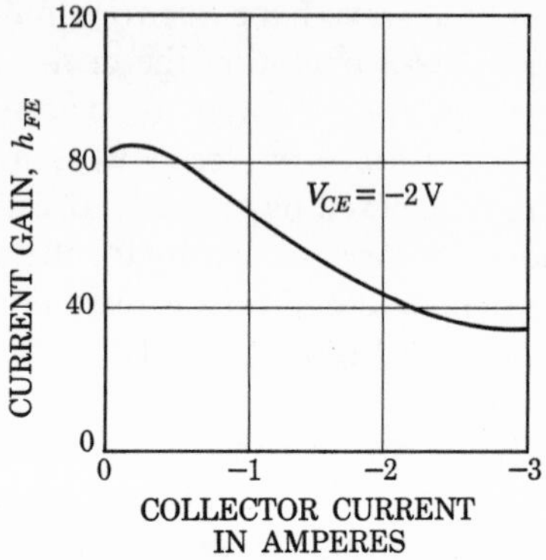

Fig. 7–8. Variation of current gain with collector current for a typical power transistor.

The current gain of a transistor is dependent upon collector current as shown in Fig. 7–8. If we imagine a stage biased at 1 A and handling a signal that ranges both positively and negatively from that point, the figure shows that the positive excursion would get considerably more amplification than the negative excursion.

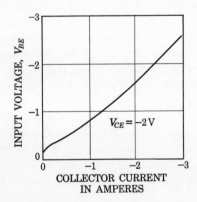

Fig. 7–9. Transfer characteristic for a typical power transistor.

The two sources of distortion described above tend somewhat to cancel each other and will result, when combined, in an over-all transfer characteristic such as that shown in Fig. 7–9. It can be noted that while this curve is a plot of base voltage vs resulting collector current, a curve of base current vs collector current could also be described as a transfer characteristic for this device.

Let us assume that, for any particular situation, the collector current will contain harmonics, and can thus be represented by a Fourier Series

$$i_c = I_Q + A_0 + A_1 \cos \omega t + A_2 \cos 2\omega t + A_3 \cos 3\omega t \ldots, \qquad (7\text{--}19)$$

where the fourth and higher-order harmonics may be omitted with negligible error. We shall further assume that the signal voltage applied to the transistor input is a pure cosinusoid and shall sample both input and output waveforms at several time intervals to obtain the coefficients of the terms of Eq. (7–19). Let us take our samples at $\omega t = 0°, 60°, 120°,$ and $180°$ with corresponding collector currents designated as I_{max}, I_x, I_y, and I_{min}. Graphically, this operation is shown in Fig. 7–10.

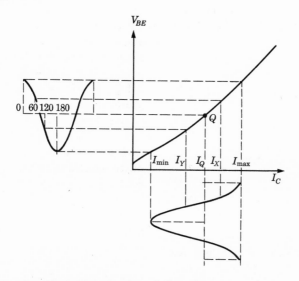

Fig. 7–10. Graphical determination of distortion content in output current.

Substitution in Eq. (7–19) yields:

$$\left.\begin{array}{ll} \omega t = 0° & I_{max} = I_Q + A_0 + A_1 + A_2 + A_3, \\ \omega t = 60° & I_x = I_Q + A_0 + A_1/2 - A_2/2 - A_3, \\ \omega t = 120° & I_y = I_Q + A_0 - A_1/2 - A_2/2 + A_3, \\ \omega t = 180° & I_{min} = I_Q + A_0 - A_1 + A_2 - A_3. \end{array}\right\} \quad (7\text{-}20)$$

The solution of these four simultaneous equations results in expressions for the harmonic amplitudes:

$$\left.\begin{array}{l} A_0 = (\tfrac{1}{6})(I_{max} + I_{min}) + (\tfrac{1}{3})(I_x + I_y) - I_Q, \\ A_1 = (\tfrac{1}{3})(I_{max} - I_{min}) + (\tfrac{1}{3})(I_x - I_y), \\ A_2 = (\tfrac{1}{4})(I_{max} + I_{min}) - (\tfrac{1}{2})I_Q, \\ A_3 = (\tfrac{1}{6})(I_{max} - I_{min}) - (\tfrac{1}{3})(I_x - I_y). \end{array}\right\} \quad (7\text{-}21)$$

The total harmonic content in a wave can be expressed as the ratio of the rms value of all harmonics to the effective value of the fundamental.

$$D = (A_2{}^2 + A_3{}^2 + \cdots)^{1/2}/A_1 \times 100\%. \quad (7\text{-}22)$$

Usually the ratio of harmonic amplitude to fundamental amplitude is of concern.

$$D_2 = (A_2/A_1) \times 100\%, \qquad\qquad (7\text{--}23)$$

and

$$D_3 = (A_3/A_1) \times 100\%. \qquad\qquad (7\text{--}24)$$

7-6. Class-A Amplification. A single transistor, biased by the methods of Chapter 3 and capable of handling the required load power, may be used as the output stage of an amplifier. The transistor may be R-C or transformer-coupled to its load and to its driver.

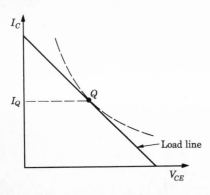

Figure 7–11 symbolizes the output characteristics of a transistor. It is desirable to provide an operating point (such as Q) that is equidistant from each axis. The Q point and load are often selected so that the maximum collector-dissipation hyperbola is tangent or nearly tangent to the load line at Q; these conditions are easily achieved with a transformer-coupled load, because a turns ratio may be chosen to reflect almost any load value into the collector circuit.

Fig. 7–11. Typical operating point for Class-A power stage requires high quiescent current.

To achieve an operating point such as Q of Fig. 7–11, a large standby collector current must be supplied to a high-power stage. This quiescent current for a Class-A power-amplifier stage may be as much as 6 or 8 amperes, and consequently it is easy to understand why Class-B amplifiers, which require almost zero quiescent current, are widely employed as output stages.

Two transistors may be connected in Class-A push–pull if more output power is required than can be supplied by a single transistor. Two such circuits are shown in Fig. 7–12. In Fig. 7–12(a), the transistors are both p–n–p and two input signals are required; these signals must differ in phase by 180°. The required phase inversion may be supplied by a transformer or by one of the active phase-inversion circuits described in a later section.

In Class-A push–pull operation both devices operate at all times, and each supplies one-half of the total load power. If the transistors are matched, the addition of the two signals in the load will result in the elimination of all even harmonic distortion, and dc magnetomotive force in the output transformer will be minimized.[6]

A Class-A push–pull stage utilizing complementary symmetry is depicted in Fig. 7–12(b). No phase inversion is required; instead, each transistor receives the same input signal. The use of opposite conductivity types, while simplifying some circuit designs, creates additional problems for the designer. In the diagram two power supplies are used, and this in itself is undesirable in many applications. The matching problems may be difficult to overcome.

The efficiency of an electronic circuit is usually defined as the ratio of the power delivered to the load to the power supplied by the power supply. We

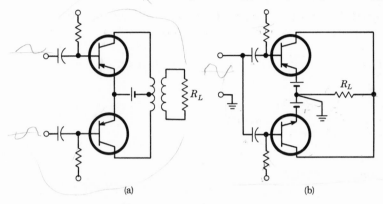

Fig. 7–12. Class-A push–pull output circuits.

may determine the theoretical efficiency of a transformer-coupled Class-A stage by initially considering the power dissipated at the collector junction:

$$P_{\text{diss}} = \frac{1}{2\pi} \int_0^{2\pi} v_C i_C \, d(\omega t) \qquad (7\text{–}25)$$

with

$$v_C = V_{CC} - kV_{CC} \sin \omega t,$$
$$i_C = (V_{CC}/R_L) + k(V_{CC}/R_L) \sin \omega t. \qquad (7\text{–}26)$$

The constant k is the ratio of the peak value of the voltage sinusoid to V_{CC}, and may take on values from 0 to 1. The effective load on the stage is R_L. Performing the integration noted in Eq. (7–25) yields

$$P_{\text{diss}} = (V_{CC}^2/R_L)[1 - (k^2/2)]. \qquad (7\text{–}27)$$

Power delivered to the load is

$$P_o = (I_{cm}/\sqrt{2})(V_{cm}/\sqrt{2}) = k^2 V_{CC}^2/2R_L. \qquad (7\text{–}28)$$

Thus the supply drain is

$$P_{\text{dc}} = P_o + P_{\text{diss}} = V_{CC}^2/R_L. \qquad (7\text{–}29)$$

The circuit efficiency becomes

$$\eta = P_o/P_{\text{dc}} = k^2/2 \times 100\%. \qquad (7\text{–}30)$$

For the maximum value of k (unity), the maximum efficiency is 50%. Because saturation and cutoff are not located exactly on the axes, actual efficiency will be slightly less than 50%. The case without transformer coupling is studied in Problem 7–11.

Power-Amplifier Design Example—Class-A. The design of a Class-A output stage by graphical methods is considered in this example.

Object. Design a transistor amplifying stage to meet the following requirements:

1. Load resistance: 2000 Ω
2. Power output: 1 W (maximum, sinusoidal)
3. Temperature: 40° C
4. Supply potential available: 12 V
5. Frequency: 400 cps

Solution. It may be assumed from the power-output specification that the stage output should enter the saturation and cutoff regions of the characteristics for any power delivery in excess of 1 W of full-load power (P_{FL}). A specification

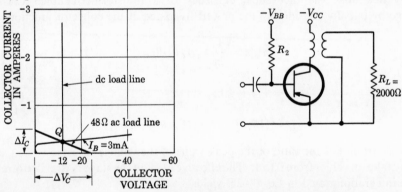

Fig. 7–13. Load lines for Class-A stage design example.

of this type is encountered when feeding a load that may be damaged by excessive signal. Since here we shall transformer-couple to the load, let us assume an output-transformer efficiency of 67%. The stage must supply

$$P_{max} = P_{FL}/\eta = 1.0/0.67 = 1.5 \text{ W}.$$

The type 2N539A power transistor is available and will be used. It is capable of handling the required power.

If we assume no dc resistance in the transformer primary, then, as can be seen in Fig. 7–13, the dc load line is vertical from 12 V. Since saturation and cutoff should exist concurrently, the collector-voltage swing will be 2(12), or 24 V. We must find the corresponding collector-current excursion.

$$P_{max} = 1.5 = [\Delta V_C/(2\sqrt{2})][\Delta I_C/(2\sqrt{2})].$$

(ΔV_C and ΔI_C are peak-to-peak values and division by $2\sqrt{2}$ yields rms.)

$$\Delta I_C = 12/24 = 0.5 \text{ A}.$$

The load seen by the transistor is

$$R_L = \Delta V_C/\Delta I_C = 24/0.5 = 48 \ \Omega.$$

The impedance ratio of the output transformer must be 48:2000.
    The quiescent point is

$$V_{CE} = 12 \text{ V},$$

$$I_C = 0.25 \text{ A},$$

and results in a 3-W standby dissipation.
    The base-circuit characteristic is defined by the plot of h_{IE} vs I_C in Appendix I. If it is assumed that the curve applies at $V_{CE} = 12$ V, then at $I_C = 0.25$ A,

$$R_i \cong h_{IE} = 135 \ \Omega.$$

h_{FE}, from the manufacturer's curve at $I_C = 0.25$ A, is

$$h_{FE} = I_C/I_B \cong I_c/I_b = 85.$$

Power gain is given by

$$G = \frac{P_o}{P_i} \cong \frac{I_c^2 R_L}{I_b^2 h_{IE}} \cong \frac{(h_{FE}I_b)^2 R_L}{I_b^2 h_{IE}} = 2570.$$

A rough calculation may be made to determine base-bias resistance R_2. The Q point is located at $I_B \cong 3$ mA.

$$R_2 \cong V_{CC}/I_B = 12/0.003 = 4000 \ \Omega.$$

The design discussed here contains no stabilization or feedback. Further investigation must be directed along those lines.

7-7. Shifting of the Operating Point. The A_0 term in the distortion discussion is necessary in the event that the performance of the transistor differs on the positive and negative half cycles of the input signal, and the resulting output waveform contains a constant or dc term in addition to the quiescent current I_Q. Because of characteristics nonlinearities, the operating point of many Class-A amplifiers will shift slightly in the presence of signal.
    Again refer to Fig. 7-11. The Q point is assumed equidistant from the two limiting regions. In the presence of a sinusoidal base-current signal that drives the stage to both extremes, the resulting collector current will be squared (the peaks will be clipped). The operating point will remain at Q and not change

from its no-signal value, because Q is equidistant. A pronounced shift in the operating point will occur, however, when the stage is driven into only one of the limiting regions (saturation or cutoff). Figure 7–14 illustrates this. The stage has a no-signal bias that determines Q. When the base-current variation is of such a magnitude as to cause the stage to saturate, clipping occurs and the quiescent point must shift because of the new average or dc value of the distorted wave. In this instance, the point shifts away from the saturation region, I_Q is reduced, and because of this the clipping is softened.

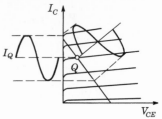

Fig. 7–14. Clipping occurs when the operating point is not in the center of the allowable range and the input signal is large.

It must be remembered that when the operating point shifts, it moves up or down the *dc load line*; the ac load line always passes through Q.

Should input variations result in collector-current excursions that tend to exceed the allowable drive, and should a stage originally be biased at a point closer to cutoff, a harder form of clipping will occur. However, it too will be somewhat softened by a shifting of the Q point, because of distortion of the current waveform. This case is characterized by a noticeable increase in I_C.

7–8. Class-B Amplification. Since Class-B operation results in conduction over one-half of the input-signal cycle, it is necessary to employ two transistors in a push–pull arrangement in order to amplify an entire sinusoidal waveform. The two halves of the waveform are added at the load re-establish the complete wave.

Class-B circuits are widely accepted because of their low standby-current requirements. It has been noted that Class-A circuits require an operating point that is characterized by a high value of collector current; for a Class-B stage or push–pull pair, little or no standby collector current is necessary, for biasing is at or near cutoff. A single-sided stage is seldom used because of its inability to reproduce the input-signal waveform.

In analyzing a push–pull arrangement, it is customary to treat only one of the transistors, since each is operating at identical levels into an identical load. Transformer load-coupling as shown in Fig. 7–15(a) is widely used, with the collector supply fed to the center tap of the output transformer. The dc load per stage consists of one half of the dc resistance of the transformer primary; this can often be assumed to be negligible when high-quality transformers are used. In each collector circuit only one half of the primary turns are applicable. Consequently the total primary resistance (R_{cc}) to alternating signals is given by

$$R_{cc} = 4R_L, \tag{7–31}$$

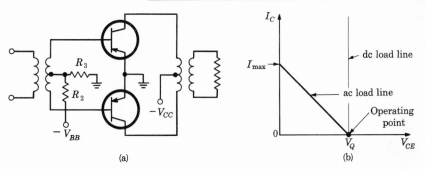

Fig. 7–15. Class B push–pull pair: (a) circuit diagram; (b) output characteristic.

where R_L is the load per transistor, and is the secondary load resistance referred to one half of the primary.

The diagram of Fig. 7–15(b) indicates an operating point set at

$$I_C = 0,$$

$$V_{CE} = V_Q.$$

A load line joins this Q point with

$$I_C = I_{max},$$

$$V_{CE} = 0.$$

This diagram assumes that cutoff is at zero current instead of I_{CO} and saturation is at zero collector voltage. Then

$$R_L = V_Q/I_{max}.$$

The power delivered by a stage that is driven through its total range (cutoff to saturation) is given by

$$P_o = \tfrac{1}{2}(V_Q/\sqrt{2})(I_{max}/\sqrt{2}) = V_Q I_{max}/4. \qquad (7\text{–}32)$$

The $\frac{1}{2}$ factor is used because we are dealing with half-wave pulses. For a push–pull pair

$$P_o = V_Q I_{max}/2. \qquad (7\text{–}33)$$

DC drawn from the collector supply is negligible during standby operation. When a sinusoidal signal of peak amplitude I_{max} is present, the dc source must supply the average current level in the pulse; during each half cycle this drain is

$$I_{dc} = I_{max}/\pi. \qquad (7\text{–}34)$$

The power from the dc supply is

$$P_{dc} = V_Q I_{max}/\pi. \qquad (7\text{–}35)$$

Therefore the maximum efficiency of each transistor is

$$\eta = P_o/P_{dc} = (V_Q I_{max}/4)/(V_Q I_{max}/\pi) = 78\%.$$

It is important to know the power being dissipated at the collector junction.

$$P_{diss} = P_{dc} - P_o = (V_Q I_{max}/\pi) - (V_Q I_{max}/4)$$

$$= 0.068 V_Q I_{max}$$

$$= 0.27 P_o. \tag{7-36}$$

Should a Class-B stage be driven to a fraction (k) of its total allowable swing,

$$\Delta V_C = k V_Q,$$

$$\Delta I_C = k I_{max}.$$

Therefore,

$$P_o = k^2 V_Q I_{max}/4 \tag{7-37}$$

per transistor.

An example of the design of a Class-B output stage is not presented at this point. In the next chapter such a design is illustrated in conjunction with a complete 10 W amplifier.

Distortion in Class-B Stages. The two transistors employed in any push–pull arrangement should be operationally matched, the degree of such matching depending upon the extent of which distortion must be minimized. In addition to the sources of distortion discussed under Class-A amplification, Class-B circuits are subject to "crossover distortion."

Crossover distortion is best understood by study of a diagram. Figure 7–16(a) shows the nonlinearity of the input characteristic of a common-emitter–connected transistor. The exponential nature of the curve signifies high input resistance at low-voltage levels; thus little base current will flow until input

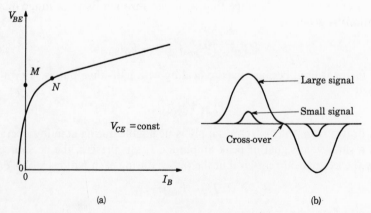

Fig. 7–16.   Crossover distortion: (a) input characteristic; (b) collector-current waveforms.

voltage exceeds some value such as *M*. Because collector current is almost directly proportional to base current, resulting collector current will be small until the input voltage is sufficiently high. The collector current for a push–pull pair is shown in Fig. 7–16(b); distortion at the "crossover" point is obvious.

To overcome this type of distortion, a base potential or current bias can be supplied that will permit operation at a more desirable point on the input characteristic, such as *N*. The summation of the alternate half-cycle signals at the load will consequently be free from a major distortion contribution and the output waveform will approximate a pure sine wave. The input biasing network composed of R_2, R_3 and V_{BB} in the circuit of Fig. 7–15(a) compensates for this type of distortion by providing the required slight forward bias. R_3 must be kept small, for signal power will be lost in that element. Often, because of temperature effects upon the transistor emitter–base characteristics, the biasing network will contain temperature-compensating elements such as thermistors or junction diodes. The addition of a bypass capacitor across R_3 is not recommended, for its discharge through that resistance will develop a potential that tends to reverse bias both transistor input junctions and, therefore, contribute to distortion.

Unbypassed emitter resistance is often used with the Class-B push–pull pair in order to improve bias stability and to reduce distortion by providing some signal degeneration.

7–9. Phase Inverters. To drive a push–pull output stage when complementary symmetry is not employed, two signals differing in phase by 180° must be supplied to the high-power pair. A transformer, with its secondary center tap grounded, is often used, the phasing of the voltage from *CT* to each end of the winding differing by 180°. When the cost, weight, or frequency requirements so dictate, a transistor phase inverter may provide the required signals. The transistor phase inverter must be capable of supplying two identical outputs of opposite polarities, and output impedances must be equal in order to satisfy the needs of each of the power transistors.

The "split-load phase inverter" is shown in Fig. 7–17(a). The input impedance

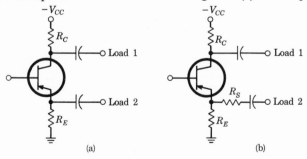

Fig. 7–17.   Split-load phase inverter: (a) basic circuit; (b) circuit modified to adjust for output impedances. Biasing not shown.

of this stage will be fairly high, because of the unbypassed emitter resistance R_E. The circuit has two sources of unbalance: if R_E is made equal to R_C as would seem natural, load #2 would receive slightly more signal, because i_e is always greater than i_c ($i_c = \alpha i_e$); also, load #2 is fed from a common-collector

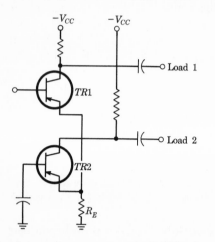

type of generator, whereas load #1 is fed from a common-emitter type of output resistance. The circuit shown in Fig. 7–17(b) employs R_S to equalize the output resistances.

In the phase inverter of Fig. 7–18, the input signal is supplied to only one transistor; TR1 emitter current, flowing through the common R_E establishes a varying emitter-to-base potential for transistor TR2. The output of TR2 consequently differs from that of the directly supplied transistor by 180°. This circuit has been called the "emitter-coupled inverter." A mathematical analysis of

Fig. 7–18. Emitter-coupled phase inverter. Biasing not shown.

operation is similar to that of the difference amplifier discussed in Chapter 10, and proceeds with the drawing of the equivalent circuit, followed by calculation of the collector voltages V_{c1} and V_{c2}. For perfect inversion $V_{c1} = V_{c2}$, and the output resistances of each transistor are identical. The emitter-coupled inverter does not quite satisfy these requirements.

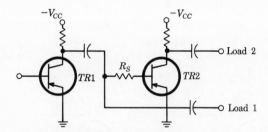

Fig. 7–19. Another type of phase inverter. Biasing not shown.

Another two-transistor phase inverter circuit is shown in Fig. 7–19. The resistor R_S can equalize the gain of TR2 to make its output signal equivalent to that of TR1. The phase inversion due to TR2 is used for load #2: the requirement, as previously stated, is a 180° difference between currents to the loads. Output resistances will tend to differ for this circuit.

7–10. Summary. An extremely important consideration in the design of large-signal stages is junction temperature and its effects upon circuit operation. Changes of transistor parameters with temperature cause variations in gain and resistance levels, but of even greater importance is the possiblity of thermal runaway. Such runaway is not always destructive because there is often external resistance in the collector-emitter circuit to limit the quiescent current to a finite and sometimes seemingly satisfactory value; investigation of the standby collector-to-emitter potential as well as the current is helpful in determining if runaway has occurred.

Because of the large standby current requirement, Class-A high-power stages have not gained wide acceptance. Class-B push–pull circuits are often used and have been refined to a high degree by the addition of thermistors and other temperature-sensitive compensating devices.

PROBLEMS

7–1. On a sketch of the 2N3242 output characteristics, show the maximum dissipation contour (500 mW at 20° C).

7–2. A particular transistor is dissipating 25 mW at its collector junction. The thermal resistance is given as 0.6° C/mW for operation in free air. At what temperature is the collector–base junction when the ambient is 40° C?

7–3. If the transistor in Problem 7–2 were attached to a clip-on sink of 1 in.² radiating surface and θ_T was found to be 0.45° C/mW, at what temperature is the junction for the ambient condition and dissipation?

7–4. The maximum allowable operating temperature for the transistor of Problems 7–2 and 7–3 is 90° C. In an ambient of 40° C, what is the permissible collector dissipation with and without the sink?

7–5. Consider a high-power transistor, mounted vertically and cooled by natural convection from a $\frac{1}{8}$-in.-thick copper sheet. Eight watts are being dissipated in the transistor, the junction-to-case resistance is 1.0° C/W, and mounting hardware is 1.0° C/W. The ambient is 30° C and maximum allowable junction temperature is 90° C. Find the minimum dimensions of the sink.

7–6. In the Class-A amplifier of the figure, $\beta = \beta_{dc} = 99$, $\theta_T = 4°$ C/W, and $(\partial I_{CBO}/\partial Tj)_{max} = 10^{-4}$A/° C. The dc resistances of the transformer windings are negligible.
(a) When connected as shown, with no signal, will the circuit thermally runaway?
(b) If a 5 Ω resistance is connected between emitter and ground, will the circuit thermally runaway?

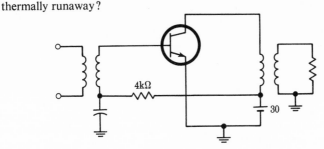

Problem 7–6.

7–7. Verify Eq. (7–13).

7–8. For an output waveform, $I_Q = 1$ A, $I_x = 1.6$ A, $I_y = 0.5$ A, $I_{max} = 2$ A, $I_{min} = 0.3$ A.

(a) Write the Fourier series for this wave with numerical coefficients through the third harmonic.

(b) Obtain the percentage of each harmonic of the fundamental.

7–9. Operating Class A, a power transistor is to deliver a maximum of 4 W of audio power to a 4 Ω load. A 12 V power supply is to be used. Assume ideal characteristics, ideal transformer coupling, and a quiescent point adjusted for symmetrical clipping. Determine the following:

(a) What transformer impedance ratio is required?

(b) What is the operating point of the stage?

(c) What is the standby-power requirement?

(d) What is the peak collector current?

7–10. Draw each of the following circuits and state which of the arramgements require phase inversion:

(a) Push–pull Class-B pair (p–n–p and p–n–p).

(b) Push–pull Class-A pair (p–n–p and n–p–n).

(c) Push–pull Class-A pair (n–p–n and n–p–n).

(d) Push–pull Class-B pair (n–p–n and p–n–p).

7–11. Prove that the maximum collector efficiency of a Class-A stage with collector load resistance R_C is 25%. When R_C is used, and the transistor coupled to $R_{L'}$ through a capacitor, is the ratio of power in R_L to dc power 6.25%? $R_{L'} = R_C$.

7–12. Verify Eq. (7–28).

7–13. For a Class-B push–pull transformer-coupled circuit, find the collector potential on the OFF transistor in terms of the direct supply potential V_{CC} when the pair is operating with full signal.

7–14. A dc meter in the V_{CC} branch of an ideal Class-B amplifier reads 0.75 A. Refer to Fig. 7–15(a). If the circuit load is 40 Ω, and an ideal output transformer with a 1 : 1 turns ratio is used, how much power is delivered to the load.

7–15. Specify the area, thickness, material, and mounting position of a flat metallic plate that can adequately serve as a heat sink for a power transistor, biased at cutoff and feeding a transformer-coupled load. The supply potential is 30 V, and the transistor is half of a Class-B pair delivering 30 W to the load when swinging from the cutoff to saturation. Consider 1.5° C/W for the transistor, 0.5° C/W for the mounting washer. The transformer has an efficiency of 75% and negligible winding resistances. Choose a heat sink that will just enable the junction to operate at 75° C in a 35° C ambient; do not include a safety factor.

7–16. A push–pull Class-B pair is wired as shown in the diagram. Crossover distortion is evident in the output waveform and it is desired to overcome this with a

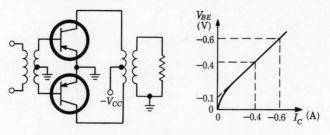

Problem 7–16.

compensating network. Working with a knowledge of the transfer curve and available supplies of $+20$ and -20 V design a resistive circuit to minimize crossover distortion and include your network in a sketch of the circuit.

7-17. A two-transistor bridge circuit with a speaker load is shown in the accompanying diagram. The bridge is adjusted to have a zero direct voltage from A to B; thus a conventional loudspeaker may be employed. Study the operation of this circuit and answer the following:

    (a) TR1 and TR2 are operating in what configurations?

    (b) What direct collector–emitter potentials exist across TR1 and TR2?

    (c) If each transistor is operating Class B, explain how the circuit will reproduce the entire signal at the speaker.

    (d) If each transistor is operating Class A, explain how the circuit will reproduce the entire signal at the speaker.

    (e) Add biasing to the diagram for Class A operation.

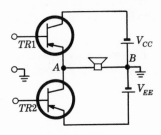

Problem 7–17.   Problem 7–18.

7-18. Repetitive power pulses of peak value P_P and time duration T_1 are applied to a thermal network consisting of thermal resistance θ_{jc} in parallel with thermal capacitance C_{jc}. At $t = T_2$ the cycle repeats. Under steady-state conditions show that the maximum rise in junction temperature, which occurs at $t = T_1$, is given by

$$\Delta T_j(t = T_1) = P_P \theta_{jc}[(1 - e^{-T_1/\tau})/(1 - e^{-T_2/\tau})]$$

where $\tau = 1/\theta_{jc}C_{jc}$.

7-19. Design a Class-A power stage using a 2N539A to meet the following requirements:

    1. Load resistance: 50 Ω

    2. Power output: 2 W (maximum, sinusoidal)

    3. Temperature: 25°C

    4. Supply potential available: -16 V

    5. Frequency: 800 cps.

Assume an output-transformer efficiency of 75% and an input-transformer efficiency of 50%, with negligible dc resistances. Sketch the circuit and determine all component values, both transformer impedance ratios, circuit gains, and the input resistance of the complete stage.

7-20. Design a push–pull Class-B stage to directly feed a center-tapped loudspeaker.

    1. Load resistance: 4 Ω each side

    2. Power output: 5 W

    3. Temperature: 25°C

    4. Potentials available: -20 and $+20$ V

    5. Frequency response: 60 to 6000 cps.

Itemize any assumptions made in the design.

REFERENCES

1. DeWitt, D., and Rossoff, A. L., *Transistor Electronics* (McGraw-Hill Book Co., Inc., New York, 1957).
2. Hunter, L. P., *Handbook of Semiconductor Electronics* (McGraw-Hill Book Co., Inc., New York, 1963), 2nd ed.
3. Hurley, R. B., *Junction Transistor Electronics* (John Wiley & Sons, Inc., New York, 1958).
4. Lo, A. W. *et al.*, *Transistor Electronics* (Prentice-Hall, Inc., Englewood Cliffs, New Jersey, 1955).
5. Riddle, R. L., and Ristenbatt, M. P., *Transistor Physics and Circuits* (Prentice-Hall, Inc., Englewood Cliffs, New Jersey, 1958).
6. Ryder, J. D., *Electronic Fundamentals and Applications* (Prentice-Hall, Inc., Englewood Cliffs, New Jersey, 1964), 3rd ed.
7. Staff, *Motorola Power Transistor Handbook*, Motorola, Inc., Phoenix, Arizona, 1960.
8. Thornton, R. D., DeWitt, D., Chenette, E. R., and Lin, H. C., *Characteristics and Limitations of Transistors* (John Wiley & Sons, Inc., New York, 1963).
9. Wolfendale, E., *The Junction Transistor and Its Applications* (The Macmillan Co., New York, 1958).

Chapter 8

MULTISTAGE AMPLIFIERS

When more amplification is required that can be supplied by a single stage, additional stages are joined to form a *composite* or *cascade* or *multistage* amplifier. Vacuum-tube stages and FET stages can easily be connected in cascade because of their isolating properties; transistors, on the other hand, because of their finite input resistance, present a considerable load to preceding circuitry, and therefore warrant special attention.

The performance of a single stage can be obtained by using the equations derived in Chapter 5; coupling networks and their effects upon gain, frequency response, and impedance levels were discussed in Chapter 6; and the high-power stage was described in Chapter 7. The problem at hand is to combine this information in order to analyze and synthesize the multistage amplifier. From the point of view of over-all requirements, the multistage amplifier must join a particular source to a particular load and provide the required amplification over the desired frequency range; it must be capable of supplying the proper power to the load, of presenting the required input resistance to the source, and of working under the environmental conditions to be expected with the power supplies available.

8–1. Analysis by Blocks. The amplifier designer can make use of systems concepts because a multistage circuit is a system of different circuits, some

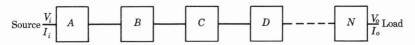

Fig. 8–1.   Block diagram of multistage circuit.

capable of supplying gain, as for example the active elements, and some providing attenuation; coupling networks and feedback paths are examples of the latter. A cascade amplifier can be depicted as in Fig. 8–1, a series of blocks each representing significant circuitry. Each block is capable of voltage and current gain, although the gain of some of the blocks may be less than unity and they therefore serve to attenuate. The block designated "A" may, in reality, be the coupling circuit between the source and the first amplifying stage marked "B." The "C" block may represent a coupling network, an equalizing network, or some other group of passive or active elements.

Since over-all operation is to be considered, the load power may be written as

$$P_o = I_o^2 R_L,$$ (8-1)

and the input power as

$$P_i = I_i^2 R_{iA}.$$ (8-2)

The power gain is

$$G = P_o/P_i = I_o^2 R_L/I_i^2 R_{iA}.$$ (8-3)

But

$$I_o = I_i(A_{iA}A_{iB} \cdots A_{iN}).$$ (8-4)

Therefore

$$G = (R_L/R_{iA})(A_{iA}A_{iB} \cdots A_{iN})^2.$$ (8-5)

The operation of a multistage amplifier can be specified in terms of the individual voltage gains, because, at the load, power can be expressed by

$$P_o = V_o^2/R_L,$$ (8-6)

and at the input by

$$P_i = V_i^2/R_{iA}.$$ (8-7)

Then power gain is

$$G = P_o/P_i = (V_o^2/R_L)/(V_i^2/R_{iA}).$$ (8-8)

But

$$V_o = V_i(A_{vA}A_{vB} \cdots A_{vN}).$$ (8-9)

Therefore

$$G = (R_{iA}/R_L)(A_{vA}A_{vB} \cdots A_{vN})^2.$$ (8-10)

Another approach is to use the power gains of each stage

$$G = G_A G_B \cdots G_N.$$ (8-11)

Equation (8-11) requires all gain factors to be numerical ratios. Should gains be given in logarithmic units (decibels), the over-all amplification is the sum of the individual gains.

To analyze the over-all performance of a multistage amplifier, it is necessary only to determine the numbers to use in an equation such as (8-5). R_L will undoubtedly be known, but the determination of R_{iA} is not as simple as might be desired. R_{iA} depends upon the load on block A, and the load on block A is the input resistance of block B, and so on. Similarly, in order to calculate any of the A_i terms, the input resistance of the following block must be known. Therefore, it may be concluded that *in order to predict the operation of a multistage transistor amplifier, it is necessary to proceed from the last element (or block) and work forward toward the initial block.*

In order to determine the output resistance of a cascaded circuit, an exception must be made to the rule quoted in the preceding paragraph, namely that analysis must proceed from the final element toward the initial element. Output resistance depends upon the properties of the driving source, and therefore its calculation is not possible until all preceding elements are adequately specified.

The frequency response of composite circuits may be considerably poorer than that of an individual stage. As a chain is no stronger than its weakest link, so a cascade amplifier is no wider than its narrowest stage (in the absence of external feedback). If the stages are more-or-less identical, over-all performance may be entirely unsatisfactory, even if the response of each individual stage contains a safety factor.

The upper half-power frequency for n identical stages is to be investigated. It is defined by reduction in voltage (or current) gain to $1/\sqrt{2}$ of the mid-band value. The gain of each stage ideally declines with increasing frequency according to the relation

$$A = A_{\mathrm{mid}}/[(1 + (f/f_h)^2)]^{1/2}. \tag{8-12}$$

f_h represents the upper cutoff frequency of a single stage. Now if the over-all performance of the cascade amplifier (A_T) is equated to that of the composite stages, at the frequency of interest we have

$$A_T/\sqrt{2} = A^n = \{A_{\mathrm{mid}}/[1 + (f/f_h)^2]^{1/2}\}^n.$$

Note that the gains A_T and $(A_{\mathrm{mid}})^n$ at the mid-frequency reference are identical. Mathematical manipulations give

$$2^{1/n} = 1 + (f/f_h)^2,$$

from which

$$f = f_h(2^{1/n} - 1)^{1/2}. \tag{8-13}$$

Equation (8-13) is an expression for the upper "cutoff" frequency (response 3-db down) for a multistage circuit consisting of n identical stages.

At the low-frequency end of the spectrum, circuit gain can be approximated by

$$A = A_{\mathrm{mid}}[1 + (f_l/f)^2]^{1/2}. \tag{8-14}$$

f_l represents the lower half-power frequency of a single stage. Hence, low-frequency cutoff is at

$$f = f_l/(2^{1/n} - 1)^{1/2}. \tag{8-15}$$

A numerical example is illuminating. Consider three stages in cascade, each with $f_l = 20$ cps and $f_h = 20,000$ cps. From Eqs. (8-13) and (8-15), the over-all bandwidth is found to be 39 to 10,200 cps. It is obvious, therefore, that the bandwidth reduction resulting from the cascading of stages is an important design factor; it may be overcome by designing all stages to have broad response, or by the use of feedback (treated in Chapter 10).

8–2. Computer Analysis. An alternate method of obtaining performance information for a multistage amplifier is by solution of the composite equivalent circuit. When several stages are included, or when feedback loops are evident, the solution of the simultaneous circuit equations becomes a laborious task, and the results of such a study may not be worth the time devoted to it. The procedure is identical with that used in Chapter 5 to analyze single-stage circuits; the equivalent circuit must be drawn, loop or nodal equations written, the equations solved to determine the unknown voltages and currents, and finally, the ratios of the important quantities determined. Examples of equations for gains and impedance levels of multistage circuits are available in the literature.[1]

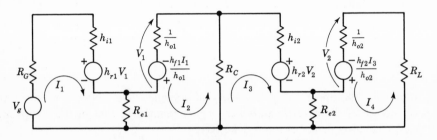

Fig. 8–2.   Circuit for computer study.

A powerful method of multistage circuit analysis particularly applicable to circuit design employs the digital computer to perform the laborious calculations and does not require solution of the simultaneous equations that always result from multiple mesh or nodal networks.

As an example of the use of the computer, consider the two-stage amplifier shown in Fig. 8–2. Its voltage gain is to be studied. Of special interest is the effect of transistor parameter variations upon the gain, and the influence of production tolerances in feedback elements R_{e1} and R_{e2}. We proceed by writing the four loop equations. Note that source transformations have been employed to eliminate current generators in the collector branches.

$$V_g = I_1\left(R_G + h_{i1} + R_{e1} - \frac{h_{r1}h_{f1}}{h_{o1}}\right) + I_2\left(R_{e1} + \frac{h_{r1}}{h_{o1}}\right) + 0 + 0,$$

$$0 = I_1\left(R_{e1} - \frac{h_{f1}}{h_{o1}}\right) + I_2\left(R_C + \frac{1}{h_{o1}} + R_{e1}\right) + I_3(R_C) + 0,$$

$$0 = 0 + I_2(R_C) + I_3\left(R_C + h_{i2} + R_{e2} - \frac{h_{r2}h_{f2}}{h_{o2}}\right) + I_4\left(R_{e2} + \frac{h_{i2}}{h_{o2}}\right),$$

$$0 = 0 + 0 + I_3\left(R_{e2} - \frac{h_{f2}}{h_{o2}}\right) + I_4\left(R_L + \frac{1}{h_{o2}} + R_{e2}\right).$$

(8–16)

Regular methods for determination of voltage gain require that these equations be solved for I_4 in terms of V_g and the circuit elements. *It is advantageous not to have to solve the equations.* Consider every element to be of known value. (If V_g is not known, it can be assumed to be 1 mV, or some other simple number.) Thus in the corresponding matrix equation,

$$[V] = [R][I], \qquad (8\text{--}17)$$

all of the elements of $[V]$ and of $[R]$ are known. These arrays are the data fed to the computer programmed to solve simultaneous linear equations. (Such a program is often a standard subroutine easily and quickly performed by any machine.) The computer solves the equations by matrix inversion. That is, it provides the elements of the $[I]$ matrix by multiplying through by the inverse of $[R]$:

$$[I] = [R]^{-1}[V]. \qquad (8\text{--}18)$$

The voltage gain is simply

$$A_v = I_4 R_L / V_g. \qquad (8\text{--}19)$$

Consider an amplifier having the following nominal values of parameters and elements:

$$R_G = 10^4, \qquad R_C = 10^4, \qquad R_L = 500,$$
$$h_i = 4000, \qquad h_f = 100, \qquad h_r = 10^{-3}, \qquad h_o = 10^{-5},$$
$$R_{e1} = 50, \qquad R_{e2} = 100.$$

Solution of Eqs. (8–16) using these values yields the reference value of A_v, 107.5. Reruns may now be made using different values for certain of the parameters in order to evaluate the effects of these changes. Of the many possibilities we select the following 10:

Change	A_v
1. Each $h_f = 50$	38.4
2. Each $h_f = 150$	179.9
3. Each $h_o = 3 \times 10^{-4}$	44.6
4. $R_C = 8000$	93.9
5. $R_{e1} = 40$, $R_{e2} = 80$	123.8
6. $R_{e1} = 60$, $R_{e2} = 120$	94.1
7. Changes 1 and 3	16.2
8. Changes 1, 3, 4 and 6	14.0
9. $R_G = 9000$	113.7
10. $R_G = 11,000$	101.9

The values for A_v given in this chart are very rapidly obtained. Additional information is available from the computer runs. For example, all of the circuit currents are available for study. The method may be extended to determine frequency response if the computer is programmed to manipulate complex numbers.

This rapid means for repeated analysis can save many hours of labor. The problem that remains, however, is for the designer to show good engineering judgment in his selection of variable changes and in his ability to analyze the data thus generated.

8–3. Analysis by h Parameters. The h-matrix parameters offer a means for determining circuit performance that is somewhat more general than the methods described in the preceding sections. Consider the two-stage equivalent circuit of Fig. 8–3. The parameters are simply h_i, h_r, h_f, and h_o, without designation of the

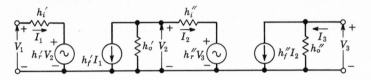

Fig. 8–3.   General h-parameter equivalent for two stages.

configuration employed, and the single prime represents the first stage whereas the double prime stands for the second stage parameters of the cascaded pair.

If a load is attached at the output terminals and a source at the input pair, equations can be written for A_i, A_v, G, R_i, and R_o in terms of the general parameters. Should stage one be common-base and stage two be common-emitter, then $h_i{}' = h_{ib}$, etc., and $h_i{}'' = h_{ie}$, etc. Therefore, one set of performance equations can suffice for the nine possible combinations of the three configurations connected as a pair. Such equations will not be offered here.

A somewhat simpler means of finding the operation of the cascaded pair is to find the *h parameters of the entire circuit*, not just for individual transistors. It must be remembered that a complete circuit such as that of Fig. 8–3 may have an h_i, which is defined as the "input impedance with output ac short-circuited," and likewise an h_r, h_f, and h_o. To determine these h parameters for the composite circuit, Fig. 8–3 may be simplified to that of Fig. 8–4(a) for the calculation of

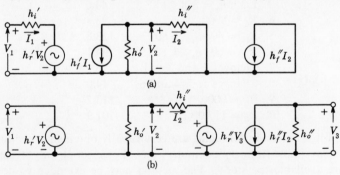

(a)

(b)

Fig. 8–4.   Simplifications of Fig. 8–3: (a) circuit for determination of h_{11} and h_{21}; (b) circuit for determination of h_{12} and h_{22}.

h_i and h_f, both of which require that the ac output be short-circuited. Figure 8–4(b) may be used to calculate h_r and h_o, for each require that the ac input circuit be opened. The results of such an analysis follow:

$$h_i = V_1/I_1 = h_i' - [h_i''h_r'h_f'/(h_i''h_o' + 1)], \tag{8-20}$$

$$h_f = I_3/I_1 = -h_f'h_f''/(h_i''h_o' + 1), \tag{8-21}$$

$$h_r = V_1/V_3 = h_r'h_r''/(h_i''h_o' + 1), \tag{8-22}$$

$$h_o = I_3/V_3 = h_o'' - [h_f''h_r'h_o'/(h_i''h_o' + 1)]. \tag{8-23}$$

After determination of the composite parameters, they can be used in the general equations of Table 5–1. Those equations are listed here for convenience:

$$A_v = -h_f R_L/(h_i + R_L\Delta^h), \tag{8-24}$$

$$A_i = h_f/(1 + R_L h_o), \tag{8-25}$$

$$R_i = (h_i + R_L\Delta^h)/(1 + R_L h_o), \tag{8-26}$$

$$R_o = (h_i + R_G)/(\Delta^h + R_G h_o). \tag{8-27}$$

Note that biasing resistances have been assumed to be of no consequence in the preceding derivations.

8–4. Analysis by a Parameters. The ABCD or a parameters noted earlier as Eqs. (4–7) are of particular use in the analysis of cascaded networks. Consider the blocks shown in Fig. 8–5. Terminal quantities are described by

$$\begin{bmatrix} V_1 \\ I_1 \end{bmatrix} = [a_A]\begin{bmatrix} V_2 \\ -I_2 \end{bmatrix} \quad \text{and} \quad \begin{bmatrix} V_2 \\ I_2 \end{bmatrix} = [a_B]\begin{bmatrix} V_3 \\ -I_3 \end{bmatrix}. \tag{8-28}$$

Because of the directions assigned to I_2 and I_3 in the diagram, all $[a_A]$ and $[a_B]$ elements are positive quantities. To describe the composite structure, we multiply the matrices according to Sec. 5–11 to obtain

$$\begin{bmatrix} V_1 \\ I_1 \end{bmatrix} = [a]\begin{bmatrix} V_3 \\ I_3 \end{bmatrix} \tag{8-29}$$

with

$$a_{11} = a_{11A}a_{11B} + a_{12A}a_{21B},$$

$$a_{12} = a_{11A}a_{12B} + a_{12A}a_{22B},$$

$$a_{21} = a_{21A}a_{11B} + a_{22A}a_{21B},$$

$$a_{22} = a_{21A}a_{12B} + a_{22A}a_{22B}. \tag{8-30}$$

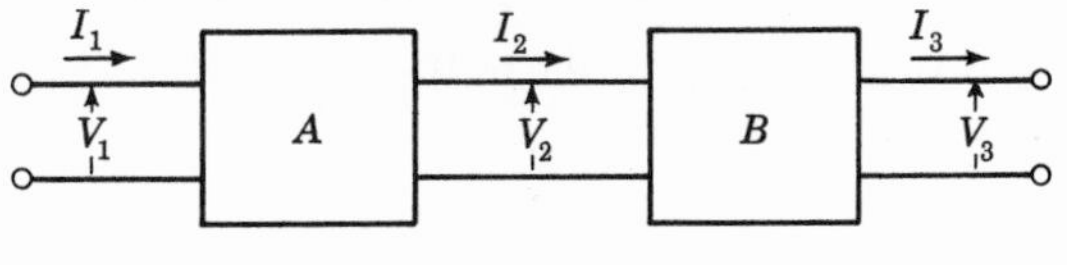

Fig. 8–5. a-parameter analysis.

The manipulations described in Eqs. (8–30) can easily be performed. The result is that the two networks have been compressed into one described by [a]. The formulas of Appendix II can be used to analyze the network when terminated.

8–5. Design of a Multistage Amplifier. An example of the design of a multistage amplifier will now be given. The purpose of this section is to familiarize the reader with the complexities involved in the design of a cascaded amplifier. This example is incomplete in the sense that further investigations may be warranted to simplify the circuitry, improve efficiency, provide adequate feedback, design power supplies, and to study temperature effects.

Design of a 10-W Servo Amplifier

Object. Design an amplifier to meet the following specifications:
1. Rated load power: 10 W
2. Load: 500 Ω (resistive), a small instrument motor
3. Overload capacity: 10%
4. Input signal to give rated output: 0.1 V
5. Input resistance: 50,000 Ω (minimum)
6. Carrier frequency: 400 cps
7. Ambient temperature: 25° ± 5° C
8. Supply potentials available: 12 and 28 V.

Solution.

General

The minimum power gain required is

$$G = P_o/P_i = 10/[(0.1)^2/50 \text{ k}] = 50 \times 10^6 \text{ or } 77 \text{ dB}.$$

A Class-B push–pull output stage can handle the required load power and provide a gain of 25–30 dB. An unstabilized driver stage can easily provide 30 dB, so a low-power amplifying stage will also be necessary. Type 2N2614 and type 2N539A transistors are available. Transformer coupling may be used where applicable.

The design will proceed according to the block approach, commencing with the final stages and working toward the low-level stages.

Push–Pull Class-B Power Stage

To supply 10 W (P_{FL}) to the load in Fig. 8–6,

$$\text{transformer primary power} = P_{FL}/\eta = 10/0.80 = 12.5 \text{ W},$$

where η represents the efficiency of the output transformer (assumed to be 80%). The stage must be capable of handling

$$(110\%)(12.5) = 13.7 \text{ W}.$$

Each power transistor is required to supply a maximum of 6.85 W.

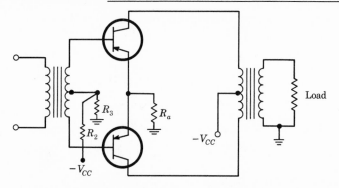

Fig. 8–6. Conventional Class-B push–pull output stage with biasing network to compensate for crossover distortion.

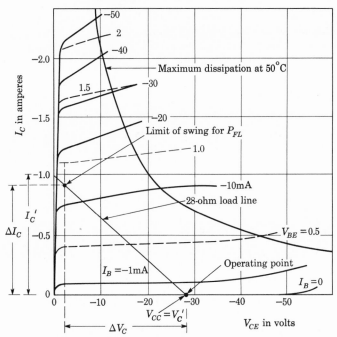

Fig. 8–7. Output and input characteristics for the 2N539A, shown on one set of axes. (This curve is not included in the section of Appendix I devoted to the 2N539A.)

The symbols $I_C{'}$ and $V_C{'}$ are explained by Fig. 8–7, and represent maximum swings in output quantities. For each transistor, under overload conditions,

$$P_{max} = V_C{'}I_C{'}/4.$$

Since this is Class B

$$V_C{'} \cong V_{CC} = 28 \text{ V},$$

so
$$I_C' = 4(6.85)/28 \cong 1.0 \text{ A.}$$

Therefore the load to be supplied by each transistor is

$$R_L = V_C'/I_C' = 28/1.0 = 28 \ \Omega.$$

For the entire primary, the reflected load resistance is

$$R_{cc} = 4(28) = 112 \ \Omega.$$

(If the factor of 4 is not clearly understood, a proof based upon turns ratios is suggested.)

Full load for each transistor is

$$P_{FL} = 12.5/2 = 6.25 \text{ W.}$$

Refer again to Fig. 8–7. To find the actual swings for rated full load, ΔI_C and ΔV_C, make use of the laws of similar triangles

$$P_{FL} = [(\Delta I_C)(\Delta V_C)]/4$$
$$= [(kI_C')(kV_C')]/4.$$

Thus $k = 0.89$. Therefore

$$\Delta I_C = kI_C' = 0.9 \text{ A,}$$
$$\Delta V_C = kV_C' = 25 \text{ V.}$$

To drive a 2N539A to 0.9 A and through a 25 V-swing requires (from Fig. 8–7)

$$\Delta I_B = 15 \text{ mA,}$$
$$\Delta V_{BE} = 0.85 \text{ V.}$$

Therefore the required input power is

$$P_i = [(\Delta I_B)(\Delta V_{BE})]/4 = [(15 \times 10^{-3})(0.85)]/4 = 3.2 \text{ mW.}$$

Nominal power gain per stage is

$$G = P_{FL}/P_i = 6.25/0.0032 = 1950 \text{ or } 32.9 \text{ dB.}$$

The gain, including output transformer losses, is

$$G = (0.80)(1950) = 1560 \text{ or } 31.9 \text{ dB.}$$

Total power to be supplied from the preceding stage $= (2)(3.2) = 6.4$ mW.

A bias circuit to prevent crossover distortion is necessary. Figure 8–8 shows input-circuit characteristics (replotted from the information of Fig. 8–7). When $I_B = 0$, approximately 0.2 V is required from base to emitter. To eliminate this type of distortion, a circuit composed of V_{CC}, R_2, and R_3 will be designed to put $+0.2$ V on the emitter. Assume $R_3 = 10 \ \Omega$; then by voltage division from the 28-V supply, $R_2 = 1400 \ \Omega$.

An unbypassed 1-Ω resistance in the emitter lead will be used for gain stabilization. Input resistance is to be determined.

$$h_{IE} \text{ (published)} \cong 60 \ \Omega \text{ (at peak of input signal)}.$$

The 1-Ω resistor affects input resistance according to

$$R_i = \beta_{dc} R_E + h_{IE} = (0.9/0.015)(1) + 60 = 120 \ \Omega.$$

Total secondary impedance load on the input transformer $= 4(R_i) = 480 \ \Omega$. The bias circuit will cause a slight loss in amplification. Since the 1-Ω resistor

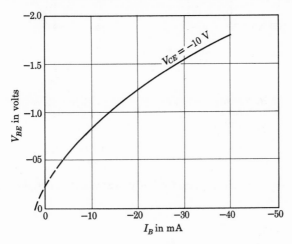

Fig. 8–8. Input characteristics for the 2N539A (obtained from Fig. 8–7).

doubles input resistance, it will cause a loss of 50% in stage gain (3 dB). Therefore it is to be expected that the stage will provide a nominal power gain of 780 (excluding the driver transformer), and that the necessary power to be supplied from the driver stage is 12.8 mW.

Driver Stage

To supply 12.8 mW to the output stage with an assumed interstage transformer efficiency of 75%, the driver must be capable of handling

$$P_{FL} = 12.8/0.75 = 17 \text{ mW}.$$

and, with overload capacity included,

$$P_{max} = 17(110\%) = 18.7 \text{ mW}.$$

A 2N2614 is capable of this loading and will be used for TR1 and TR2. Examine the diagram of Fig. 8–9. Single-battery bias is employed, with operating-point stability offered by R_{12}. Since V_{CC} is fixed, the dc load line will have a slope of $-1/450$ from -12 V; this can be seen on the characteristics of Fig. 8–10 (200 Ω

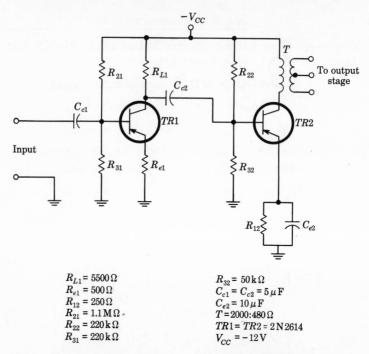

$R_{L1} = 5500\,\Omega$
$R_{e1} = 500\,\Omega$
$R_{12} = 250\,\Omega$
$R_{21} = 1.1\,\text{M}\,\Omega$
$R_{22} = 220\,\text{k}\,\Omega$
$R_{31} = 220\,\text{k}\,\Omega$

$R_{32} = 50\,\text{k}\,\Omega$
$C_{c1} = C_{c2} = 5\,\mu\,\text{F}$
$C_{e2} = 10\,\mu\,\text{F}$
$T = 2000\!:\!480\,\Omega$
$TR1 = TR2 = 2\,\text{N}\,2614$
$V_{CC} = -12\,\text{V}$

Fig. 8–9.   Circuit diagram for low-power stages of design example.

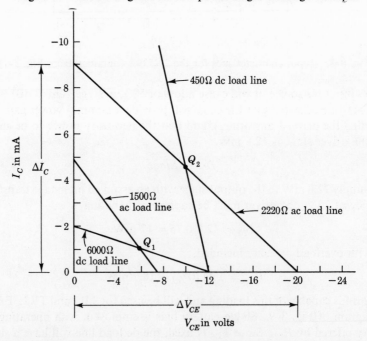

Fig. 8–10.   Load lines on the collector characteristics of the 2N2614.

for the transformer resistance and 250 Ω for R_{12}). An ac line of 2220 Ω drawn through the Q point will allow generally undistorted output power of

$$P = [(\Delta I_C)(\Delta V_{CE})]/8 = [(9 \times 10^{-3})(20)]/8 = 22.5 \text{ mW}.$$

The operating point chosen is

$$I_C \cong I_E = -4.5 \text{ mA and } V_{CE} \cong -10 \text{ V},$$

and the circuit elements are as shown in Fig. 8–9. If R_{32} is chosen to be 50 kΩ, and a nominal value of 150 used for h_{FE}, $R_2 = 220$ kΩ.

The nominal values of the small-signal parameters at 1 mA, 6 V, 1000 cps, were determined from tests:

$$h_{fe} = 150, \qquad h_{re} = 10 \times 10^{-4},$$

$$h_{ie} = 4550 \text{ Ω}, \qquad h_{oe} = 60 \times 10^{-6} \text{ mho}.$$

These values must be corrected for the operating point chosen. Correction information is given in Fig. 8–11. Therefore the parameters for this stage are:

$$h_{fe} = (150)(0.75)(1.25) = 140, \qquad h_{re} = (10 \times 10^{-4})(1.3)(0.8) = 10.4 \times 10^{-4},$$

$$h_{ie} = (4550)(0.25)(1.25) = 1420, \qquad h_{oe} = (60 \times 10^{-6})(3.9)(0.9) = 210 \times 10^{-6}.$$

The characteristics of the stage are obtained from the equations of Table 5–1:

$$A_v = 175, \qquad G = 16{,}800 \text{ or } 42.2 \text{ dB},$$

$$A_i = 96, \qquad R_i = 1200 \text{ Ω}.$$

The required power at the base is

$$P_{FL}/G = 17 \text{ mW}/16{,}800 = 1 \text{ μW}.$$

Signal current loss in R_{32} is expected to be

$$R_i/(R_{32} + R_i) = 2.3\%.$$

1st Amplifying Stage

In order to meet the 50,000 Ω input-resistance specification, we shall use a common-emitter stage with a degenerative emitter-leg feedback. The nominal value of h_{fe} is 150; if a 500-Ω resistance is used, the input resistance of the transistor alone will be about 75,000 Ω. This seems satisfactory when we realize that R_{21} and R_{31} will parallel the input of this stage. An operating point is chosen at

$$I_C = -1 \text{ mA}, V_{CE} = -6 \text{ V}.$$

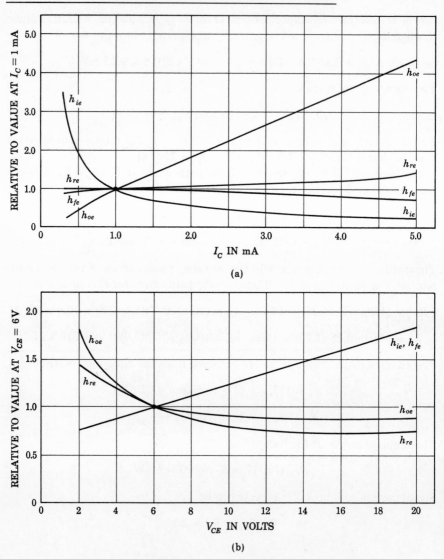

Fig. 8–11. Parameter variation information for 2N2614.

Because the collector supply is -12 V, the collector load resistance must be 5500 Ω. If R_{31} is chosen as 220,000, it follows that R_{21} must be 1.1 MΩ. Calculations using nominal parameters and a load of 5500‖1200 yield, for the first stage,

$$A_v = 1.8, \qquad G = 270 \text{ or } 24.3 \text{ dB},$$

$$A_i = 150, \qquad R_i = 72,000 \ \Omega.$$

The base-biasing network reduces this input resistance to a nominal value of 51,500 Ω.

TRANSFORMER SPECIFICATIONS

	Output	*Driver*
Maximum primary power	13.7 W	25 mW
Impedance ratio	112CT : 500	2000 : 480CT
Turns ratio $- N_1 : N_2$	0.472	2.0
Unbalanced dc in primary	none	5 mA
Maximum primary 400 $\sim$ voltage	20 (rms)	7 (rms)

PERFORMANCE SUMMARY

	Power Out	*Gain*	*Power In*
Output transformer	10 W	0.8	12.5 W
Output stage	12.5 W	975	12.8 mW
Driver transformer	12.8 mW	0.75	17 mW
Driver stage	17 mW	16,800	1 μW
Coupling	1 μW	0.8	1.2 μW
1st stage	1.2 μW	270	0.005 μW
Coupling	0.005 μW	0.72	0.007 μW

Over-all power gain $= P_o/P_i = 10/(7 \times 10^{-9}) = 1.4 \times 10^9 = 91.4$ dB

Results and Conclusions. The amplifier designed here was built and tested and the following notes pertain to its performance:

(a) Over-all gain 85 dB vs 91.4 dB calculated.

(b) Input resistance measured 60,000 Ω.

(c) In order to meet the requirement that 10 W be delivered to the load, the 28-V power supply must be well regulated, for the amplifier draws nearly an ampere from the supply.

The gain and input resistance of this amplifier is highly dependent upon the h_{fe} parameters of the particular transistors used. In order to provide a tolerable level of gain stability, negative feedback should be employed. Feedback is the subject of Chapters 9 and 10.

Additional study of this amplifier is considered in Problem 8–10.

8–6. Synthesis of Voltage Transfer Functions. In order to shape the frequency response of a network, for the purpose of filtering or of equalizing, circuits employing FET's along with passive components are particularly applicable and are easily synthesized. It was shown that the voltage gain of a single FET stage feeding a resistive load is $g_m R_L$. For a complex load $Z(s)$, the voltage transfer function $A(s)$, defined as the complex ratio of output to input voltages, is

$$A(s) = g_m Z(s). \tag{8–31}$$

s represents the Laplace operator and, in general, $s = \sigma + j\omega$. For sinusoidal steady-state analysis, $s = j\omega$.

The problem to be considered here is the realization of a network that provides the required $A(s)$. With $A(s)$ given and g_m a known constant, the problem is to find $Z(s)$. From Eq. (8–31),

$$Z(s) = A(s)/g_m. \qquad (8\text{–}32)$$

The question to be initially answered is "is $Z(s)$ realizable?" Stated differently, is there a combination of passive elements that will present a driving-point impedance equal to $A(s)/g_m$? This quantity may be represented by the ratio of polynomials in s:

$$Z(s) = \frac{A(s)}{g_m} = \frac{a_o s^n + a_1 s^{n-1} + \cdots a_n}{b_o s^m + b_1 s^{m-1} + \cdots b_m} = \frac{p(s)}{q(s)}. \qquad (8\text{–}33)$$

In alternate form, Eq. (8–33) is

$$\frac{p(s)}{q(s)} = H \frac{(s - s_1)(s - s_2) \cdots (s - s_n)}{(s - s_a)(s - s_b) \cdots (s - s_m)}. \qquad (8\text{–}34)$$

H is a_o/b_o; s_1, s_2 etc., are referred to as the *zeros* of the function, and s_a, s_b etc., as the *poles*. Values of the zeros and poles are referred to as the *critical frequencies* of the network.

If we are initially restricted to considering a *single* FET stage, it is possible to realize $Z(s)$ if

$Z(s)$ is real when s is real,

$Re\ Z(s) \geq 0$ for $Re\ s \geq 0$.

These are the requirements for a driving-point impedance to be a *positive real function*. A positive real (p.r.) function may be realized using passive circuit elements. Description of the mathematical tests to determine whether a particular $Z(s)$ is realizable are not reproduced here; such discussions are available in the literature.[3] However, from the summary of the properties of positive real functions given below, it is possible to visually test a function and immediately reject certain functions as nonrealizable. Properties of p.r. functions are:
  1. The coefficients of all terms in Eq. (8–33) are real and positive.
  2. The degree of numerator and denominator polynomials differ at most by 1.
  3. The lowest degree terms in $p(s)$ and $q(s)$ differ in degree at most by 1.
  4. Poles and zeros must have negative or zero real parts.
  5. Poles on the imaginary axis of the complex s plane must be simple.

The reference to the complex s plane in 5 above can be clarified by considering Fig. 8–12. The figure shows the poles and zeros of a sample function plotted in a complex s plane. Poles are denoted by x and zeros by o. Any function described by Eq. (8–34) can be so plotted.

Example.   Consider the function

$$Z(s) = 10^3 \frac{s^2 + 4s + 4}{s^3 + 2s^2 + 2s + 40} = 10^3 \frac{(s + 2)^2}{(s + 4)(s^2 - 2s + 10)}.$$

This function is non-p.r. because it has two poles with positive real parts and thus violates rule 4. The poles are located at $s = -4$, and $s = 1 \pm j3$. If the required function is non-positive real, this simply means that the function cannot be realized by a single stage of the type of Fig. 8–13.

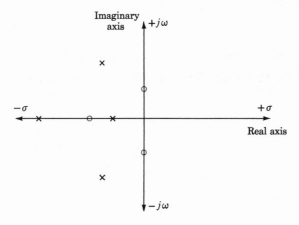

Fig. 8–12.   Complex *s*-plane showing typical arrangement of poles and zeros. The function is of the form $A(s) = (s + a)(s^2 + b^2)/(s + c)(s + d)(s^2 + e^2)$.

To realize a p.r. function, the methods of Foster will be the only ones considered here. *For a given impedance function to be realized as an RC network it is necessary that*

1. All the zeros and poles be simple and have negative or zero real parts (no imaginary parts).

2. The zeros and poles alternate.

3. The critical frequency of lowest magnitude be a pole. To be an *RC admittance*, substitute zero for pole in statement 3. To synthesize an *RL admittance*, the three rules given apply directly. An *RL impedance* function is treated as *RC* admittance. Rules for *RLC* networks will not be considered here.

If the function corresponds to an *L–C* network,

1. The poles and zeros are simple and fall on the imaginary axis as conjugate pairs.

2. The poles and zeros alternate.

Foster's methods are summarized here:

1. *RC* impedance. Expand $Z(s)$ by partial fractions.
2. *RC* admittance. Expand $Y(s)/s$ by partial fractions.
3. *RL* impedance. Expand $Z(s)/s$ by partial fractions.
4. *RL* admittance. Expand $Y(s)$ by partial fractions.
5. *LC* impedance. Expand $Z(s)$ by partial fractions.
6. *LC* admittance. Expand $Y(s)$ by partial fractions.

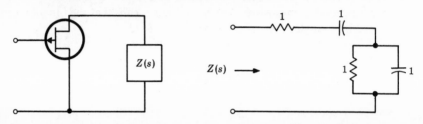

Fig. 8–13. Single FET stage with load   Fig. 8–14. Realization of $Z(s)$ as given
$Z(s)$.   in the example.

Example.   Consider the synthesis of the p.r. driving-point impedance function

$$Z(s) = \frac{s^2 + 3s + 1}{s(s + 1)}.$$

Dividing denominator into numerator, one obtains

$$Z(s) = 1 + \frac{2s + 1}{s(s + 1)} = 1 + \frac{2(s + \frac{1}{2})}{s(s + 1)}.$$

The first term, 1, is a series resistance of 1 Ω. It is obvious that the poles and zeros alternate, and the lowest critical frequency is a pole at $s = 0$. Therefore we may realize an *RC* network. A partial fraction expansion yields

$$Z(s) = 1 + 1/s + 1/(s + 1).$$

The $1/s$ term is recognized as a series capacitor of 1 F, and $1/(s + 1)$ as the parallel resultant of 1 Ω and 1 F.* The resulting network is shown in Fig. 8–14. Note that if a $Y(s)$ equal to the given $Z(s)$ had to be realized, the expansion would have provided negative terms.

To synthesize a non-positive real function, we can make use of cascaded FET stages, for any $p(s)/q(s)$ with poles and zeros in the left half plane or on the imaginary axis may be expressed as the product of positive real functions.[3] Once the function is broken into p.r. parts, each part can be the load on a FET stage.

---

*Ridiculous values such as 1-F capacitances are used here for simplicity of presentation. By normalizing techniques a real problem could be stated in similar terms if desired.

Examples.

non-p.r. functions	break into	
1. $\quad s^2$	s	s
2. $\quad \dfrac{s+2}{s(s+1)}$	$\dfrac{s+2}{s}$	$\dfrac{1}{s+1}$
3. $\quad \dfrac{s^2+1}{s^2+4s+16}$	$\dfrac{s^2+1}{s}$	$\dfrac{s}{s^2+4s+16}$
4. $\quad \dfrac{10^6}{s(s+1)(s+2)}$	$\dfrac{10^6}{s}$ $\quad\dfrac{1}{s+1}$	$\dfrac{1}{s+2}$

A network that will provide the $A(s)$ required by Example 4 is shown in Fig. 8–15. Other networks are possible, for the non-p.r. function can be broken into an infinite number of products.

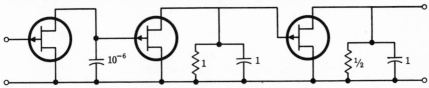

Fig. 8–15. Realization of Example 4.

In order to practically synthesize a given $A(s)$, it is assumed that FET stages, including their gate biasing, do not load down the preceding circuitry. In addition it is also required that the V_{DD} supply be provided for each stage. In Fig. 8–15, V_{DD} can be supplied to stages 2 and 3 through the 1-Ω resistors; for stage 1 a large-valued resistance could parallel the capacitance for this purpose.

PROBLEMS

8–1. Confirm Eqs. (8–16).

8–2. Using Eqs. (8–16), verify that the voltage gain equals 123.8 when change No. 5 is made to nominal element values in the example of Sec. 8–2.

8–3. Two transistors are connected in cascade to supply a 2000-Ω load. Each has the following parameters: $h_{ib} = 50\ \Omega$, $h_{rb} = 10^{-4}$, $h_{fe} = 60$, and $h_{ob} = 10^{-6}$ mho.
  (a) Calculate the power gain of the pair if the first is connected common-base and the second common-emitter.
  (b) Calculate the current gain of the pair if both transistors are being operated common-emitter.
To arrive at answers to parts (a) and (b), utilize the composite h-parameter method.

8–4. Consider the circuit shown in the accompanying figure. Base-biasing resistances are very large and may be neglected. Bypassed resistances are assumed to have no effect upon circuit gains and impedances. Each transistor has $r_e = 25$ Ω, $r_b = 1300$ Ω, $r_c = 10^6$ Ω, and $\alpha = 0.975$. You are asked to calculate the following by using any convenient method:

(a) The current gain of the composite amplifier.

(b) The input resistance of the composite amplifier.

8–5. For the two-stage circuit of Problem 8–4, calculate the following:

(a) The over-all voltage gain.

(b) The amplifier output resistance when the first stage is connected to a source of 4000-Ω internal resistance.

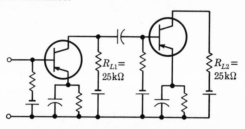

Problem 8–4.

8–6. Three non-identical stages are cascaded. From the data given below, determine the over-all bandwidth.

	f_l(cps)	f_h(cps)
Stage one	30	42,000
Stage two	44	50,000
Stage three	60	80,000

8–7. Show that an interative (repeating) arrangement of common-base stages with direct or capacitive coupling provides no usable power amplification.

8–8. Confirm Eqs. (8–20) through (8–23).

8–9. A particular coupling transformer is designated as 4000CT : 1000CT; the numbers represent the nominal impedance ratio, and CT indicates that the center tap of each winding is brought out. For this transformer, calculate the following.

(a) The resistance reflected into the entire primary if the entire secondary is connected to 400 Ω.

(b) The reflected resistance if each half of the secondary is joined to 400 Ω.

(c) The resistance reflected to one half of the primary if the entire secondary is connected to 900 Ω.

8–10. For the servo-amplifier design example, calculate the following, using 2N539A information available in Appendix I:

(a) The power being disspated at the collector junction of each Class-B transistor at maximum overload.

(b) The minimum size of a vertical, square, $\frac{3}{32}$-in. aluminum heat sink necessary to keep junction temperature below 60° C in a 40° C ambient. Allow 1.0° C/W for the washer.

8–11. "Decoupling" is usually necessary in high-gain multistage circuits.

(a) What is decoupling?

(b) How can decoupling be incorporated into the second design example? Sketch.

8–12. Consider two cascaded common-emitter stages, with emitter resistance R_{e2} in the second stage and collector-load resistance R_{c1} at the output of the first. Is there a value of R_{e2} that will maximize the over-all voltage gain?

8–13. The compound connection of two transistors as shown in the accompanying figure is sometimes useful for signal amplification. Consider each transistor to be characterized by only two parameters, h_{ie} and h_{fe}. Derive expressions for the h_i and the h_f parameters of the pair. The transistors are not to be considered identical.

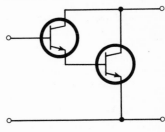

8–14. It is required to analyze the unipolar-bipolar cascade shown. The FET is characterized by $I_{DSS} = 5$ mA, $V_P = 5$ V, and is operating at $V_{GS} = 1$ V. The device behaves according to the square-law relation, $I_D = I_{DSS}(1 - |V_{GS}/V_P|)^2$. The conventional transistor is operating at $I_C = 1.5$ mA, with $h_{fe} = 50$, $r_{bb'} \cong 0$. Consider gate current to be negligible. Find:

Problem 8–13.

(a) The gate-to-ground direct voltage, I_D, g_m, and V_{DS}.
(b) The dynamic load on the FET at its drain terminal.
(c) The signal voltage at point X with $V_g = 1$ mV.
(d) The over-all voltage gain, $|V_o/V_g|$.

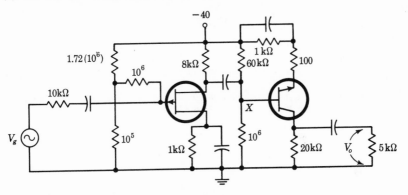

Problem 8–14.

8–15. Use the minimum number of cascaded FET stages necessary in order to synthesize the following voltage-transfer functions: K represents the gain constant.

(a) $\dfrac{K(s+1)(s+2)(s+3)}{s}$

(c) $\dfrac{Ks(s+10^5)(s+10^4)^2}{(s+10^6)}$

(b) $\dfrac{K(s^2+4)(s+1)}{s^4(s+2)}$

(d) $\dfrac{K(s+5)}{s^2+s+1}$

Design Problems. In the problems that follow, perform the operations necessary in order to obtain a circuit that will meet the listed requirements. For each solution, select transistor types from Appendix I, and choose a biasing arrangement. Correct the design-center parameters for operating point and temperature, and in each solution itemize any assumptions made and clearly indicate the steps leading to your choice of each component.

8–16. Requirements.
1. Carrier frequency: 800 cps
2. Load resistance: 100 Ω
3. Input resistance: 2000 $\pm$ 200 Ω
4. Load power: up to 5 W
5. Power gain: 45 dB (minimum)
6. Temperature: 0° to 50° C
7. Supplies available: designer's choice

8–17. Requirements:
1. Frequency response: 10,000 to 30,000 cps
2. Load resistance: 1000 Ω
3. Input resistance: 10,000 $\pm$ 1000 Ω
4. Voltage gain: 100 minimum (ratio of load voltage to amplifer input voltage)
5. Source characteristics: resistance of 10,000 Ω in series with a generator of 0 to 10 mV
6. Temperature: 25° C
7. Power supply available: $+10$ V

REFERENCES

1. Coblenz, A., and Owens, H. L., *Transistors: Theory and Applications* (McGraw-Hill Book Co., Inc., New York, 1955).
2. Shea, R. F., *Transistor Circuit Engineering* (John Wiley & Sons, Inc., New York, 1957).
3. Van Valkenburg, M. E., *Introduction To Modern Network Synthesis* (John Wiley and Sons, Inc., New York, 1961).

Chapter 9

GAIN STABILITY

The problem of linearly amplifying time-varying electrical signals electronically with a satisfactory degree of predictability has demanded the attention of engineers since deForest's invention of the audion tube in 1906. In his words, "... anyone who has had considerable experience with numerous audion bulbs must admit that the behavior of different bulbs varies in many particulars, and to an astonishing degree".[2]

Improved production techniques eventually overcame the wide variations observed by deForest, but the problem of aging remained. With the advent of the "ageless" transistor in 1948, the basic problem of parameter variations became even more acute. A transistor amplifier must provide stable amplification in the light of unit-to-unit variations in significant characteristics that may be as great as $4:1$. In addition to the variations in static characteristics and in parameters caused by wide manufacturing tolerances, the effects of ambient-temperature excursions upon the active device must be overcome.

The commercial availability of field-effect transistors, with their attendant characteristics spreads, has made it further evident that unit-to-unit variations and temperature effects represent significant problems to be overcome in the successful employment of modern devices.

The usual method employed to overcome parameter variations is the use of degenerative feedback. This chapter will investigate the effect of local feedback upon the operation of simple single-stage circuits. The discussion will be limited to stabilization of the voltage gain of such circuits. Stability of current gain and impedance levels are appropriate topics for study, but are beyond the scope of this treatment.

9–1. Transistor Dynamic Stability. The voltage gain V_o/V_g of the single stage depicted in Fig. 9–1 was given in Chapter 5 as

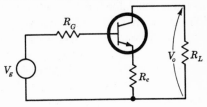

Fig. 9–1. Simple transistor amplifying stage with feedback element R_e.

$$A_v \cong g_m h_{fe} R_L / [h_{fe} + g_m R_x + g_m R_e (1 + h_{fe})], \qquad (9\text{–}1)$$

229

with $R_x = r_{bb'} + R_G$. The most significant parameter is h_{fe} in Eq. (9–1). The effect of this parameter upon A_v is evident in the numerator or current-gain portion and in the denominator or input-resistance part of that equation. Because h_{fe} may exhibit a spread of $3:1$ or greater with a given transistor type, the problem of overcoming its variation is a real one. To assist in swamping h_{fe} variations, feedback element R_e is used.

We shall assume that the significant parameter h_{fe} can take on values from a low represented by h_{fe} to a high represented by $h_{fe} + \Delta h_{fe}$. For convenience, the following definitions will apply:

$$A_v \equiv A_v(h_{fe}) = A_{v1}, \qquad A_{v2} \equiv A_v(h_{fe} + \Delta h_{fe}),$$

$$\Delta A_v \equiv A_{v2} - A_{v1}.$$

This investigation will be limited to a study of the effects of changes in h_{fe} upon the voltage amplification of a transistor stage. Although variations may be expected in the transconductance parameter g_m that can have an equally important effect upon operation of a stage, they can be controlled by biasing-circuit design that prevents the operating point from significantly changing when transistor substitution or temperature alter the value of h_{FE} of the active element, as discussed in Chapter 3.

The effect of R_e and of R_x upon voltage amplification is pictorially represented in Fig. 9–2(a). A_{v2}, *the gain at the maximum expected value of* h_{fe}, is used as the ordinate because the expressions then assume a form similar to those useful in the discussion of S_T (to follow). The multiplier $(1/g_m R_L)$ is used to normalize A_{v2}, and $A g_m/(h_{fe} + \Delta h_{fe})$ to normalize R_x. In order to use the curve when feedback is present, we note that R_e and R_x affect gain similarly. Therefore, from the denominator of the A_{v2} expression, we define the constant A as follows:

$$AR_x = R_x + R_e(h_{fe} + \Delta h_{fe}). \qquad (9–2a)$$

It is assumed that h_{fe} is much larger than unity. Solving Eq. (9–2a) for R_e yields:

$$R_e = (A - 1)R_x/(h_{fe} + \Delta h_{fe}). \qquad (9–2b)$$

The minimum value for A is unity, and occurs when feedback is absent ($R_e = 0$).

The graph may be used to determine the upper limit of amplification possible with a given amount of feedback. Consider the following example: $g_m = 0.1$, $h_{fe} + \Delta h_{fe} = 100$, $R_x = 1000$, $R_L = 1000$. Without feedback, $A = 1$, the absissa $= 1$, and the ordinate is 0.5. Therefore $A_{v2} = 50$. Adding $R_e = 10$ yields $A = 2$, and the ordinate is 0.33, corresponding to $A_{v2} = 33$.

Now we consider the effects of variations in h_{fe} upon the gain of a stage. Using Eq. (9–1), one may derive the following expression:

$$\frac{\Delta A_v}{A_v} \equiv \frac{A_{v2} - A_{v1}}{A_{v1}} = \frac{\Delta h_{fe}}{h_{fe}} \left[\frac{g_m(R_e + R_x)}{g_m(R_e + R_x) + (h_{fe} + \Delta h_{fe})(g_m R_e + 1)} \right]. \qquad (9–3)$$

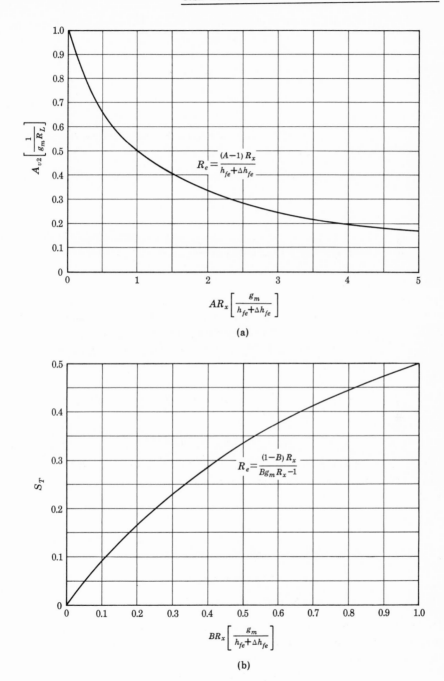

Fig. 9–2. (a) Normalized voltage gain vs. normalized R_x; (b) S_T vs. normalized R_x.

Δh_{fe} is the maximum change in h_{fe} to be expected, and is considered as a positive quantity in all discussions that follow.

The sensitivity function discussed by Truxal will be used.[7] The sensitivity of a transmission function T to changes in a parameter x is

$$S \equiv \frac{d(\ln T)}{d(\ln x)}.\tag{9-4}$$

This S is the reciprocal of the function originated by Bode.[1] A practical form of Eq. (9–4), useful for transistor-circuit studies, is

$$S_T = \frac{\Delta A_v/A_v}{\Delta h_{fe}/h_{fe}}.\tag{9-5}$$

Equation (9–5) becomes, after manipulations,

$$S_T = \left\{1 + (h_{fe} + \Delta h_{fe})\left[\frac{g_m R_e + 1}{g_m(R_x + R_e)}\right]\right\}^{-1}\tag{9-6}$$

It can be noted that the dynamic sensitivity function S_T is independent of the load resistance, generally decreases with increase in R_e, and increases with R_x.

A low value of S indicates that the amplification of the stage is highly stable; it is less sensitive to changes in the significant parameter than one having a high value of S. The maximum value of S_T is given by Eq. (9–6) with $R_e = 0$, and is

$$S_{T\max} = [1 + (h_{fe} + \Delta h_{fe})(1/g_m R_x)]^{-1}.\tag{9-7}$$

A minimum value of S_T may be predicted when the assumptions that $g_m R_e \gg 1$ and $R_e \gg R_X$ are valid; then

$$S_{T\min} = [1 + (h_{fe} + \Delta h_{fe})]^{-1}.\tag{9-8}$$

A physical feeling for the nature of the sensitivity function is helpful. When the fractional change in the significant parameter ($\Delta h_{fe}/h_{fe}$) is unity, S_T is simply equal to $\Delta A_v/A_v$, the fractional change in gain caused by the parameter variation.

Further study of Eq. (9–6) is of interest.

$\partial S_T/\partial R_e$ is negative when $R_x < 1/g_m$;

$\partial S_T/\partial R_e$ is zero when $R_x = 1/g_m$;

$\partial S_T/\partial R_e$ is positive when $R_x < 1/g_m$.

The circuit conditions for zero and positive derivatives are not of great practical importance, for simulating them requires that the stage be biased at a very low level of collector current to achieve a low value of g_m or that R_X be quite small. A low value of R_x in essence requires that $r_{bb'}$ be low valued, but the value of that parameter is not under the direct control of the circuit designer.

Other investigators have used the current-generator equivalent tee model for their analytical studies of gain sensitivity. In terms of symbols used here, the sensitivity relation given by Mulligan and Shamis[5] is

$$S_T = \{1 + (\beta + \Delta\beta)[(R_e + r_c)/(R_e + r_b + r_e + R_G)]\}^{-1}. \qquad (9\text{--}9)$$

Under the assumptions made in discussion of the modified hybrid π, it can be shown that tee parameters r_b and r_e are equivalent to $r_{bb'}$ and $r_{e'}$ through parameter interrelations given earlier. Consequently, Eq. (9–9) differs from Eq. (9–6) by only a small factor in the denominator of the bracketed term.

A form of the "ideal transistor" would be a device characterized by the modified hybrid-π model with *zero* base-spreading resistance. When such a device is fed from an ideal voltage source, it provides a voltage gain of $g_m R_L$, and thus A_v would be independent of h_{fe}. With such a device we could jump to the conclusion that no gain stability problem exists, for, regardless of the transistor used, voltage gain is simply a function of the operating point chosen, the ambient temperature, and the load resistance. When one considers source resistance, however, *complete cancellation of h_{fe} from numerator and denominator of the A_v expression does not occur*, so the real problem is evident even with the ideal device, and is accentuated by the magnitude of source resistance.

The effect of source resistance upon the sensitivity factor is shown in Fig. 9–2(b). R_x has been normalized by the multiplier $[Bg_m/(h_{fe} + \Delta h_{fe})]$. For a stage with no local feedback, the constant $B = 1$. The figure also is of value for circuits with feedback element R_e. By equating terms of the denominator of the S_T expression with and without R_e, one obtains

$$(g_m R_e + 1)/(R_e + R_x) = 1/BR_x.$$

Solving for R_e results in

$$R_e = (1 - B)R_x/(Bg_m R_x - 1). \qquad (9\text{--}10)$$

In practice, the constant B can have values from $1/g_m R_x$ to unity.

A numerical example will illustrate the use of Fig. 9–2(b). Let it be required that $S_T < 0.2$. Then, from the figure, $BR_x g_m/(h_{fe} + \Delta h_{fe}) < 0.25$. With known values of $g_m = 0.04$, $(h_{fe} + \Delta h_{fe}) = 200$, and $R_x = 2000$, we obtain $B < 0.625$. Since $B \neq 1$, feedback is necessary. From Eq. (9–10), $R_e = 15.3\ \Omega$.

The gain-to-sensitivity ratio is a figure of merit that is of value in the discussion to follow:

$$A_{v2}/S_T = (h_{fe} + \Delta h_{fe})R_L/(R_e + R_x). \qquad (9\text{--}11)$$

A_{v2} is used here to simplify the expression. A large value of this quotient is obviously desirable. One can note, however, that local feedback can only decrease the quotient.

Amplifier design. The concepts previously discussed can be mathematically packaged and an amplifier design method formulated to provide all element values in order to realize a single-stage circuit that meets prescribed specifications on static and dynamic stability as well as on voltage gain. In addition, it is possible to find the maximum voltage gain that can be provided by a given transistor stage feeding a known load from a known source when predetermined static and gain-stability requirements are to be met. This design procedure is contained in the paper "A Method for Designing Gain-Stabilized Transistor Stages."[3]

The procedure noted allows freedom in operating-point selection in order to assist in meeting input impedance, noise, and/or bandwidth requirements. The required calculations are best performed on a digital computer; a FORTRAN program is included for that purpose. The paper is recommended to those interested in an advanced design method.

9–2. FET Dynamic Stability. A single FET stage is shown in Fig. 9–3. According to Eq. (5–46), an approximate expression for the voltage gain of this circuit, V_o/V_g, is

$$A_v = g_m R_L/(1 + g_m R_e). \tag{9–12}$$

The significant parameter g_m has great effect upon voltage gain, as evidenced by study of Eq. (9–12). We may define a dynamic sensitivity function S_F for the FET as follows:

$$S_F \equiv \frac{\Delta A_v/A_v}{\Delta g_m/g_m}. \tag{9–13}$$

When Eq. (9–12) is used to determine ΔA_v, the S_F function becomes

$$S_F = [1 + (g_m + \Delta g_m)R_e]^{-1}. \tag{9–14}$$

In the absence of local feedback, $S_F = 1$. This represents an exceptionally high sensitivity to changes in the significant parameter, and implies that, unless other means are used to reduce ΔA_v, a great deal of feedback is necessary to gain stabilize the FET stage.

The gain-to-sensitivity ratio is of interest:

$$A_{v2}/S_F = (g_m + \Delta g_m)R_L. \tag{9–15}$$

This figure of merit is independent of R_e.

A comparative analysis of conventional transistor and FET stages with regard to dynamic stability is in order. A typical transistor stage fed from a 1500-Ω source with $g_m = 0.04$, $r_{bb'} = 500 \ \Omega$, and $h_{fe} + \Delta h_{fe} = 200$ would have a dynamic sensitivity factor S_T of 0.285, assuming no feedback were employed. This value is contrasted to unity as obtained for a comparable FET stage. S_T is minimized by the fact that h_{fe} is present in both numerator and denominator of the voltage-gain expression and some cancellation occurs.

A typical FET stage may be characterized by $g_m + \Delta g_m = 0.004$. For a 5000-Ω load, the gain-to-sensitivity ratio is 500 for the conventional transistor while only 20 for the FET stage. The exceptionally high dynamic sensitivity of the

FET stage without feedback and the low transconductance of that device suggests that a method to achieve gain stability by using means other than degenerative feedback be sought. The result of study of this problem is the "floating-Q" method of stage biasing.

9–3. Floating-Q Biasing.[4] In the floating-Q method the operating point adjusts to the static characteristics of the particular active device introduced into the network. If such adjustments are judiciously allowed, the Δg_m quantity may be significantly reduced and, although S_F is not improved (it will always be unity for $R_e = 0$), ΔA_v is correspondingly reduced. In principle floating-Q requires

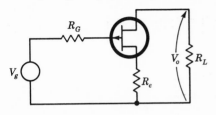

Fig. 9–3. Simple FET amplifying stage with feedback element R_e.

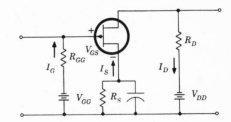

Fig. 9–4. Single FET amplifying stage.

that the biasing network accept the extremes of the production variations in units of a given type, and provide an operating point for each unit that results in an identical g_m. Consider the complete FET stage of Fig. 9–4; no dynamic feedback is being used. With the assumptions that $I_D = I_S$, and that $I_G R_{GG}$ is small compared with other terms, one obtains, for the gate–source loop,

$$I_D R_S = V_{GG} + V_{GS}. \tag{9–16}$$

The incremental form of Eq. (9–16) that must hold when V_{GG} is invariant is

$$R_S = \Delta V_{GS}/\Delta I_D. \tag{9–17}$$

It is necessary to choose the allowed excursions in the operating-point coordinates, ΔV_{GS} and ΔI_D, so that g_m is constant when unit-to-unit differences in the static characteristics are encountered. An analytic procedure for the determination of these quantities will be considered.

The relation given by Sevin and noted earlier as Eq. (4–71) will be used here to describe the junction FET transfer characteristic[6]:

$$I_D = I_{DSS}(1 - |V_{GS}/V_P|)^2. \tag{9–18}$$

The value of g_m may be obtained from Eq. (9–18):

$$g_m = \partial I_D/\partial(-V_{GS}) = (2I_{DSS}/V_P)(1 - |V_{GS}/V_P|). \tag{9–19}$$

The equations that follow are useful for those FET types characterized by the square-law relation, Eq. (9–18). The method may be extended to units described by other power-law relations.

The transfer characteristics of two FET units exhibiting the maximum and minimum I_{DSS} values to be encountered in an application of the device are shown in Fig. 9–5. At $V_{GS} = 0$, g_{m1} and g_{m2} represent the transconductances of the units and I_{DSS1} and I_{DSS2} the respective drain currents. In the majority of applications, operation of the stage will not take place at $V_{GS} = 0$, so subscript A is used to designate the desired operating point of unit 1, and subscript B the operating point of unit 2. The transconductances g_{mA} and g_{mB} may be expressed in terms of measurable parameters through application of Eq. (9–19). *Equality of the transconductance expressions yields*

$$V_{GSB} = \frac{2I_{DSS2}}{g_{m2}} - \frac{I_{DSS2}}{I_{DSS1}} \left[\frac{g_{m1}}{g_{m2}}\right]^2 \left[\frac{2I_{DSS1}}{g_{m1}} - V_{GSA}\right] \qquad (9\text{--}20)$$

and

$$I_{DB} = I_{DA} \frac{I_{DSS2}}{I_{DSS1}} \left[\frac{g_{m1}}{g_{m2}}\right]^2. \qquad (9\text{--}21)$$

The selection of an operating point for the extremal unit designated as No. 1 in Fig. 9–5 is made in conjunction with requirements on the signal size to be handled and the amplification to be attained. Since stage gain is directly determined by this selection, it is necessary, for maximum gain, to bias this unit near I_{DSS}; thus V_{GSA} and I_{DA} are determined. From the known constants of the devices, V_{GSB} and I_{DB} can be obtained by substitution of values into Eqs. (9–20) and (9–21). In terms of the quantities obtainable from Eqs. (9–20) and (9–21), Eq. (9–17) becomes

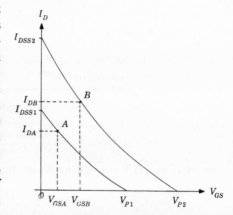

Fig. 9–5. Transfer characteristics for extremal units.

$$R_S = (V_{GSB} - V_{GSA})/(I_{DB} - I_{DA}). \qquad (9\text{--}22)$$

The gate–return resistance R_{GG} may be selected in accordance with the constraints imposed by input-impedance level and the assumption made in writing Eq. (9–16), and V_{GG} may be determined from that equation by using values at either extremal operating point.

Although the preceding discussion has centered upon an analytic procedure for determination of the biasing elements, a graphical analysis is equally valid. Figure 9–6 shows the measured variations of g_m with respect to V_{GS} and I_D for three FET units. If it is assumed that units 1 and 2 represent extremals, the values of ΔV_{GS} and ΔI_D to determine R_S are easily found at the desired g_m level.

The floating-Q method may be modified to take into account the increased output conductance expected from units with large I_{DSS}. In practical circuits, this conductance acts to reduce output voltage by paralleling the load; it can be thought of as reducing g_m. Therefore, in order to compensate for reduction in gain expected from such units, g_{mB} can be increased from its nominal value of

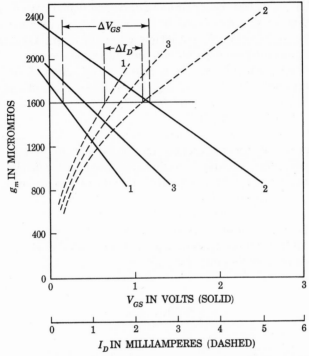

Fig. 9–6.   Variation of g_m with I_D and V_{GS}.

g_{mA}, in direct proportion to the reduction in load resistance caused by the conductance parameter. The modified form of Eqs. (9–20) and (9–21), valid for an increase in g_m of 10% from unit 1 to unit 2, would contain a 1.1 multiplier in the second term of Eq. (9–20) and on g_{m1} in Eq. (9–21).

Experimental Results.   Three FET units having vastly different static characteristics were used to obtain the plot of Fig. 9–6. Measured data follow:

Unit No.	I_{DSS}
1	1.5 mA
2	5.1 mA
3	2.4 mA

In order to evaluate the floating-Q method, two tests were made with differing load resistances (R_D). A g_m level of 1600 μ mhos was initially selected, and R_{GG}

arbitrarily chosen to be 10 MΩ. From the graphs showing the dependence of g_m upon operating point, one obtains $R_S = \Delta V_{GS}/\Delta I_D = 1.0/(0.95 \times 10^{-3}) = 1050 \, \Omega$. Equation (9–16) requires that V_{GG} be 1.1 V.

Test data indicate that with a low value of R_D (2700 Ω), the gain compensation is extremely effective.[4] The fractional variation in gain, $\Delta A_v/A_v$, which would have been 23.6% if I_D were constant at 1.5 mA, and would have been 56.2% if V_{GS} were held at 0.5 V, was reduced to less than $\pm 2\%$. With a higher value of R_D (10,000 Ω), we find that the paralleling effects of output conductance and reduction in g_m on unit 2 require additional consideration, for $\Delta A_v/A_v = -2.5\%$.

To overcome the reduced value of g_m caused by operation of unit 2 at a significantly lower level of V_{DS}, the biasing elements were recalculated to provide a 2.5% increase in g_m for that unit. With $R_S = 880 \, \Omega$ and $V_{GG} = 0.9$ V, the resulting $\Delta A_v/A_v$ was less than 0.7%.

It is evident from the preceding discussion that gain variations caused by production differences in the static characteristics of certain FET types can be successfully overcome without resorting to dynamic feedback. However, floating-Q biasing is not a panacea for the FET; it does not automatically compensate for gain changes caused by temperature excursions. Temperature-derived gain variations can be minimized if the temperature coefficient of R_S is selected to have the appropriate positive value. When working with dual-gate units it is possible to utilize the extra degree of freedom provided by the additional electrode for compensation purposes.

PROBLEMS

9–1. Confirm Eq. (9–2b).

9–2. Confirm Eq. (9–3).

9–3. Confirm Eq. (9–6).

9–4. Confirm Eq. (9–9).

9–5. Confirm Eq. (9–10).

9–6. A transistor with $r_{bb'} = 0$, $g_m = 0.03$, $h_{fe1} = 100$, $h_{fe2} = 150$, is to be used in a circuit fed from a signal source with 2500 Ω internal resistance. The load is 2000 Ω.

(a) Find the maximum voltage amplification provided by this stage.

(b) Determine S_T for this stage if unstabilized.

(c) What value of R_e must be used to reduce S_T to 0.1?

(d) For the stabilized stage of (c), find the maximum and minimum values of voltage gain to be expected from units having current transfer ratios of h_{fe1} and h_{fe2}.

9–7. If $\Delta A_v/A_v$ is to be limited to 0.1, and the transistor parameters, source, and load characteristics are as given in Problem 9–6, find the necessary value of R_e.

9–8. Confirm Eqs. (9–20) and (9–21).

9–9. Curves 1 and 2 in Fig. 9–6 represent the behavior of a particular FET type. A stage using that type is to be designed having a constant g_m level of 1200×10^{-6} mho.

(a) Graphically determine I_{DA}, V_{GSA}, I_{DB}, V_{GSB}.

(b) From (a) find R_S.

(c) Use Eqs. (9–20), (9–21) and (9–22) to obtain R_S.

(d) Find V_{GG} for this stage. Consider that $I_G = 0$.

9–10. Use Eq. (5–45), which describes the bandwidth (B) of a simple transistor stage, to derive a relation for the fractional sensitivity $(\Delta B/B)$ caused by variations in h_{fe}.

REFERENCES

1. Bode, H., *Network Analysis and Feedback Amplifier Design* (D. Van Nostrand Co., Inc., Princeton, New Jersey, 1945).
2. DeForest, L., discussion to paper by E. H. Armstrong, "Some Recent Developments in the Audion Receiver," *Proc. IRE*, **3** (September, 1915).
3. Fitchen, F. C., *A Method for Designing Gain-Stabilized Transistor Stages* (Engineering Experiment Station Report, South Dakota State University, Brookings, South Dakota, 1966).
4. Fitchen, F. C., "Gain Stability for Field-Effect Transistor Stages," *Solid-Stage Design*, **5**, No. 11 (November 1964).
5. Mulligan, J. H., Jr., and Shamis, S. S., "Transistor Amplifier Stages with Prescribed Gain and Static and Dynamic Sensitivity," *Communication and Electronics*, No. 55 (July, 1961).
6. Sevin, L. J., "A Simple Expression for the Transfer Characteristic of FET's," *Electronic Equipment Engineering*, **11**, No. 8 (August, 1963).
7. Truxal, J. G., *Automatic Feedback Control System Synthesis* (McGraw-Hill Book Co., Inc., New York, 1955).

Internal structure of a high-gain, high-current Darlington amplifier. Note the two separate transistor structures. At $I_C = 5$ A, h_{FE} has a minimum value of 1200. Maximum continuous collector current rating is 10 A, and maximum power dissipation is 50 W at 100°C case temperature. (Photo courtesy Texas Instruments, Incorporated.)

Chapter 10

FEEDBACK

The discussion of transistor equivalent circuits and parameters presented earlier leads to the conclusion that circuit gain is "at the mercy" of parameter variations. It is also true that input and output resistance, frequency response, and phase shift are highly dependent upon transistor parameters. Parameter variations are due to many causes: manufacturing tolerances cause units of the same type to differ; aging of semiconducting materials results in parameter changes; operating-point shift, frequency, and climatic conditions also affect the resistances and capacitances of the transistor.

To overcome the expected variations, feedback, the addition of a portion of the output signal to the input signal, is employed. Reduction of the magnitude ⌐of the input signal by addition of a feedback signal is called *inverse, degenerative,* or *negative* feedback, while an increase in total input due to this summation is termed *direct, regenerative,* or *positive* feedback. The use of negative feedback is widespread and will be the only type considered here, although positive feedback certainly is employed in oscillator circuits and occasionally in radio-receiver circuits.

10–1. Feedback—General Theory. The block diagram of Fig. 10–1 can be used to illustrate feedback in an elementary way. The output voltage v_o of an amplifier with a voltage gain of A supplies a load; v_o is also available to the feedback network, and Bv_o, a fraction of v_o, is added to the input circuit. (B, as used here should not be confused with beta, the common-emitter short-curcuit current-amplification factor.) The nominal amplifier gain is

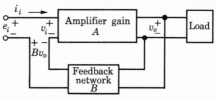

Fig. 10–1.   General feedback diagram.

$$A = v_o/v_i. \qquad (10\text{–}1)$$

If we take polarities into account A will normally be negative and may be

241

complex. B normally will be positive, and also may be complex. In the presence of a feedback signal, a summation at the input yields

$$v_i = e_i + Bv_o. \tag{10-2}$$

The voltage amplification of the composite network A_f is

$$A_f = v_o/e_i = v_o/(v_i - Bv_o) = A/(1 - BA). \tag{10-3}$$

Equation (10–3) will now be interpreted. In the absence of feedback ($B = 0$), the amplifier exhibits a gain of A. If the magnitude of the denominator is greater than unity, the over-all amplification will be less than A and the feedback is degenerative; the converse of this statement also applies, If the entire output voltage is supplied to the input ($B = 1$), the composite gain is less than unity. When $BA = 1$, the resultant gain is infinite, and the circuit has an output independent of any external input voltage.

If $|BA| \gg 1$, then the amplification approaches

$$A_f \rightarrow 1/B. \tag{10-4}$$

Equation (10–4) signifies that gain is independent of elements in the forward path, usually a highly desirable condition. Because B is often a passive network, A must be very large to satisfy the condition specified by Eq. (10–4). Since B is usually a fraction, A_f can be a large number. Aging, tolerances, and temperature would certainly have negligible effect upon an amplifier that behaves according to Eq. (10–4).

The price to be paid for the advantages of feedback (they will be considered in detail in the following sections) is reduction in over-all gain. A given amplifier having an open-loop gain of A, will have a closed-loop gain of less than A because of incorporation of any negative feedback circuitry. But the advantages of feedback are so numerous that it generally pays to design our original amplifier with sufficient gain so that added feedback will not reduce gain below the desired value. The inclusion of additional gain to offset feedback losses is a small price to pay when compared with the advantages as indicated in the paragraphs to follow.

Stabilization of Gain. The performance of a feedback amplifier of gain A_f is compared with that of an unstabilized amplifier having open-loop gain A. Of course, for A, when a change in amplification is experienced,

$$dA/dA = 1. \tag{10-5}$$

Differentiation of Eq. (10–3) yields the following expression for the fractional gain sensitivity of the feedback amplifier:

$$dA_f/A_f = [1/(1 - BA)](dA/A). \tag{10-6}$$

We may conclude that the feedback amplifier will show a much greater stability with respect to the internal factors that cause gain changes.

Consider an amplifier with a gain of -10^4. The fraction B is to be $1/100$. Then, from Eq. (10–3), feedback will reduce the gain to approximately -100. For a 10% variation in forward gain, the over-all gain of the feedback amplifier will suffer less than a 0.1% change. Variations in gain will be reduced by the same amount as forward gain.

Reduction in Distortion. In earlier discussions it was evident that nonlinear distortion increases with the swing or level of the output signal.

Consider that distortion D is being generated in the final stage of an amplifier. The output voltage including distortion (v_o') is given by

$$v_o' = v_o + D. \tag{10–7}$$

The new equation at the summation point is

$$v_i = e_i + Bv_o + BD. \tag{10–8}$$

So

$$v_o = Ae_i + ABv_o + ABD, \tag{10–9}$$

and

$$v_o = \frac{Ae_i}{1 - BA} + \frac{ABD}{1 - BA}. \tag{10–10}$$

Therefore

$$v_o' = v_o + D = \frac{Ae_i}{1 - BA} + \frac{D}{1 - BA}. \tag{10–11}$$

The distortion factor for a closed loop system is

$$D_f = D/(1 - BA). \tag{10–12}$$

Since $|1 - BA|$ is usually much greater than one, nonlinear distortion will be reduced by a factor equivalent to the amount of gain reduction.

It may seem reasonable that if one is reducing amplifier gain by the addition of feedback, signal swings will be proportionally reduced and therefore nonlinearities will be less evident in the output of the feedback circuit. This reasoning is true, but reduction in signal amplitude was not of concern in the above analysis, distortion having been handled by using a lumped term D rather than $f(v_o)$. The reduction in the harmonic content of the output voltage can be visualized if we consider that we are sampling the distortion and adding the amplified, out-of-phase sample to the original distorted waveform in order to cancel a portion of it. It is important to realize that output-signal swing can be the same with or without feedback.

Reduction in Noise Content of Output. Noise or extraneous signals may be reduced by the addition of feedback, but, under certain practical conditions, the over-all noise level may be increased because of the requirement for higher forward gain and thus more stages of amplification.

Consider the diagram of Fig. 10–1 with another input signal e_n, which can be assumed to be a noise voltage introduced in the first stage. Equation (10–2) becomes

$$v_i' = e_i + Bv_o + e_n. \tag{10–13}$$

Since this equation tells us that the noise signal will be treated in the same manner as e_i, e_n will be reduced by the same amount as e_i, namely,

$$e_n' = e_n/(1 - BA). \tag{10–14}$$

Feedback has no effect on the signal-to-noise ratio.

Change in Input Impedance. Input impedance of a multistage amplifier without feedback was given in Chapter 5 as a function of R_L and the transistor parameters. From Fig. 10–1, in the absence of feedback, the corresponding relationship is

$$Z_i = e_i/i_i = v_i/i_i. \tag{10–15}$$

With the feedback loop closed, Eq. (10–15) becomes

$$Z_{if} = (v_i - Bv_o)/i_i. \tag{10–16}$$

Since

$$v_o = Av_i,$$

then Eq. (10–16) becomes

$$Z_{if} = [v_i(1 - BA)]/i_i. \tag{10–17}$$

Therefore

$$Z_{if} = Z_i(1 - BA). \tag{10–18}$$

The presence of the $(1 - BA)$ term indicates an increase in input impedance due to closing of the loop, for that term is always greater than unity in systems employing negative feedback.

Change in Output Impedance. The method used previously for determining output impedance is to connect a hypothetical generator of voltage e_o across the output terminals of a circuit or device and measure or calculate the current i_o with the input signal source short-circuited. Then, for the amplifier without feedback,

$$Z_o = e_o/i_o. \tag{10–19}$$

With the feedback loop closed, as in Fig. 10–2,

$$v_i = Be_o. \tag{10–20}$$

The output loop current is

$$i_o = (e_o - BAe_o)/Z_o. \tag{10–21}$$

Therefore, the effective output impedance is

$$Z_{of} = e_o/i_o = Z_o/(1 - BA). \tag{10–22}$$

The conclusion that can be drawn is that output impedence is reduced by the addition of inverse feedback. This reduction is not caused, in this case, by the paralleling of Z_o by the feedback network, because in the treatment given here it was assumed that no current was drawn from e_o by the feedback network.

Increase in Bandwidth. To investigate the effects of feedback upon the bandwidth of a circuit, we must assign frequency dependence to the forward amplifier gain. A good assumption may be that

$$A = A_o/[1 + jf/f_{3dB}] \tag{10-23}$$

where f_{3dB}, as used in Chapter 6, is the upper cutoff frequency, and A_o is the mid-frequency reference gain. Substitution of Eq. (10–23) into Eq. (10–3) yields

$$A_f = A_o/[1 - BA_o + jf/f_{3dB}]. \tag{10-24}$$

Now the denominator will be of the form $K + jK$ when

$$f/f_{3dB} = 1 - BA_o. \tag{10-25}$$

Equation (10–25) indicates that the new cutoff or half-power frequency (f_f) occurs at

$$f_f = f_{3dB}(1 - BA_o). \tag{10-26}$$

In conclusion, the upper cutoff frequency has been increased, and the bandwidth extended by an appreciable amount. For analysis of low-frequency performance, see Problem 10–2.

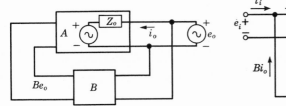

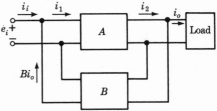

Fig. 10–2. Feedback diagram for calcu-   Fig. 10–3. General current-feedback dia-
lation of output impedance.   gram.

Current Feedback. The preceding discussion provides a basis for understanding the reasons why feedback is so frequently employed in electronic circuits. The discussion was limited to what is usually called "voltage" or "shunt" feedback; the output voltage is sampled, operated upon by the feedback network, and returned to the input circuit. It is also possible to employ "current" or "series" feedback in which the load current is sampled and a version of that current fed back and combined with signal source current at the amplifier input terminals.

In the current feedback amplifier shown in Fig. 10–3, one may consider that the block B does not load the amplifier output, and thus $i_2 = i_o$. At the input port a current summation takes place. Consequently,

$$i_i = i_1 - Bi_o.$$

Since A is the ratio of i_2 to i_1, it can be shown that

$$A_{if} = i_o/i_i = A/(1 - BA). \tag{10-27}$$

Normally A would provide phase reversal and therefore carry a negative sign. B, usually a positive quanitity, represents the ratio of current fed back to load current.

Current feedback lowers the input impedance and increases the output impedance of an amplifying network. Otherwise, its use is equivalent to the voltage-feedback case discussed in preceding sections of this Chapter (see Problem 10-4).

Instability in Feedback Circuits. The benefits derived from the use of negative feedback are great, but are achieved at the expense of gain. Additional low-level stages may usually be added to compensate for the loss of gain. Another drawback to be contended with is the possibility of self-oscillation because forward and feedback elements are frequency sensitive. At low and also at high frequencies, the output voltage may be shifted in phase and changed in magnitude relative to the mid-frequency value. The summation of output and input voltages in a feedback circuit may, because of this additional phase shift, result in regeneration and possibly oscillation.

Self-oscillation can be visualized with the help of Eq. (10-3), which is repeated here:

$$A_f = A/(1 - BA).$$

When $BA \to +1$, $A_f \to \infty$, a condition intolerable in amplifiers, and represents an output limited only by the saturation and cutoff regions of the characteristics. Should BA approach some positive value lower than unity, regenerative operation results.

For BA to be positive the combination of B and A must contribute the 360° phase shift required to cause a summation of in-phase signals at the amplifier input. Although B is often a mere resistive network, wiring capacitances may cause unwanted phase shift. 180° of shift is normally supplied by an active circuit consisting of an odd number of common-emitter stages. Each stage is frequency sensitive, and with three in cascade, each only need shift an additional 60° in order for one oscillation requirement to be satisfied—namely, for BA to be positive. If this requirement is satisfied, and in addition the magnitude of the loop gain (BA) is equal to or greater than unity, the network will oscillate.

To test the stability of a circuit we may plot $-BA$ on polar coordinates and examine the length of the phasor when 180° of additional phase shift is apparent. *According to the Nyquist criterion, oscillations will exist if the locus of $-BA$ encloses the $(-1,0)$ point.*[8]

A measure of the amount of feedback employed in an amplifier is given by the "number of dB of feedback." This term can be defined as the ratio of the gain of an amplifier without feedback to the gain of that same amplifier including feedback, the ratio being expressed in decibels.

Example. A three-stage transistor amplifier with the feedback loop open was found to have a frequency response that could be approximated by the relation

$$-BA = \frac{5}{(1 + jf10^{-4})^3}.$$

The ratio of measured values Bv_o and e_i gives this equation. It is desired to investigate the stability of this amplifier.

A polar plot of this function is the curve of Fig. 10–4. From the equation, the intersection of the plot with the negative real axis will occur when the imaginary part of $-BA$ is zero. Therefore

$$f^2 10^{-8} = 3$$

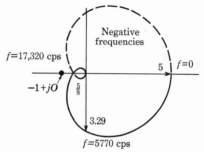

Fig. 10–4. Nyquist diagram for text example.

or $f = 17,320$ cps. The magnitude of $-BA$ at this frequency is $5/(1 - 3f^2 10^{-8}) = -\frac{5}{8}$. This is less than -1, and as seen from the curve, no encirclement of the $-1 + j0$ point is apparent at this value of gain. In fact, for this example the gain could be increased by $\frac{8}{5}$ before $-1 + j0$ is intersected (the total gain could become $(\frac{8}{5})(5)$ or 8). A condition for absolute stability for networks having this form of open-loop transfer function is

$$|BA| < 8$$

at the reference frequency.

10–2. Local Feedback. The term "local feedback" as used here, pertains to feedback that is applied to a single amplifying stage. Two examples of local feedback were given in Chapter 6: the unbypassed emitter resistor, and the resistor from collector to base. At that point in the text complete fomulas were given for the performance of these simple circuits. The use of local feedback is widespread, owing in part to the simplicity of calculating the effects of the feedback elements upon operation.

Feedback from Collector-to-Base. As shown in Fig. 10–5(a), it is only necessary to connect a resistor such as R_c in order to provide the circuit input with a signal proportional to the output of the stage. The 180° phase shift inherent in the common-emitter stage provides the necessary subtraction of signals at the base terminal.

It is advantageous to study this connection from the standpoint that current splitting is taking place at the collector terminal. The ratio of current fed back to load current is

$$B_i = [1/R_c + R_i)]/G_L \cong G_c/G_L. \tag{10-28}$$

Equation (10–28) assumes that source resistance is large and transistor input resistance is small compared to R_c.

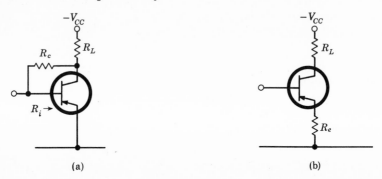

Fig. 10–5. Local feedback: (a) collector-to-base feedback element; (b) emitter-lead feedback element.

In order to predict the operation of this stage it can be assumed that voltage gain will not be affected nearly as much by the presence of R_c as will current gain, particularly when one considers a low value of R_L, possibly several thousand ohms, and a fairly high value of R_c, possibly 100,000 Ω. If we modify Eq. (10–27) it becomes

$$A_{if} = A_i/(1 - B_iA_i). \tag{10-29}$$

The approximate expression for A_i of a normal stage, is, from Table 5–2,

$$A_i \cong h_{fb}/[h_{ob}R_L + (1 + h_{fb})]. \tag{10-30}$$

Insertion of Eqs. (10–28) and (10–30) into Eq. (10–29) gives

$$A_{if} = h_{fb}/[R_L(h_{ob} - G_ch_{fb}) + (1 + h_{fb})], \tag{10-31a}$$

or, for $h_{fb} \cong -1$,

$$A_{if} \cong h_{fb}/[R_L(h_{ob} + G_c) + (1 + h_{fb})]. \tag{10-31b}$$

This result should agree with the derived equation in Chapter 5 for the case of G_c paralleling h_{ob}. It is only necessary to add G_c to h_{ob} in Eq. (10–30) to modify that equation for the feedback element. The obvious agreement between Eq. (10–31b) and modified Eq. (10–30) provides a basis for examination of more complex circuity by the methods of this chapter.

Feedback in Emitter Circuit. The circuit of Fig. 10–5(b) contains local feedback because it is obvious that load current flowing through R_e causes a potential drop which is "felt" by the input circuit. Although this scheme is often called "current feedback," the presence of R_e will not materially affect current amplification since R_L will usually be many times larger than R_e. The voltage gain of such a stage, will, however, be severely altered. Voltage gain is given by the following approximate formula from Table 5–2:

$$A_v \cong h_{fb}R_L/[h_{ib}(1 + R_Lh_{ob})].$$ (10–32)

It is to be remembered that the equivalent circuit used for derivation of this formula would place R_e in series with h_{ib}. The equation, including feedback, is

$$A_{vf} \cong h_{fb}R_L/[(h_{ib} + R_e)(1 + R_Lh_{ob})].$$ (10–33)

The method of this chapter requires the definition of a feedback fraction, in this case

$$B_v = R_e/(R_L + R_e) \cong R_e/R_L.$$ (10–34)

We recall that

$$A_{vf} = A_v/(1 - B_vA_v).$$ (10–35)

A_v is given by Eq. (10–32) and B by Eq. (10–34); substitution into Eq. (10–35) yields

$$A_{vf} \cong h_{fb}R_L/[h_{ib}(1 + R_Lh_{ob}) - R_eh_{fb}].$$ (10–36)

Equation (10–36) agrees with Eq. (10–32) since h_{fb} is negative and approximately of unit magnitude, and $R_Lh_{ob} \ll 1$.

10–3. Multistage Feedback. Consider a multistage amplifier composed of m identical stages each capable of providing a gain of A. The total amplification will be

$$A_t = A^m$$ (10–37)

and

$$dA_t = mA^{m-1}dA.$$ (10–38)

Equation (10–38) tells us that a 0.1 change in stage gain (dA) will result in a change in over-all amplifier gain of 20 times that amount (for two stages each with an A of 10).

Let us now design a multistage feedback amplifier having n identical stages each providing a gain of A. Thus

$$A_f = A^n/(1 - BA^n).$$ (10–39)

This feedback amplifier should do the same job as the one employing no feedback, so

$$A_t = A_f.$$ (10–40)

It follows that

$$A^m = A^n/(1 - BA^n).$$ (10–41)

The feedback fraction may be derived from Eq. (10–41)

$$B = (A^m - A^n)/A^{m+n}.$$ (10–42)

If Eq. (10–39) is differentiated, and the value of B from Eq. (10–42) substituted,

$$dA_f/dA = nA^{2m-n-1}. \qquad (10\text{–}43)$$

Insertion of Eq. (10–38) into Eq. (10–43) yields

$$\frac{dA_f}{dA} = \frac{nA^{2m-n-1}}{mA^{m-1}} \frac{dA_t}{dA}. \qquad (10\text{–}44a)$$

This may be simplified to

$$\frac{dA_f}{A_f} = \left(\frac{n}{m}\right) \frac{1}{A^{n-m}} \frac{dA_t}{A_t}. \qquad (10\text{–}44b)$$

Equation (10–44) can most easily be interpreted with the aid of numbers. If the amplifier without feedback has one stage ($m = 1$) with a gain of 50, the feedback amplifier with three stages ($n = 3$) requires a B of approximately A^{-1} or $1/50$ according to Eq. (10–42). The relative drift in the feedback amplifier due to changes in A compared with the drift in the nonfeedback circuit due to the same cause is $1/833$.

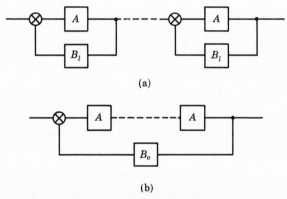

(a)

(b)

Fig. 10–6.   Comparison of local and over-all feedback.

Superiority of Over-all Feedback.   The preceding discussion compared the relative stability of feedback and nonfeedback networks. We now seek to compare local feedback with over-all feedback. In Fig. 10–6(a), n identical cascaded stages stabilized by local feedback are shown. The forward gain of each stage is A and the feedback factor is B_l. Assuming no loading effects, the over-all amplification is

$$A_{lf} = [A/(1 - B_l A)]^n. \qquad (10\text{–}45)$$

An amplifier with over-all feedback also having n stages is shown in Fig. 10–6(b). The gain of this network is

$$A_{of} = A^n/(1 - B_o A^n). \qquad (10\text{–}46)$$

The fractional gain change of the local feedback amplifier caused by changes in A is obtained by differentiating Eq. (10–45):

$$\frac{dA_{lf}}{A_{lf}} = \frac{n}{1 - B_l A}\left(\frac{dA}{A}\right). \tag{10–47}$$

The corresponding expression applicable to the over-all feedback case is

$$\frac{dA_{of}}{A_{of}} = \frac{n}{1 - B_o A^n}\left(\frac{dA}{A}\right). \tag{10–48}$$

We wish to express the ratio of Eq. (10–48) to Eq. (10–47) in consistent symbols. Because $A_{lf} = A_{of}$, it follows that

$$(1 - B_l A)^n = 1 - B_o A^n.$$

Therefore

$$\frac{dA_{of}/A_{of}}{dA_{lf}/A_{lf}} = \frac{1}{(1 - B_l A)^{n-1}}. \tag{10–49}$$

For values of n greater than unity, Eq. (10–49) suggests that the *fractional gain variations of the network employing over-all feedback will always be less than the corresponding quantity for a network using local feedback*. $[(1 - B_l A) > 1$ for negative feedback]. This conclusion is independent of the fractional gain variation dA/A of each forward element.

10–4. Feedback Networks. It is possible to write loop and node equations for multistage feedback amplifiers, and solve the simultaneous equations in order to analyze a given network for its terminal characteristics and amplificational properties. This turns out to be a particularly lengthy procedure, unsuitable for most purposes. Instead, it is infinitely more convenient to attack the problem with a block approach.

Each stage of a feedback amplifier has associated voltage and current gain properties. Cascades of stages may also be treated by considering only the overall properties. Thus the symbol shown in Fig. 10–7 may be useful to represent either a single stage or several cascaded stages. The letter A stands for the capability of amplification of either voltage or current. In a particular arrangement we may wish

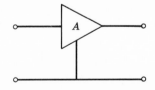

Fig. 10–7. Symbol used for amplifying stage.

to make use of only the voltage-gain properties, or consider only the current-amplification properties of the network.

Four feedback amplifier networks will be discussed. In each instance the active device will provide 180° of phase shift per stage; thus we are in a sense considering only common-emitter and common-source stages. However, it is not difficult to extend the analysis to cascades utilizing other configurations. Transformers may also be useful for phase inversion and for insertion of feedback signals, but will not be considered in the text examples.

Shunt Feedback. A widely accepted feedback scheme is shown in Fig. 10–8, with multistage feedback from the collector of the third stage to the base of the

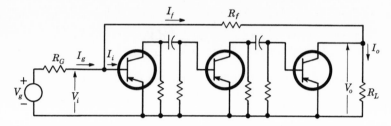

Fig. 10–8.   Three-stage amplifier with over-all shunt feedback.

first. In the following analysis A_v and A_i represent the gains of the forward path, from first base to load. Equations may be written to relate the important quantities:

$$V_o = A_v(V_g - I_g R_G),$$

$$V_g - V_o = (I_g - I_i)R_f + I_g R_G, \qquad (10\text{--}50)$$

$$(V_g - I_g R_G) = I_i R_I.$$

The input resistance of the first stage is R_I. Solution of Eqs. (10–50) yields

$$A_{vf} = \frac{V_o}{V_g} = \left(\frac{R_f}{R_G}\right)\left\{-1 \middle/ \left[1 - \frac{1}{A_v}\left(1 + \frac{R_f}{R_I} + \frac{R_f}{R_G}\right)\right]\right\}. \qquad (10\text{--}51)$$

It is obvious from Eq. (10–51) that $A_{vf} \to -R_f/R_G$ as $A_v \to \infty$. *Because of the directions assumed for currents and the polarities assumed for the voltages in Fig. 10–8, it is necessary to assign a negative sign to A_v when using Eq. (10–51).* With $R_G = 0$ the circuit is fed from a pure voltage source. Equation (10–51) reduces to

$$A_{vf} = A_v = A_{v1}A_{v2}A_{v3}. \qquad (10\text{--}52)$$

We conclude, then, that this shunt feedback connection may often have only a slight effect upon the voltage amplification of the network.

The current amplification is more seriously affected. We may again use Eqs. (10–50). Upon elimination of I_i and V_g, solution yields

$$A_{if} = \frac{I_o}{I_g} = \left(\frac{R_f}{R_L}\right)\left\{-1 \middle/ \left[1 - \frac{1}{A_v}\left(\frac{R_I + R_f}{R_I}\right)\right]\right\}. \qquad (10\text{--}53)$$

This equation may be transformed to include the internal current gain A_i instead of A_v by making the substitution $A_v = A_i R_L/R_I$. For the usual case, $R_f \gg R_I$,

Eq. (10–53) reduces to

$$A_{if} \cong \frac{A_i}{1 - A_i(R_L/R_f)}. \qquad (10\text{–}54)$$

For an odd number of common-emitter stages, A_i will have a negative value. The corresponding feedback factor $B_i = R_L/R_f$.

Voltage gain has not been materially affected by feedback of this type, but since current gain is reduced, input resistance must be reduced by a like amount, hence

$$R_{if} \cong \frac{R_I}{1 - A_i(R_L/R_f)}. \qquad (10\text{–}55)$$

As used here, R_{if} is the ratio of V_i to I_g.

Series Feedback. A series type of feedback may be applied to the three-stage amplifier. Such a connection is depicted in Fig. 10–9. The element R_e is common to all stages, and will be of a small value because the large signal current of

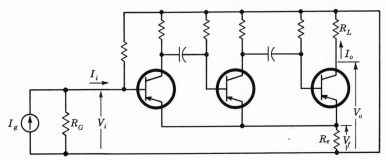

Fig. 10–9. Three-stage amplifier with over-all series feedback.

the final stage passes through it. As can be noted from current-gain expressions previously derived for single stages, emitter resistance in general has little effect upon current amplification. Therefore,

$$A_{if} \cong A_i = A_{i1}A_{i2}A_{i3}. \qquad (10\text{–}56)$$

A more precise expression is obtained by solving the appropriate equations:

$$I_i = I_g - (V_i/R_G),$$

$$I_o = A_iI_i, \qquad (10\text{–}57)$$

$$I_iR_I + (I_i - I_o)R_e = V_i.$$

Therefore:

$$A_{if} = \frac{I_o}{I_g} = \left(\frac{R_G}{R_e}\right)\left\{-1\Big/\left[1 - \frac{1}{A}\left(1 + \frac{R_I}{R_e} + \frac{R_G}{R_e}\right)\right]\right\}. \qquad (10\text{–}58)$$

Equation (10–58) reduces to Eq. (10–56) for $R_G \to \infty$. $A_{if} \to -R_G/R_e$ for a very large value of forward gain A_i. To apply the equation successfully, R_I must represent the input resistance of the first transistor—it is not equal to V_i/I_i.

The lower pair of Eqs. (10–57) may be solved for the over-all voltage gain of the circuit. The result is:

$$A_{vf} = \frac{V_o}{V_i} = \left(\frac{R_L}{R_e}\right)\left\{-1 \Big/ \left[1 - \frac{1}{A_i}\left(\frac{R_I + R_e}{R_e}\right)\right]\right\}. \qquad (10\text{–}59)$$

For the usual case, $R_I \gg R_e$, Eq. (10–59) reduces to the simpler form

$$A_{vf} \cong \frac{-A_v}{1 - A_v(R_e/R_L)}. \qquad (10\text{–}60)$$

The corresponding $B_v = R_e/R_L$.

Input resistance of this series feedback network is larger than that of a network without feedback. From the preceding, for unaltered current gain but voltage gain reduced,

$$R_{if} \cong R_I(1 - A_v R_e/R_L). \qquad (10\text{–}61)$$

Shunt-Series Pair. Two common-emitter stages, joined by an appropriate coupling network, could employ neither the over-all shunt feedback nor the over-all series feedback of the preceding section, on account of phasing. If, however, an "interior" signal is fed to an "exterior" point, or an "exterior" signal is fed to an "interior" point, the phasing will be correct for the degenerative form of feedback.

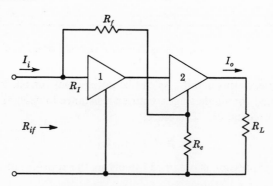

Fig. 10–10. Shunt-series pair.

One such arrangement, often referred to as the shunt-series feedback pair, is shown in Fig. 10–10. A signal, taken from the emitter resistor of stage two, is made available to the input circuit through R_f. This form of feedback principally affects current gain. An applicable expression for A_{if} is

$$A_{if} \cong A_i'/(1 - B_i A_i'). \qquad (10\text{–}62)$$

The feedback factor B_i is again the ratio of current fed back to load current and is given by

$$B_i \cong -R_e/(R_f + R_e) \cong -R_e/R_f. \qquad (10\text{–}63)$$

Note the minus sign in Eq. (10–63). That sign is necessary since the current fed back to the input in this network does not strengthen or increase the input signal, as is the case in the idealized network of Fig. 10–1. Since the forward gain of the two-stage amplifier cannot provide phase reversal, B_i contains the negative sign necessary for the feedback to be degenerative.

When calculating the gain of the forward channel, one must include elements R_f and R_e, but discount the mutual effects by opening the feedback path. Thus $A_i{}'$ is the current gain of the two stages with R_f connected between first base and ground, and R_e included in stage two.

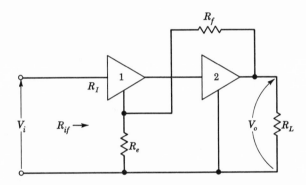

Fig. 10–11. Series-shunt pair.

The voltage gain of this pair is reduced by addition of feedback, but the effect is not pronounced until a large amount of feedback is employed. Consequently, for $|B_i| < 0.1$, we may generally assume that the input resistance of this connection is

$$R_{if} = R_I/(1 - B_iA_i'). \qquad (10\text{–}64)$$

Ghausi has described a design method to achieve a *maximally flat magnitude* frequency response. His article is recommended for those working with the shunt-series feedback pair.[2]

Series-Shunt Pair. An alternate method for incorporating feedback in a two-stage amplifier is shown in Fig. 10–11, with the signal at the second stage collector fed back to the emitter of the first stage. In the series-shunt pair, voltage gain is primarily affected by the inclusion of feedback. The expression for voltage gain is

$$A_{vf} \cong A_v'/(1 - B_vA_v'). \qquad (10\text{–}65)$$

The feedback factor B_v, the ratio of voltage fed back to voltage at the load, is

$$B_v \cong -R_e/(R_f + R_e) \cong -R_e/R_f. \qquad (10\text{–}66)$$

Again the feedback factor is considered as a negative quantity because the voltage fed back bucks the signal voltage V_i. The forward gain used in Eq. (10–65) must include local effects of the feedback elements. Thus $A_v{}'$ is the product of the voltage gain of stage one with R_e connected in its emitter lead, and the gain of stage two with R_f connected between collector and ground.

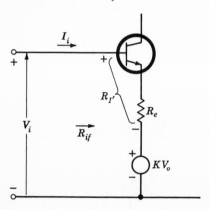

Fig. 10–12. Feedback amplifier quantities of interest.

A high level of input resistance is possible with the series-shunt pair. An expression for R_{if} is

$$R_{if} = R_I{}'(1 - B_vA_v{}'). \qquad (10\text{–}67)$$

The term $1 - B_vA_v{}'$ is naturally positive and considerably greater than unity. $R_I{}'$, essentially the input resistance of stage one, must include the local effect of R_e. This situation is clarified by reference to Fig. 10–12. The voltage *fed back* is symbolized by the voltage generator KV_o. A summation of voltages around the input loop yields

$$V_i = KV_o + I_iR_I{}'.$$

We may substitute $V_o = A_v{}'I_iR_I{}'$. Upon using this substitution, and cognizance of the fact that $K = -B_v$, we may obtain R_{if}, the ratio of V_i to I_i, as given by Eq. (10–67).

Design Example.

Object. Design a two-stage amplifier to meet the following requirements:

1. Voltage gain: 100 ± 3
2. Input resistance: 50,000 Ω (minimum)
3. Bandwidth: 50 cps to 1 Mc (minimum)
4. Load: 2200 Ω
5. Source characteristics: $0 - 1$ mV, 100 Ω
6. Temperature: $25° \pm 5°$ C
7. Transistor parameters for 0.5 to 1 mA, 2 to 10 V:
   $100 \le h_{fe} \le 300$
   $3000 \le h_{ie} \le 8000 \qquad V_{BE} = 0.5$ V
   $100 \le h_{FE} \le 300$

Naturally, low values exist together. Other parameters may be considered negligible. These parameter variations are primarily caused by manufacturing tolerances, although the effects of operating-point variations, as noted, are included.

8. Power supply available: +10 V
9. DC not permitted in source and in load.

Solution. A series-shunt pair will be used since it provides high input resistance. The bandwidth requirement will not be difficult to meet, for quite a large amount of feedback may be employed to meet the gain specification. Ambient-temperature excursions present no problem. Consequently, top priority is assigned to meeting the gain requirement.

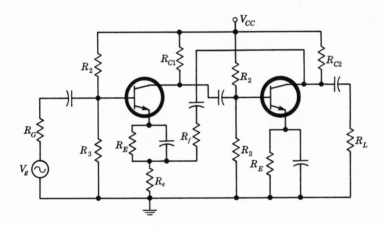

Fig. 10–13. Feedback amplifier text example.

Bias Considerations. Using the lowest value of h_{FE}, 100, we select an operating point for each stage at $I_C = 0.5$ mA, $V_{CE} = 6$ V. The dc load line is 8000 Ω. At the highest h_{FE} value, we arbitrarily select an operating point at $I_C = 1.0$ mA; therefore, $V_{CE} = 2.0$ V. Thus the bias stabilization circuit will permit I_C to change by 2:1 when h_{FE} varies 3:1. From the extremal analysis discussion of Sec. 3–11, with no significant variation in V_{BE},

$$R_E = \frac{\Delta I_B}{\Delta I_C} R_B = \frac{1.67 \times 10^{-6}}{0.5 \times 10^{-3}} R_B = 3.33 \times 10^{-3} R_B.$$

A selection of 1000 Ω for R_E requires $R_B = 300{,}000 \,\Omega$. Such a large value will not adversely affect input resistance. Therefore, $R_C = 7$ kΩ, $R_E = 1$ kΩ, $R_2 = 3$ MΩ, $R_3 = 333$ kΩ. The circuit is shown in Fig. 10–13.

Gain Considerations. Using minimum parameter values, $R_C = 7$ kΩ and $R_L = 2200$ Ω, we can expect the voltage gain of a stage to be about 55. The gain of the pair, without feedback, will consequently approach 3000. For a high forward gain, from Eq. (10–3), the feedback factor $B_v = 1/A_f = 0.01$. From Eq. (10–66), $B_v = R_e/R_f$. Further study is necessary in order to determine specifically either R_e or R_f.

An approximate relation for the forward gain is

$$A_v = A_{v1}'A_{v2}' \cong \frac{h_{fe1}R_{L1}}{h_{ie1} + (1 + h_{fe1})R_e} \cdot \frac{h_{fe2}R_{L2}}{h_{ie2}},$$

with $R_{L1} = R_{C1} \| R_{in2}$ and $R_{L2} = R_L \| R_f \| R_{C2}$. R_f may be eliminated from this equation by using $R_f = R_e/B_v$. With this substitution we note that R_e is the only unknown in the expression for A_v. It may be differentiated with respect to R_e. Setting the derivative to zero yields the value of R_e that provides a maximum forward gain:

$$R_e = \left[\frac{B_v h_{ie1}}{(1 + h_{fe1})(G_L + G_{C2})} \right]^{1/2} \tag{10–68}$$

For minimum parameter values, $R_e = 22$ Ω. Therefore R_f will be approximately 2200 Ω.

The minimum gain of stage two, with R_f, R_L and R_C comprising the load, is 32. The minimum gain of stage one, with $R_C \| R_{in2}$ as a load, *and R_e included*, is 40. Consequently the minimum forward gain with feedback elements included (but no over-all feedback employed) is 1280. We may now determine B_v from Eq. (10–3), using $A_{vf} = 98$ as a minimum to include a safety factor:

$$98 = \frac{1280}{1 + B_v(1280)}.$$

Hence $B_v = 0.0095$. We shall retain $R_e = 22$ and make $R_f = 2320$.

To check the gain with maximum parameters, we calculate $A_{v2} = 36.3$, $A_{v1} = 76.8$, $A_v = 2780$. Thus from Eq. (10–3), $A_{vf} = 101$, which is well below the 103 upper limit.

Bandwidth and Input Impedance. The major factor affecting these two network properties is $(1 - BA)$. In this design, the term has a minimum value of 13.2. The low value of input resistance, with feedback loop open, is 5200 Ω. Therefore we may expect the minimum input resistance to be 68,500 Ω. Base biasing will not reduce this below the specified minimum.

In order to meet that bandwidth requirement, it is necessary for the open-loop frequency response to be flat from about 500 to 100,000 cps. This can easily be achieved with standard bypass and coupling capacitances, and many general-purpose transistor types.

Attention must be given to several other characteristics of this amplifier. The output resistance is quite low, generally a desirable feature. The frequency response may exhibit a hump at high frequencies. This may be eliminated by paralleling R_f with an appropriate capacitance, thus increasing the feedback factor over the portion of the spectrum where additional feedback is necessary.

Certain designs of this type will self-oscillate at a very low frequency (< 10 cps) because the loop gain may be greater than unity when the phase shift caused by coupling capacitances equals 180°. These oscillations may be eliminated by choosing more appropriate values for coupling elements.

10–5. Automatic Gain Control. Closely allied with any discussion of feedback is the *automatic gain control* (AGC) system employed in communications receivers. The function of such a system is to maintain a relatively constant signal at the *second detector* stage of a receiver regardless of the strength of the

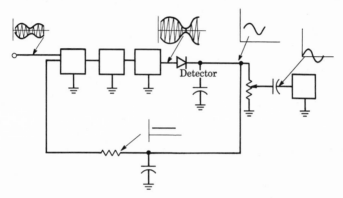

Fig. 10–14. General AGC circuit showing waveforms at various points.

incoming signal, that is, the signal at some previous section of the circuitry. The detector, also called a *demodulator*, separates intelligence from a carrier frequency and discards the carrier. In the prototype system it is normal to sample the detector output, which is intelligence superimposed upon dc, and feed the average level of this signal back to a preceding stage to control the grid bias of a tube that is operating in a nonlinear region of its characteristics, and thereby control the gain of a stage by utilizing the magnitude of the output of a later stage. Such a system actually controls the intelligence level by controlling the carrier magnitude, since both carrier and modulation are amplified equally. The rectification and low-pass filtering accomplished by the detector stage leaves a dc signal to be fed back whose amplitude is proportional to carrier amplitude.

Figure 10–14 describes the operation of an AGC circuit by showing the important waveforms. A simple demodulator is described by the diode, while the associated shunt capacitance helps eliminate high frequencies (the carrier) from the audio or video stages that follow. In the feedback line further filtering is employed to smooth the waveform, since only the average value is of importance.

When working with transistor circuits, we must find a means of controlling gain by altering the quiescent or dc conditions of an amplifier. The variations of parameters with operating point were discussed in Chapter 4, and in Chapter 6 the results of an investigation of the relation of performance to operating point were presented. Other investigations have been made and the results are depicted in Fig. 10–15 and 10–16. A considerable variation in gain can be achieved if either emitter current or collector voltage is varied. In the case of AGC this operating point change is caused by the fedback signal.

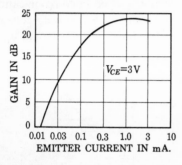

Fig. 10–15. Variation of gain due to emitter current for a typical common-emitter stage.

Fig. 10–16. Variation of gain due to collector voltage for a typical common-emitter stage.

To change either emitter current or collector voltage, power is required. Again we encounter the difference between vacuum-tube and transistor technologies. The output of the second detector must supply power to the controlled stage or stages. This control power requirement can be minimized if the dc is made available to a base rather than an emitter. Figure 10–17(a) illustrates an

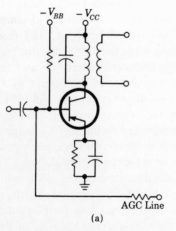
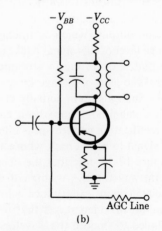

Fig. 10–17. (a) Emitter current AGC; (b) collector voltage AGC.

AGC that controls the emitter current of a transistor by altering base bias. Of course emitter current depends upon base current and his scheme can be studied by considering the controlled transistor to be a dc amplifier that is amplifying the AGC signal. Emitter-current variations cause variations in the potential drop across the bypassed emitter resistance and therefore changes in the available voltage across the transistor; one may reason that these two effects (I_E and V_{CE} control) tend to cancel, with no resulting gain variation. For this type of circuit, the collector voltage must be fairly large, or, in other words, not in the sensitive region of operation.

It is possible, of course, to directly control emitter current by means of the AGC voltage, if sufficient power is available, or to include a separate AGC amplifier.

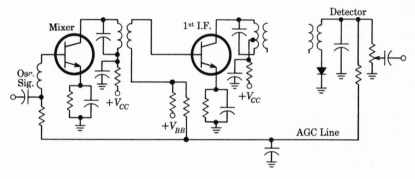

Fig. 10–18. Practical AGC system.

Maximum sensitivity of control is achieved at low values of emitter current, below 100 μA for the transistor whose operation is depicted in Fig. 10–15, and at low collector potentials, below 500 mV. These facts essentially limit the swing of applied signals to very small values, as are encountered in the radio-frequency (R.F.), converter, and first intermediate-frequency (I.F.) stages of a superheterodyne receiver. If a large collector resistor is added to the circuit of Fig. 10–17(a) as shown in Fig. 10–17(b), and the emitter bias current made fairly large, then a small collector-to-emitter voltage is available. An AGC signal that alters base current will also change emitter current and thereby alter available collector voltage. The changing collector potential provides gain control. Quiescent emitter current for this circuit should be fairly large and therefore not in the sensitive region of operation.

Figure 10–18 shows a practical circuit. AGC is used to control the base bias of both the mixer and first I.F. amplifier stages of a receiver. Although resistors are in both collector circuits, they are of too low a value (1000 Ω) to provide collector-voltage control; the stages are I_E controlled. The variable resistance at the detector output provides manual volume control for the entire circuit.

Automatic gain-control systems must operate so that when the incoming signal is strong, the fedback voltage or current is of such a polarity as to reduce amplifier gain, and vice versa.

When changing the operating point of a transistor we might expect input and output impedances also to change. Since loads are normally tuned circuits in receiver circuitry, the resonant frequency and bandwidth of such tuned circuits will be altered as a result of changing transistor impedances. Collector capacitance is a function of collector voltage, and thus a degree of detuning is almost certain to occur. It is desirable that the bandwidth of tuned circuits be wide when input signals are strong, and narrow when signals are weak. This is accomplished when using a collector-voltage AGC system, for the input impedance of the controlled stage is reduced when I_E increases, thereby detuning the input tuned circuit. On the other hand, when I_E is used for the direct control of gain, the input impedance of a stage will be increased and bandwidth narrowed when I_E decreases. Selectivity should be accomplished elsewhere in the receiver for such a system.

10-6. Direct-Coupled Amplifiers. Also called a direct-current or a direct-voltage amplifier, a direct-coupled (dc) amplifier has, as its main application, the amplification of signals below several cps and down to the dc signal. It is to be realized that the circuits discussed thus far have used transformers and capacitors for coupling between stages; these elements are capable of passing time-varying signals exclusively, and severely attenuate the lower frequencies.

It is possible to remove the blocking capacitors from an *R-C* amplifier, thereby placing the direct potential at the second-stage base at the same level as the first-stage collector. This may be acceptable provided that the emitter and collector potentials of the second stage are adjusted to maintain the required operating voltages. Therefore, because of the need for adjusted potentials, we might expect to encounter numerous power supplies in any dc amplifier. The amplifier will be sensitive to these supplies since a change in any supply voltage will be amplified just as a dc input signal is amplified. When appearing at the load this amplified supply variation would be indistinguishable from signal.

The dc amplifier supplies, to its load, a signal that is proportional to its input. As would be expected, the magnitude of the output quantity is dependent upon the amplification factors of the various circuits. However, since we are dealing with direct current, and usually desire that zero voltage exist at the load when zero input signal is impressed, then a change in gain may actually cause an output voltage even in the absence of input signal. This will be apparent from the circuit to be discussed directly. It is important to note that an output other than zero will result when the operating point of any stage changes, as a result, for example, of changes in temperature, because in the absence of isolation any operating-point variation will alter the operating points of the succeeding stages.

I_{co} is a problem because of its extreme sensitivity to temperature, and, in general, must be compensated for. Compensation can be achieved by circuitry employing temperature-sensitive resistors and diodes. Both thermistors and diodes exhibit negative temperature coefficients of resistance, and, when used in conjunction with resistors having zero or positive temperature coefficients, networks may be designed having almost any desired temperature sensitivity.

These three causes of trouble for dc amplifiers—power supply variations, parameter changes due to temperature and age, and changes in leakage current—are the prime contributors to *drift*. Drift can be defined as a variation in the amplifier output independent of the designated input.

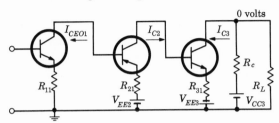

Fig. 10–19. Simple dc transistor amplifier.

Let us discuss the dc amplifier of Fig. 10–19. This diagram is not a simplification, but actually represents all circuit elements necessary for a complete workable circuit. The first and third stages are *n–p–n* units, while the second stage is *p–n–p*. Reasoning behind the choice of different types will be clear after investigation of base and collector current directions.

Since the base circuit of the first stage has no driving voltage, no base current exists. A collector current, I_{CEO}, will be apparent and will be in the direction as shown on the diagram. I_{CEO} of the first stage *is* I_B of the second stage, and since transistor-conductivity types alternate, the current direction is correct for Class-A amplification. If stage two has a current gain of h_{FE2}, then its collector current is

$$I_{C2} = h_{FE2}I_{CEO1}.$$

I_{C2} is in the proper direction, and serves as base current for stage three. The collector current of stage three is

$$I_{C3} = h_{FE3}I_{C2} = h_{FE2}h_{FE3}I_{CEO1}.$$

Should a fourth stage be required, it must be *p–n–p*.

Examine collector-to-emitter voltages. The output stage collector is at ground potential, and the emitter is made negative by supply V_{EE3}; thus the collector is more positive than the emitter. Base potential is approximately that of emitter number three and is common to collector two. V_{EE2} is in series with V_{EE3} and together they supply the collector potential for stage two. Stage number one has a collector potential approximately equal to V_{EE2}. As shown, the base of the first stage is not at zero volts, but could be made so by additional circuitry. Actually, the circuit shown was fed from a differential amplifier and R_{11} was several thousand ohms to provide a high input impedance. R_{21} and R_{31} are low-valued resistors that provide degenerative feedback, and although they do not materially affect the current gain of any particular stage, they tend to increase the stability of collector current with respect to temperature variations.

In the amplifier as constructed, $I_{C1} = 6$ μA, $I_{C2} = 220$ μA, and $I_{C3} = 9$ mA, indicating that $h_{FE2} \cong 37$ and $h_{FE3} \cong 41$. The sensitivity of such a circuit to ambient temperature is apparent. The signal supplied to the load is based upon I_{CEO} of stage number one, and although silicon transistors were employed, we might expect a change of about 5% per degree Centigrade in that current. Even if I_{CEO} were not the quiescent current of the first stage, I_{CEO} would make up a sizable portion of it. Temperature compensation is a must for such an amplifier even if it is expected that the only temperature excursions will be those as encountered in a normal room.

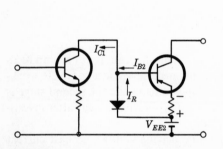

Fig. 10–20. Use of a semiconductor diode to temperature-compensate an amplifier.

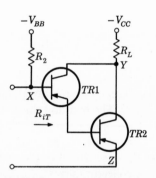

Fig. 10–21. Common-emitter compound connection.

The semiconductor diode is often used for temperature compensation because the temperature coefficient of resistance of the diode material is equivalent to the rate at which transistor leakage (I_{CO}) varies with temperature. For example, in the circuit of Fig. 10–20, it is desired to maintain I_{B2} constant although I_{C1} (which may be I_{CEO} of the first stage) is subject to variations because of climatic conditions. The diode is biased negatively, and we are concerned with the reverse current, I_R. Since V_{EE2} is the only circuit source,

$$I_{B2} = -I_R + I_{C1}. \qquad (10–69)$$

It is required that $dI_{B2}/dT = 0$. Therefore, for perfect compensation,

$$dI_R/dT = dI_{C1}/dT. \qquad (10–70)$$

The diode should have leakage properties indentical to those of the transistor.

Compound connection. An extremely interesting circuit is the *compound-connection* shown in Fig. 10–21. This circuit is also referred to as the *Darlington pair.* The emitter terminal of TR1 is directly connected to the base of TR2; the collectors of both units share a common load. The two transistors present only three terminals to the external circuit (X, Y, and Z in the figure).

Since TR2 is in the common leg of TR1, it will provide negative feedback that serves to gain-stabilize the composite circuit, and the resulting input resistance (R_{iT}) is much greater than that of a single common-emitter stage. For normal Class-A operation, resistance R_2 is chosen so that both stages are operating in the active region of their collector characteristics. It is of course easy to saturate TR2 by supplying too much base current to TR1, since the operating point of the second transistor depends upon

$$I_{B2} = I_{E1} \cong h_{FE1}I_{B1},$$

and

$$I_{C2} \cong h_{FE1}h_{FE2}I_{B1}.$$

Since the collector currents of both transistors flow through the common load, each will contribute to total load signal, but the extent of that contribution differs by the magnitude of the current amplification of TR2. Refinements can be made to the circuit shown. Bypassed emitter resistance for TR2 may be added, single-battery biasing (or other forms) may be used, or an additional stage added by connecting its base to the emitter of TR2, its collector to the common load, and its emitter to ground.

A Darlington pair, enclosed in a single case, is shown in the photograph at the beginning of this chapter. The circuit has a minimum $h_{FE} = 1200$ at $I_C = 5A$, and allowable power dissipation of 50 W at a case temperature of 100° C. Other pairs have been assembled with current gain in excess of 30,000. Naturally, input impedance is high.

The Differential Amplifier. A popular circuit often employed in dc amplifiers is the differential *amplifier*, so called because its output voltage is proportional to the difference of two voltages supplied to its two separate inputs. Two transistors are necessary to perform the subtraction operation, as can be seen in Fig. 10–22, and if they are matched, the output voltage, which can be taken between collectors, is independent of parameter changes and changes in the value of I_{CO} of either transistor. In the figure, two inputs, V_1 and V_2 are shown. However, the circuit will amplify if only one input port is supplied, and the other grounded through an appropriate impedance. Occasionally, one input port is used for the signal to be amplified, while the other input port may be the termination of a feedback line.

In principle, the causes of drift are not eliminated, but if each transistor of a differential pair is subjected to the same ambient, and the transistors are made as identical as possible, an output taken between the two devices will be free from the major drift experienced in a single-ended system. The collector voltages V_{C1} and V_{C2} may be fed to another differential pair for further amplification.

An analysis of this circuit may be made on a dc or an ac basis. Here an ac analysis is presented in order to prove the differential operation and the amplification constant of the circuit. In the analysis, r_c is assumed to be much larger than R_L, the channels are assumed indentical, and the transistor parameter r_b is lumped with generator resistance R_G to form a composite, which is termed R_S.

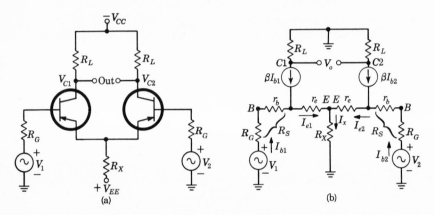

Fig. 10–22.   Common-emitter differential amplifier: (a) circuit; (b) ac equivalent.

The Kirchhoff equations for Fig. 10–22(b) are:

$$V_1 = I_{b1}R_S + I_{e1}r_e + I_xR_x,$$

$$V_2 = I_{b2}R_S + I_{e2}r_e + I_xR_x,$$

$$I_x = I_{e1} + I_{e2};$$

$$(10\text{--}71)$$

$$I_{e1} = (\beta + 1)I_{b1}, \text{ and } I_{e2} = (\beta + 1)I_{b2}.$$

For $R_x \gg r_e$ and $(\beta + 1)R_x \gg R_S$,

$$I_{b1} \cong \frac{V_1 - V_2}{2[R_S + (\beta + 1)r_e]}$$

and

$$I_{b2} \cong \frac{V_2 - V_1}{2[R_S + (\beta + 1)r_e]}.$$

The voltage between collectors is

$$V_o = \beta R_L I_{b1} - \beta R_L I_{b2}.$$

Therefore

$$V_o = \frac{(V_1 - V_2)\beta R_L}{R_S + (\beta + 1)r_e}.$$

$$(10\text{--}72)$$

A similar analysis for a single-sided output application, with output between C_2 and ground, yields *one-half* the output voltage predicted by Eq. (10–72). If the assumption of a large R_x or a small R_S is not valid, differential operation will still occur, but V_1 and V_2 will have differing coefficients in Eq. (10–72).

Common Mode operation results when identical in-phase voltages are simultaneously applied to the inputs; according to Eq. 10–72, there is theoretically no output voltage. Thus any interference voltage, as from stray electromagnetic pickup in an ungrounded system, is cancelled. The *common-mode rejection factor* is the ratio of the output with equal input voltages of opposite phase (differential mode) to the output voltage obtained with equal, in-phase inputs. In quality circuits, this factor is extremely large.

Chopper Amplifiers. Because of the many problems associated with direct-coupled circuits, a widely accepted method of amplifying low frequencies and direct signals is to convert the signal to ac, amplify this ac and then rectify to re-establish the dc. To change dc to ac, a switching scheme may be used. The switch may be a circuit or device that will alternately pass and reject the dc input as a function of time. The common name for this operation is "modulation." A modulator may be an electromechanical switch, such as a vibrator, or a circuit comprised of diodes, vacuum tubes, or transistors, or it may be electromagnetic, such as a magnetic modulator. The vibrator has moving parts, and consequently a relatively short lifetime, and is limited to operation below 1000 cps. However, since it is practically drift free and exhibits a low noise level, the vibrator is often used for this application.

A "demodulator" must be used when it is necessary to remove the alternating carrier and re-establish the dc signal; its action is basically rectification and filtering. In a system using both a modulator and a demodulator, it is desired that the over-all circuit be polarity conscious. For example, if $+10$ mV is to be amplified 1000 times, we normally expect the output to be $+10$ V, and a negative load voltage to result from an input signal of negative polarity. It is therefore necessary that the demodulator be phase sensitive. Should modulator action result in an alternating current of a certain phase (with respect to any convenient reference) for a given polarity of dc signal, then the demodulator will sample that phasing and supply the load with dc of the correct polarity. The accepted names for this rectification circuit are "phase-sensitive demodulator," "phase-sensitive discriminator," or "phase-sensitive detector."

A complete dc amplifier making use of the foregoing principle is shown in Fig. 10–23. The dc input is shorted to ground (through resistances of low value) when the square-wave modulator excitation is of the correct polarity for both diodes to conduct. On alternate half cycles neither diode can conduct and the dc signal is passed through the modulator circuit to the amplifier. The resulting potential at A is a square wave with one half of its cycle at ground potential. This square wave, with a fundamental frequency of the chopper excitation, passes through C_{c1} to the gate of TR1. The FET presents a high input impedance and

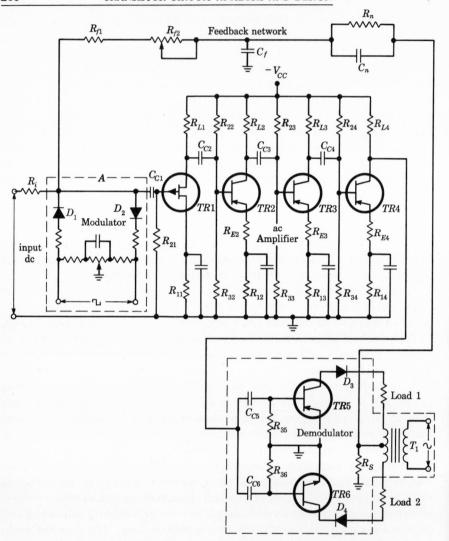

Fig. 10–23. DC chopper amplifier showing modulator and demodulator.

therefore does not load down the chopper. The square wave is amplified by three additional stages, each having a high degree of bias stability as well as some local feedback. The collector voltage of TR4 is made available to the bases of both TR5 and TR6.

A four-terminal load is being supplied by the amplifier of this figure and could represent a hydraulic valve actuated by dc, the motion of the valve dictated by the difference in the direct current flowing through its two windings. The operation of the demodulator circuit will now be discussed. Consider the lower terminal of transformer T_1 to be instantaneously positive. Diodes D_3 and D_4 are connected so that each transistor has the proper collector-voltage polarity. But since the transistors are of opposite conductivity types and are being operated Class B, the transistor that will conduct and hence supply load current is the one being correctly stimulated by base signal. Each transistor is receiving the same base signal, and the detector is said to be phase sensitive because if the bases are instantaneously positive, only TR6 will conduct, causing current downward through load #2. However, if the bases were going negative during the half cycle when each collector is correctly excited, then only TR5 will conduct, resulting in a current downward through load #1. During the other alternation of supply to T_1, neither transistor can conduct.

All load currents flow through R_S, a small resistor, which supplies feedback voltage. In the feedback loop, R_n and C_n help to shape the frequency response characteristic of the amplifier, and C_f is useful in filtering the feedback signal. The amount of feedback is dictated by R_{f1} and adjustable resistance R_{f2}, and is added to the amplifier input at A.

Chopper amplifiers have been found useful for many applications; the dc output of thermocouples, thermopiles, strain gauges, and certain pressure sensors as well as many other process transducers must be amplified for indication and control of process variables, and chopper amplifiers have been widely accepted. The bandwidth of such circuits is narrow and a general rule of thumb is that a chopper amplifier can be used to amplify signals up to 1/10 of the modulating frequency. The reader may verify the bandwidth limitation.

Operational Amplifiers. The term "operational amplifier" has been used to describe the circuit comprised of a dc amplifier and associated external impedances that together "operate" upon a direct voltage or current in some mathematical way. Applications for such amplifiers in the measurement and computer fields are numerous.

Prior to the transistor, vacuum-tube operational amplifiers, characterized by their high input resistance and high voltage gain, took on certain standard forms. With transistor circuits, however, high or low input resistance is available. In the following circuits both resistance levels will be considered. The operations to be discussed are summation, integration, and differentiation.

A dc amplifier with no load and high input resistance is depicted in Fig. 10–24 with two input voltages, v_1 and v_2, available. More than two inputs are, of course, possible,. It is desired that the output voltage, v_o be proportional to the sum of v_1 and v_2. Thus

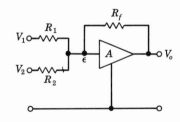

Fig. 10–24. Summing amplifier.

$$v_o = K(v_1 + v_2). \tag{10–73}$$

A summation of currents at the significant node yields

$$\frac{v_1 - \varepsilon}{R_1} + \frac{v_2 - \varepsilon}{R_2} = \frac{\varepsilon - v_o}{R_f}. \tag{10-74}$$

For the amplifier alone, including phase reversal,

$$A = - v_o/\varepsilon. \tag{10-75}$$

For a very large value of A, Eq. (10-73) becomes

$$v_o \cong - R_f \left(\frac{v_1}{R_1} + \frac{v_2}{R_2} \right) \tag{10-76}$$

Should all resistances be of equal magnitude,

$$v_o = -(v_1 + v_2). \tag{10-77}$$

It can be proved easily that if finite amplifier input resistance had been considered, input resistance would have acted as if it were parallel with R_1 and R_2. However, a large A would result in an expression identical with Eq. (10-76).

For a single input to the circuit of Fig. 10-24, the expression for output voltage including phase inversion is

$$v_o = -v_1 A R_f / [R_f + (1 + A)R_1]. \tag{10-78}$$

Equation (10-78) represents a standard feedback circuit that, for large values of A, exhibits a gain of

$$v_o/v_1 \cong - R_f/R_1. \tag{10-79}$$

Consider the amplifier with single input channel shown in Fig. 10-25. Impedances Z_F and Z_I will determine the operation of the over-all circuit. Because this circuit is very similar to the case just discussed, the output voltage, for large A, is given by a modification of Eq. (10-79) applicable to the steady-state

$$V_o = - V_i(Z_F/Z_I). \tag{10-80}$$

Let Z_I be resistive and equal R, and let Z_F be capacitive. In Laplace notation, $Z_F = 1/sC$. Equation (10-80) can be written

$$V_o(s) = - \frac{V_i(s)}{RCs}. \tag{10-81}$$

In the time domain, the corresponding expression is

$$v_o = - \frac{1}{RC} \int v_i \, dt. \tag{10-82}$$

The circuit will integrate the input voltage.

If the positions of the capacitor and resistor are interchanged, that is if $Z_I = 1/sC$ and $Z_F = R$, then, from Eq. (10–80),

$$V_o(s) = -V_i(s)RCs. \tag{10–83}$$

In the time domain, this corresponds to

$$v_o = -RC\frac{dv_i}{dt}. \tag{10–84}$$

The input voltage is differentiated if the amplifier gain is large.

Equation (10–80) suggests that the feedback amplifier of Fig. 10–25 could be employed to synthesize voltage transfer functions. When a given transfer function can be expressed as the quotient of realizable impedances, $Z_F(s)/Z_I(s)$, a high-gain operational amplifier with appropriate feedback elements provides a convenient method for the realization of equalizing and filtering functions.

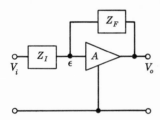

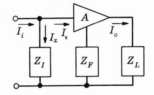

Fig. 10–25.   Computing amplifier.   Fig. 10–26.   Current analog of 10–25.

The possibility of using low input resistance transistor amplifiers has led to the so-called current-analog operational amplifier shown in Fig. 10–26. It is assumed that the input impedance of A is low compared with Z_F, and A is primarily a current amplifier, so

$$A = -I_o/I_\varepsilon. \tag{10–85}$$

Summing potential drops around the inner loop gives

$$I_x Z_I = (I_\varepsilon - I_o)Z_F. \tag{10–86}$$

It is obvious that

$$I_i = I_x + I_\varepsilon.$$

A solution of these equations for load current yields

$$I_o \cong -I_i(Z_I/Z_F), \tag{10–87}$$

for large values of A. To integrate the input current, Z_I may be a capacitor and Z_F a resistor. To differentiate, the elements may be interchanged.

The operational amplifiers described above are subject to the drifts inherent in dc amplifiers even though a large amount of feedback may be employed. Use could be made of chopper amplifiers, subject to their inherent high-frequency limitations. Automatic balancing circuits based upon chopper stabilization have proved very successful because the freedom from drift of the chopper amplifier and the superior high-frequency response of a conventional dc amplifier are both realized.[3]

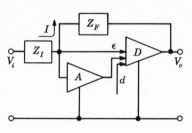

Fig. 10–27.   DC amplifier with automatic stabilization.

In the circuit of Fig. 10–27, D represents a dc amplifier having a wide bandwidth, but drift, denoted by d, will be present and can be referred to the circuit input. D has a differential amplifier input stage of high input resistance. The amplifier A is a chopper circuit that will pass all low frequencies (often included with A is a low-pass filter while in the path to D a filter may be used to block dc and pass the highs). Low-frequency amplification is the product of A and D; high frequencies will exhibit a gain of D, modified by the appropriate networks.

It is desired to eliminate or at least greatly reduce the amount of d which is present at the output. By Kirchhoff's second law:

$$\varepsilon = V_i - IZ_I = V_i - \frac{(V_i - V_o)}{Z_I + Z_F} Z_I.$$

Output voltage is

$$V_o = -AD\varepsilon - Dd - D\varepsilon.$$

Solution of these equations results in

$$V_o \cong -V_i\left(\frac{Z_F}{Z_I}\right) - \frac{d}{A}\frac{(Z_I + Z_F)}{Z_I}. \tag{10–88}$$

It can be seen that the unwanted signal has been decreased by a factor close to $1/A$.

PROBLEMS

10–1. The voltage gain of an amplifier is nominally -60 but varies $\pm 5\%$ from that value owing to changes in its power supples. The addition of over-all feedback with $B = 0.06$ will result in what nominal over-all amplification? Determine the percentage variation in A_f.

10–2. If the response of an amplifier at low frequencies can be approximated by

$$A = A_0/[1 - (jf_{3dB}/f)]$$

with A_0 the mid-frequency gain and f_{3dB} the low half-power frequency, derive an expression for f_f, the lower cutoff or half-power frequency for a feedback amplifier in terms of A_0, B, and f_{3dB}.

10–3. Analyze the current feedback circuit of Fig. 10–3 in order to prove Eq. (10–27).

10–4. Extend the analysis of Problem 10–3 in order to derive expressions for Z_{if} and Z_{of}.

10–5. Consult an information source such as Reference 7 to study phase-sensitive discriminators and draw three transistorized circuits of that type.

10–6. The network shown could be used in the feedback path of an amplifier.

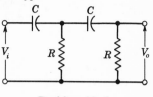

Problem 10–6.

(a) Derive an expression for the voltage transfer function (V_o/V_i).

(b) Is it possible for the network to provide a 180° phase shift? Explain.

(c) Derive an expression for the unloaded input impedance.

(d) Sketch the frequency response of this circuit.

10–7. For a common-emitter-connected transistor with $h_{ib} = 40$ Ω, $h_{rb} = 10^{-4}$, $h_{fb} = -0.972$, and $h_{ob} = 10^{-6}$ mho, make a plot of voltage gain vs R_e for five values of feedback resistance, 0, 10, 10^2, 10^3, 10^4. Consider that $R_L = 2000$ Ω.

10–8. For the transistor whose parameters are specified in Problem 10–7, show the variation in input resistance caused by emitter feedback.

10–9. For the transistor of Problem 10–7, plot current gain vs R_c for five values of that element, ∞, 10^5, 10^4, 10^3, 10^2.

10–10. Again using the transistor of Problem 10–7, show the variation of input resistance caused by collector-to-base feedback as noted in Problem 10–9.

10–11. Amplifiers with open-loop voltage gains of 10,000, 5000, 700, and 300 have their gains reduced to 100 by feedback. Express the amount of feedback in dB for each amplifier.

10–12. Compare the sensitivity of over-all amplification to internal-stage gain variations of a three-stage amplifier without feedback to a five-stage amplifier with over-all feedback. Both circuits have the same over-all gain, and are composed of identical individual stages.

10–13. In the absence of feedback, the input resistance of a three-stage transistor amplifier is 1000 Ω when the amplifier is feeding a 1000 Ω load. Each stage amplifies voltage 100 times and current 100 times. If feedback is to be added to this amplifier from the collector of stage number three to the base of stage one, of what value must the feedback resistance be in order to reduce the over-all power gain by 50%? What has happened to the input resistance?

10–14. Derive Eqs. (10–51) and (10–53).

10–15. Derive Eqs. (10–58) and (10–59).

10–16. Derive Eq. (10–68).

10–17. An alternate method for investigating the performance of the series-shunt pair is to write Kirchhoff equations relating the important quantities while using a block approach to describe the active elements. Confirm the following equations for A_{if} and A_{vf} using figures (a) and (b), respectively. Note that A_{v1} does not include R_e.

(a) $$A_{if} = \frac{A_{i1}A_{i2}(R_e + R_f) + A_{i1}R_e + R_e}{R_e + R_f + R_L},$$

(b) $$A_{vf} = \frac{A_{v1}A_{v2}R_{i2}(R_e + R_f)}{R_e[A_{v1}A_{v2}R_{i2} + A_{v2}R_{i2} + (A_{v1} + 1)R_f] + R_{i2}(R_e + R_f)}.$$

10–18. Derive the equation for the output voltage of a common-emitter differential amplifier driven from sources of high internal resistance. The assumption that $(B + 1)$ $R_x \gg R_S$ is not to be used.

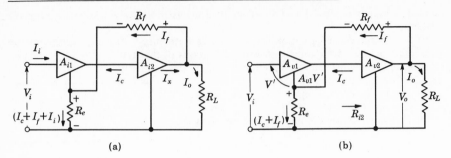

(a)   (b)

Problem 10–17.

10–19. Derive an expression for the output voltage of a common-emitter differential amplifier with dc input signals. Include parameters V_{BE} and h_{FE} for each transistor.

10–20. To study the input resistance of a common-emitter differential amplifier stage, consider that the other transistor base is returned to ground through R_G, and R_x is a very large-valued resistance. Confirm that

$$R_i \cong 2[r_b + r_e/(1 - \alpha)]$$

for the circuit of Fig. 10–22. Note that the second transistor appears as a common-base stage in the emitter branch of the transistor under study.

10–21. By sketching show the effect of chopping upon a low-frequency alternating waveform, and consequently attempt to confirm the statement that a chopper amplifier will successfully pass frequencies up to a fraction of the frequency of the chopping action.

10–22. It is desired to analyze the circuit diagram and answer questions concerning it. Knowledge of the transistor material thus far presented in the text and ability to extend these concepts to a new circuit is being tested.

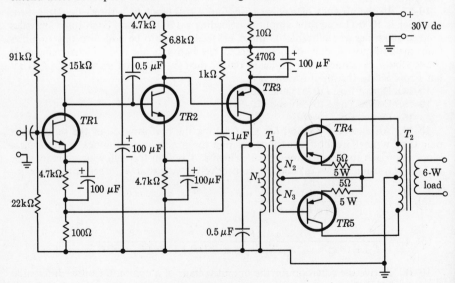

Problem 10–22.

(a) In what configuration is each transistor operating?

(b) Briefly discuss the methods of coupling employed between stages, and at source and load ports.

(c) In what mode (Class A or B) is each transistor operating? Give a reason for your answers.

(d) Discuss the purpose of each of the following components:
   (1) 0.5 μF in TR3 collector
   (2) 5 Ω in TR4 and TR5 emitters
   (3) 10 Ω in TR3 emitter
   (4) 100 Ω in TR1 emitter
   (5) 4.7 kΩ and 100 μF in TR1.

(e) All the transistors are germanium. If TR3 has a quiescent collector current of 32 mA, calculate all direct potentials in the first three stages, and the collector currents of stages 1 and 2. Assume that the winding resistance of T_1 is negligible.

(f) Draw a complete small-signal low-frequency equivalent for the first two stages in terms of h parameters with "e" subscripts. Include all pertinent R's and C's.

10–23. The network is the current analog of Fig. 10–27. Show that

$$I_o \cong -I_i\left(\frac{Z_I}{Z_F}\right) - \frac{d}{A}\left(\frac{Z_I}{Z_F}\right),$$

provided that I_x may be considered negligible and the amplifiers considered as having zero input impedance.

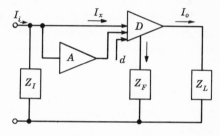

Problem 10–23.

10–24. Consider a current source I_o with parallel resistance R_o feeding R_L. Shunting the source and the load is a negative resistance device, $-R$. Show that this circuit may provide current amplification, and determine the condition for oscillation.

REFERENCES

1. Arguimbau, L. B., and Adler, R. B., *Vacuum-Tube Circuits and Transistors* (John Wiley & Sons, Inc., New York, 1956).

2. Ghausi, M. S., "Optimum Design of the Shunt Series Feedback Pair with a Maximally Flat Magnitude Response," *IRE Trans. Circuit Theory* (December, 1961).

3. Goldberg, E. A., "Stabilization of Wide-Band D-C Amplifier for Zero and Gain," *RCA Rev.*, **11** (June, 1950).

4. Hoffait, A. H., and Thornton, R. D., "Limitations of Transistor DC Amplifiers," *Proc. IEEE*, **52**, No. 2 (February, 1964).

5. Korn, G. A., and Korn, T. M., *Electronic Analog Computers* (McGraw-Hill Book Co., Inc., New York, 1956).

6. Middlebrook, R. D., *Differential Amplifiers* (John Wiley & Sons, Inc., New York, 1964).

7. Murphy, G. J., *Basic Automatic Control Theory* (D. Van Nostrand, Co., Inc., Princeton, New Jersey, 1957).

8. Nyquist, H., "Regeneration Theory," *Bell System Tech. J.*, **11** (January, 1932).

9. Ryder, J. D., *Electronic Fundamentals and Applications*, (Prentice-Hall, Inc., Englewood Cliffs, New Jersey, 1964), 3rd ed.

Chapter 11

COMMUNICATIONS AMPLIFIERS

Additional considerations in the analysis and design of amplifying networks are discussed in this chapter. The subject of electrical noise is important in the design of low-signal-level systems. Gain-control and frequency-response-shaping networks are required in most amplifying systems. Broad-frequency-band (video) amplifiers are necessary in television and radar because they serve to amplify signals of high information content and consequently warrant our attention. The narrow-band or tuned amplifying stage has many uses in radio, television, and military electronics, and will also be discussed in the pages to follow.

11-1. Types of Noise. Noise in electronic devices is any spurious signal, and is almost always unwanted. In radio and television receivers, noise is apparent to the ear and the eye as "static" and "snow", respectively. Actually, noise has two general classifications: "external" noise caused by atmospheric disturbances, motor commutation, aircraft and auto ignition, and any sparking device; and "internal" noise generated in the receiver as a result of the physics of the materials and components used. External noise will not be discussed here because its existence bears no relation to the transistor; it can be eliminated or minimized by shielding, antenna location or design, and prayer.

Our concern with noise is at the load portion of a circuit, in the loudspeaker or cathode-ray tube or other terminating device, but the important sources of internal noise are in the low-signal portion of a circuit. The first stage of any receiver and the signal source are the areas that must be investigated to determine whether their operational sensitivity is too severely limited, for noise sets a limit on such sensitivity; any signal too weak when compared with the noise level will be covered up or masked by it. Often discussed is the output "signal-to-noise ratio" for an electronic circuit. This ratio, which is sometimes a specification to be met by the circuit designer, can be used as a performance yardstick. Typical acceptable S/N ratios, expressed in decibels, are in the 15 to 60 dB range, and of course depend to a great extent upon the application.

Internal noise is generated in resistors, vacuum tubes, transistors, and, in fact, any conductor, and is due to many causes. It is said to be "random" in the sense that it is a completely unpredictable function of time, in contrast to normal electrical quantities whose future variations can be predicted from past performance or other information. A voltage described by $V = V_m \sin \omega t$ is obviously not random, for its past history is accurately known, and its future can be completely predicted. Random noise, on the other hand, contains terms of many frequencies with varying amplitudes.

It is possible by means of frequency analysis to classify noises. If the spectrum of frequencies in a wave is said to be "flat", then the wave contains equal magnitudes of all frequences. Noise of this type is "white" noise or "thermal" noise; the latter name is derived from the fact that a familiar source of this type of noise is a function of temperature.

Thermal Noise. Thermal noise, also referred to as Johnson noise, is the noise associated with random carrier movements in an electrical conductor. These movements, caused by thermal agitation, are apparent in every conductor, even if unconnected to a complete electrical circuit. Thermally caused noise has been investigated and the mean-square value of the associated noise voltage, $\overline{v_t^2}$, is given by the *Nyquist relation*,

$$\overline{v_t^2} = 4kTRB, \tag{11-1}$$

where k = Boltzmann's constant = 1.38×10^{-23} W-sec per degree Kelvin,

R = resistance of the conductor in ohms,

T = temperature of the conductor in degrees Kelvin,

B = bandwidth of the measuring system in cps.

For computational purposes, it is convenient to use mean-squared values of noise currents and voltages. Equation (11-1) provides us with a relationship for the thermal noise voltage across a given resistance. The value of noise voltage (and noise power) depends upon the bandwidth of the measuring device, for, since the noise spectrum is flat, a wider band contains more noise. When speaking of bandwidth in this application, the word technically refers to an ideal pass and rejection characteristic, although the frequency span between half-power points may be used as an approximation.

Equation (11-1) informs us that to minimize thermal noise, the use of high-valued resistances must be limited. That equation best approximates the noise behavior of wire-wound resistors. An additional noise source is found in carbon resistors because the passage of direct current forms minute arcs between carbon granules, resulting in high noise generation. Internal contact noise of this type can be eliminated by the use of low-noise resistors in critical applications and should not be confused with thermal noise.

As an example of the amount of thermal noise generated, consider a 1-MΩ resistor at 20° C (293° K) and a 4 Mc bandwidth, as is used in television video amplifiers. From Eq. (11-1) we could expect 254 μV rms of thermal noise.

For the noise analysis of a circuit, a noisy resistance can be replaced by a noiseless ideal resistance of equal value in series with a voltage generator described by Eq. (11–1). Figure 11–1(a) shows such a representation. Noise sources are defined in mean-squared terms; an equivalent noise source has no polarity.

If the circuit containing a noisy resistance R is completed by loading it down with another practical resistance of any value R_L, it may be noted that in thermal equilibrium the transfer of energy from R to R_L is exactly balanced by the noise energy transfer from R_L to R (Problem 11–2).

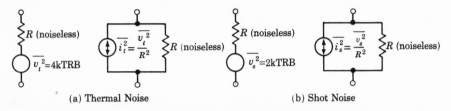

(a) Thermal Noise   (b) Shot Noise

Fig. 11–1. Representations of noise sources.

A primary source of thermal noise in any electronic circuit is the resistance of the signal source, R_G. Naturally, resistive biasing elements will also contribute noise. Within the transistor, the base resistance $r_{bb'}$ is a primary source of thermal noise.

Shot Noise. Although the motion of carriers that constitute a direct electrical current is well organized for their direction and average number are known and controlled, the actual passage of individual charge carriers across a potential barrier is a series of independent random events. These random variations about an average give rise to fluctuations in the average current and constitute *shot noise.*

Shot noise for transistors may be characterized by Schottky's equation originally proposed for vacuum diodes

$$\overline{i_s^2} = 2qI_{dc}B. \qquad (11–2)$$

We may select I_E as the direct current in Eq. (11–2) for studying emitter-junction shot noise in a conventional transistor. This current source would be paralleled by the dynamic resistance of the emitter–base junction, r_e'. Since it is known that $r_e' = kT/qI_E$, the shot noise, represented by a voltage generator, becomes

$$\overline{v_s^2} = 2qI_E r_e'^2 B \qquad (11–3a)$$

or

$$\overline{v_s^2} = 2kTr_e'B \qquad (11–3b)$$

The resistance r_e' is not itself a thermally noisy component, for it is a dynamic resistance and not a bulk or material characteristic. Note that the form of the shot-noise voltage generator given by Eq. (11–3b) is almost identical to the thermal noise voltage expression Eq. (11–1), with the exception that an additional multiplier of 2 is apparent in the thermal noise case.

Partition Noise. The random nature in which the emitter current divides or partitions between collector and base paths provides an additional source of noise in the collector current of a transistor. The electron–hole recombinations in the base region give rise to *partition noise*. At low frequencies this noise may be represented by

$$\overline{i_c^2} = 2qI_C(1 - \alpha_o)B. \tag{11-4a}$$

The low-frequency value of α is α_o. In high-frequency operation, base current increases; a more general representation of partition noise to cover a wide spectrum is

$$\overline{i_c^2} = 2qI_C [1 - (|\alpha|^2/\alpha_o)]B. \tag{11-4b}$$

Partition noise is also found in multigrid vacuum tubes.

1/f Noise. Another type of noise is present in transistors, and in other devices, the so-called *semiconductor* or *1/f* noise. Noticeable particularly at low frequencies, the power density (watts per unit frequency) varies inversely with frequency and it is believed that this phenomenon arises from surface recombination and leakage currents across the reverse-biased collector junction; it is dependent upon collector voltage, current, and temperature.[2] Above a frequency of from several hundred to several thousand cycles per second, white noise predominates; below that range *1/f* noise is important. The original transistor, the point-contact variety, was extremely noisy; *1/f* noise predominated throughout the usable frequency spectrum.

Since semiconductor noise power per unit frequency is inversely proportional to frequency, it is possible to determine the noise content of a band by integration of $K_1 f^{-1}$ over the range of frequencies in which our interest lies. The resulting relationship is

$$\text{Noise power} = K_1 \ln(f_h/f_l) \tag{11-5}$$

from which the mean-squared value of the noise voltage is

$$\overline{v_f^2} = K \ln(f_h/f_l) \tag{11-6}$$

In the above equations, the K symbol always represents a constant term, and f_h and f_l are the upper and lower frequency limits of the band being considered. A means for the evaluation of K is given in the next section.

Sensitive circuits for low-frequency amplification are degraded by the presence of *1/f* noise. It appears in the FET as well as the conventional transistor. Fortunately, the planar manufacturing technique results in devices in which the *1/f* noise is not a serious limiting factor except in the most sensitive of circuits.

11–2. Noise Figure.   The measure of the noise quality of an electronic device is the *noise figure*; it is customarily given for transistors that are to be employed in low-level circuits. Noise figure F is defined in several ways, probably most widely accepted is the following definition:

$$F = \frac{\text{total available noise power at load}}{\text{available noise power at load due to thermal noise from } R_G}. \quad (11\text{–}7)$$

This definition obviously takes into account the ever-present thermal noise attributable to the source resistance R_G. If the amplifying device contributes no noise, F is unity. Naturally, a low value of F is desirable. To express noise figure in decibels, it is simply necessary to multiply $\log_{10} F$ by 10. (Available power assumes impedance matching.)

Noise figure can be expressed in terms of available S/N ratios by

$$F = \frac{S_i/N_i}{S_o/N_o}. \quad (11\text{–}8)$$

Subscripts i and o refer to input and output quantities, respectively. Since $S_o/S_i = G_a$, the available power gain, and available thermal noise power is $N_i = \overline{v_f^2}/4R_G$, Eq. (11–8) can be written as

$$F = N_o/G_a kTB. \quad (11\text{–}9)$$

In noise-figure calculations, it is useful to note that $G_a = A^2(R_G/R_o)$: R_o is the output resistance of the entire circuit, R_G is the signal-source resistance, and A is the ratio of open-circuit load voltage to the voltage of the signal source.

Generally, the total noise power in the load, the numerator of Eq. (11–7), is the result of several sources of noise acting simultaneously in the circuit. *When the noise sources are defined in mean-squared terms, and are uncorrelated, the mean-squared values may be added arithmetically.* The thermal noises generated in different resistances are examples of uncorrelated or statistically independent quantities. It is not valid to add rms noise voltages or currents; instead, the sum of rms noise voltages V_{n1} and V_{n2} is $(V_{n1}^2 + V_{n2}^2)^{1/2}$.

It is sometimes convenient to use a *spot noise figure*, F_o, which applies at a specific test frequency such as 1000 cps, with a given source resistance and a narrow bandwidth, commonly 1 cps. As an example of the conversion of a spot noise figure to the regular or *broadband* figure F, let us consider a transistor with $1/f$ the predominant noise form, and F_o given at 1000 cps for a 1-cps bandwidth. The broadband F, from Eq. (11–7) is

$$F = \frac{kTB + K' \ln(f_h/f_l)}{kTB}. \quad (11\text{–}10)$$

Equation (11–10) assumes that $1/f$ noise and the available thermal noise from R_G, kTB, are amplified equally, and that those sources are uncorrelated. Let us evaluate Eq. (11–10) when $B = 1$ cps, $f_l = 1000$ cps, and $f_h = 1001$ cps. The natural logarithm of f_h/f_l is 0.001. Then

$$F_o = 1 + \frac{K'(0.001)}{kT} = 1 + 25K'(10^{16}) \qquad \text{at } 20° \text{ C.}$$

From this equation we may determine K' by knowing F_o. Thus

$$K' = (F_o - 1)(0.04 \times 10^{-16}).$$

Substitution of this relationship into Eq. (11–10) and rearrangement gives

$$F = 1 + \frac{1000(F_o - 1)\ln(f_h/f_l)}{B}. \tag{11–11}$$

Equation (11–11) enables us to find the noise figure for any bandwidth from the "1 cps at 1000 cps" figure, provided that the source resistance encountered is of approximately the same magnitude as that used to determine F_o, and also provided that we are in the $1/f$ noise region.

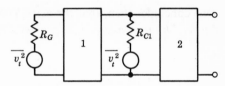

Noise in Cascaded Networks. Consider two networks in cascade as shown in Fig. 11–2. We wish to determine an expression for the noise factor of the

Fig. 11–2. Cascaded networks.

overall network in order to study the importance of stage gain upon performance. The available noise power at the input to network 2, N_{i2}, is

$$N_{i2} = F_1 G_1 kTB + kTB. \tag{11–12}$$

The first term in Eq. (11–12) is simply a rearrangement of Eq. (11–9), and the second term is the noise contribution of the load resistance R_{C1}. The second stage, *consider separately*, behaves according to

$$F_2 = N_{o2}/G_2 kTB. \tag{11–13}$$

The noise originating in the second stage is $N_{o2} - G_2 kTB$, or from Eq. (11–13) it is

$$F_2 G_2 kTB - G_2 kTB = (F_2 - 1)G_2 kTB. \tag{11–14}$$

The total output noise N_{oT} is given by the sum of terms from Eqs. (11–12) and (11–14):

$$N_{oT} = G_2(F_1 G_1 kTB + kTB) + (F_2 - 1)G_2 kTB = (F_1 G_1 G_2 + F_2 G_2)kTB. \tag{11–15}$$

It follows that the noise figure of the cascaded pair is

$$F_{12} = N_{oT}/G_1 G_2 kTB. \tag{11–16}$$

By substitution of Eq. (11-15) into Eq. (11-16) we obtain

$$F_{12} = F_1 + (F_2/G_1).$$ (11-17a)

If the anlysis is extended to three stages, we obtain

$$F_{123} = F_1 + \frac{F_2}{G_1} + \frac{F_3}{G_1 G_2}.$$ (11-17b)

This development differs slightly from the classical study by Friis, because here we consider the contribution of noise from collector load resistances.[3] If they were not included, the anlysis would yield the more familiar expression:

$$F_{123} = F_1 + \frac{F_2 - 1}{G_1} + \frac{F_3 - 1}{G_1 G_2}.$$ (11-18)

One concludes then, that *the noise figure of a cascaded network is primarily in-fluenced by first-stage noise, provided that the gain of that stage is large.*

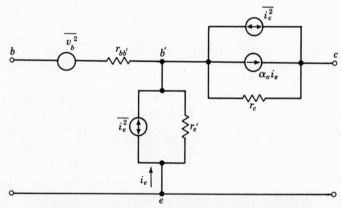

Fig. 11-3. Noise model suitable for low frequencies.

Junction Transistor Noise Figure. Nielsen has described the noise behavior of a conventional transistor by the use of three noise sources: a current generator across each junction and a voltage generator in series with the base-spreading resistance.[8] An approximate equivalent circuit useful for this study is shown in Fig. 11-3 for the transistor in the common-emitter orientation. The emitter shot noise is represented by

$$\overline{i_e^2} = 2qI_E B$$ (11-19)

and collector-junction partition noise at low frequencies by

$$\overline{i_c^2} = 2qI_C(1 - \alpha_o)B.$$ (11-20)

The base-resistance thermal noise is expressed by

$$\overline{v_b^2} = 4kTr_{bb'}B. \tag{11–21}$$

For the analysis that follows, it is convenient to represent the sources of noise by voltage generators. Thus

$$\overline{v_e^2} = \overline{i_e^2}r_e'^2 = 2kTr_e'B \tag{11–22}$$

and

$$\overline{v_c^2} = 2qI_C(1 - \alpha_o)r_c^2B = (2kT\alpha_o/r_e')(1 - \alpha_o)r_c^2B. \tag{11–23}$$

In order to include the effects of higher frequencies, collector capacitance and frequency variations in α must be included in $\overline{v_c^2}$.

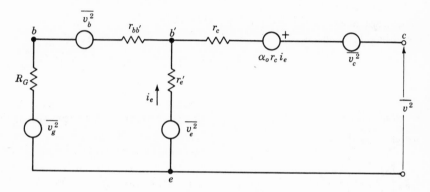

Fig. 11–4. Circuit for determination of F.

The complete circuit for calculation of F is shown in Fig. 11–4. The model is left unconnected to any load because noise figure is independent of load, if the assumption is made that the load resistance is noiseless. For the purpose of this analysis, it is necessary to temporarily assign a polarity to certain noise voltages in order to assess their contribution to output noise. The open-circuit output noise is made up of four parts, $\overline{v_c^2}$, $\overline{v_e^2}$, $\overline{(\alpha_o r_c i_e)^2}$, and $\overline{(i_e r_e')^2}$. Thus, upon summation, we obtain

$$\overline{v_o^2} = \overline{v_c^2} + \overline{v_e^2} + (\alpha_o r_c)^2\left(\frac{\overline{v_e^2} + \overline{v_b^2} + \overline{v_g^2}}{(\Sigma R)^2}\right) - r_e'^2\left(\frac{\overline{v_e^2} + \overline{v_b^2} + \overline{v_g^2}}{(\Sigma R)^2}\right) \tag{11–24}$$

with

$$\Sigma R = r_{bb'} + R_G + r_e'.$$

Since $\alpha_o r_c \gg r_e'$, Eq. (11–24) can readily be simplified by elimination of the final term. To determine F, we divide Eq. (11–24) by the fraction of $\overline{v_o^2}$ caused by $\overline{v_g^2}$, in other words by $(\alpha_o r_c)^2 \overline{v_g^2}/(\Sigma R)^2$. Therefore

$$F = 1 + \frac{\overline{v_b^2}}{\overline{v_g^2}} + \frac{\overline{v_e^2}}{\overline{v_g^2}} + \frac{(\overline{v_e^2} + \overline{v_c^2})(\Sigma R)^2}{(\alpha_o r_c)^2 \overline{v_g^2}} \qquad (11\text{--}25)$$

or

$$F = 1 + \frac{r_{bb'}}{R_G} + \frac{r_e'}{2R_G} + \frac{[2kTr_e'B + 2kT\alpha_o(1 - \alpha_o)r_c^2 B/r_e'](\Sigma R)^2}{4kTBR_G\alpha_o^2 r_c^2}. \qquad (11\text{--}26)$$

For $\overline{v_e^2} \ll \overline{v_c^2}$,

$$F = 1 + \frac{r_{bb'}}{R_G} + \frac{r_e'}{2R_G} + \frac{(1 - \alpha_o)(\Sigma R)^2}{2R_G\alpha_o r_e'}. \qquad (11\text{--}27)$$

It can be shown that the noise figure for a common-base stage is also given by Eq. (11–27) (see Problem 11–4).

The more general form of Eq. (11–27) that includes frequency effects is derived in Problem 11–5 and is

$$F = 1 + \frac{r_{bb'}}{R_G} + \frac{r_e'}{2R_G} + \frac{(1 - \alpha_o)(\Sigma R)^2}{2R_G\alpha_o r_e'} \left\{ 1 + \left[\frac{f}{f_{\alpha b}(1 - \alpha_o)^{1/2}} \right]^2 \right\}. \qquad (11\text{--}28)$$

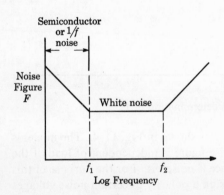

Fig. 11–5. Noise output of a typical transistor.

The curve of Fig. 11–5, a plot of noise figure vs. frequency, summarizes transistor noise. Semiconductor noise is responsible for high values of F below f_1; white noise predominates above f_1. The expression for F, Eq. (11–28), predicts the high-frequency rise. For some transistor types f_1 is in the neighborhood of 100 cps, and some high-frequency devices are available with f_2 in the hundreds of megacycles.

Minimizing the Noise Figure. The noise figure for a transistor stage depends to a large extent upon the source resistance of the circuit under consideration and upon the selected operating point. These conclusions may be reached from examination of the test data shown in Fig. 11–6, and from analytic study of Eq. (11–27). R_G is evident in that equation, and the operating point is implied in the value of r_e'.

To find a minimum of F with respect to R_G, we set $dF/dR_G = 0$ from Eq. (11–27). The resulting optimum of R_G is

$$R_{G(\text{opt})} = r_{bb'} \left[1 + \frac{(r_e'/r_{bb'})^2 + 2r_e'/r_{bb'}}{1 - \alpha_o} \right]^{1/2}. \qquad (11\text{--}29)$$

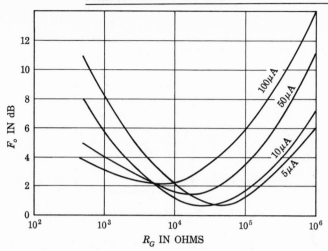

Fig. 11–6. F_o vs. R_G at 1 kc for various values of I_C. $B = 200$ cps. Sample is a silicon planar transistor.

The minimum noise figure is available from Eq. (11–27) with R_G given by Eq. (11–29), and is

$$F_{\min} = 1 + \frac{1}{\beta_o r_e'} \{[(r_{bb'} + r_e')^2 + (r_{bb'} + r_e'/2)2\beta_o r_e']^{1/2} + (r_{bb'} + r_e')\}. \quad (11\text{–}30)$$

The optimum value for R_G as given by Eq. (11–29) is close to the value of the input resistance of a transistor connected common-emitter, but differs considerably from the input resistance of a common-base stage. Therefore, if the optimum R_G is used with a common-base stage, the optimum amplification will not be achieved.

The noise-figure expression, Eq. (11–27), can be alternately visualized as the result of two noise generators, rather than three. The simple terms involving $r_{bb'}$ and r_e' can be combined into a single element, an equivalent noisy resistance of value

$$R_{eq} = r_{bb'} + r_e'/2 \quad (11\text{–}31)$$

in series with the base terminal. The final term is of the form of a shot noise source representable by

$$\overline{i_n^2} = 2q(I_E/\beta_o)B. \quad (11\text{–}32)$$

It is convenient to use the assumption that $I_E/\beta_o = I_C/h_{FE}$. This two-generator representation is given in Fig. 11–7. In terms of ac resistances and operating-point quantities, the optimum source resistance is found to be

$$R_{G(\text{opt})} = \left(\frac{R_{eq}h_{FE}}{20I_C}\right)^{1/2}, \quad (11\text{–}33)$$

where $20 = q/2kT$ at $290°$ K. Equation (11–33) also may be obtained from Eq. (11–27); it is not necessary to utilize the two-generator method; however, such an approach is often discussed in the literature.

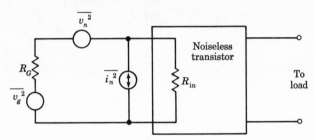

Fig. 11–7.   Two-generator noise model.

Noise in FET circuits. Noise in field-effect transistors results from several sources: thermal noise in the channel and the bulk resistances, shot noise at the gate–channel junction, and some *1/f* noise. The analysis of behavior of the device is complicated by considerable feedback of noise through C_{gd} to the input.

A noise figure for the junction FET stage that neglects *1/f* noise has been given by Bechtel[1] and is

$$F = F_{opt} + R_n R_G (G_G - G_o)^2. \qquad (11-34)$$

In Eq. (11–34) F_{opt} is the optimum noise figure ($F = F_{opt}$ when $G_G = G_o$), and G_G the conductance of the signal source. The quantity F_{opt} is decribed by

$$F_{opt} \cong 1 + 2R_n G_o \qquad (11-35)$$

with $G_o \cong \omega(C_{gs} + C_{gd})$ and $R_n \cong \lambda/g_m$. The constant λ has been measured and values of 0.3 to 0.8 obtained. Equation (11–34) shows F to have considerable dependence upon source resistance R_G. The optimum noise figure is seen to be dependent upon device capacitances, transconductance, and frequency. Test data on typical units show F to be quite independent of V_{DS} and I_D.

Noise testing. A common test for noise figure uses a *noise* diode operating in its temperature-limited emission mode; it is known to produce a noise current

$$\overline{i_{nd}^2} = 2qI_{dc}B \qquad (11-36)$$

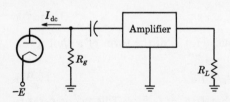

Fig. 11–8.   Noise diode test arrangement.

The direct plate current is I_{dc}. When the amplifier in Fig. 11–8. is not loading the input circuit, the rms value of diode noise voltage across R_G is

$$V_{nd} = I_{nd}R_G. \qquad (11-37)$$

A reading of true rms amplifier output, V_l, may be taken with zero noise diode current. V_l is composed of amplified thermal noise from R_G, and transistor noise, but the amplification need not necessarily be known. Upon adjustment of the direct current through the diode so that an amplifier output of *twice* the preceding power level is attained,

$$2\left(\frac{V_l^2}{R_L}\right) = \frac{(A_v V_{nd})^2}{R_L} + \frac{V_l^2}{R_L}. \qquad (11\text{--}38)$$

Equation (11–38) may be solved for A_v with the result that

$$A_v = V_l/V_{nd}. \qquad (11\text{--}39a)$$

To determine the no-load voltage gain, we note that

$$A = A_v(R_L + R_o)/R_L. \qquad (11\text{--}39b)$$

From the definition, noise figure is the ratio of total available output noise power ($V_o^2/4R_o$) to thermal noise power due to R_G as given by Eq. (11–1). This ratio is

$$F = \frac{V_o^2/4R_o}{G_a V_t^2/4R_G} = \frac{V_o^2/4R_o}{A^2(R_G/R_o)(V_t^2/4R_G)} = \frac{V_{nd}^2}{V_t^2} \qquad (11\text{--}40)$$

Therefore, at room temperature,

$$F = \frac{2qI_{dc}R_G^2 B}{4kTBR_G} = 20I_{dc}R_G. \qquad (11\text{--}41)$$

Noise figure can be determined from knowledge of the source resistance and the diode direct current required to double output noise power.

11–3. Volume Control. It is often necessary to provide a manual means for setting or adjusting the gain of many types of circuits: audio amplifiers, servo amplifiers, radio and television receivers. The placement of a variable resistance in a transistor circuit for this purpose is complicated by the absence of isolation between stages, and therefore the choice of location for the control requires a great deal of study. When deciding upon a location, attention must be paid to the following:

1. The volume control should usually provide for complete attenuation of the signal.
2. DC biasing should not be upset by the adjustment of the control.
3. Over-all frequency response should not suffer as a result of changed impedance levels.
4. The load on a stage should not be shifted by adjustment of the control because of distortion considerations.
5. If the control is located too near the circuit input, the S/N ratio may be adversely affected.

6. Location of the control too near the circuit output may allow over-loading of prior stages.
7. Direct current through the control will contribute to circuit noise.
8. The taper specification for the potentiometer should not be unrealistic.

In nearly all installations, a compromise results, as circumvention of all the limitations posed by the items listed is impossible. Generally, the location of the control is near the circuit input, often items 3 and 4 cannot be completely satisfied, and consequently frequency response is dependent to some extent upon control setting.

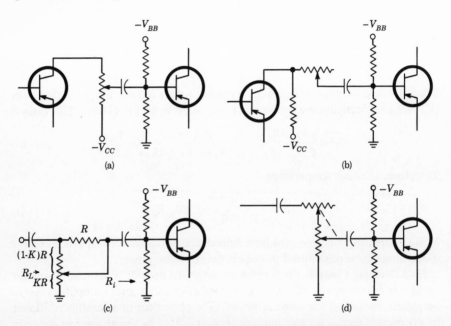

Fig. 11–9.   Volume control placement and arrangements.

Indiscriminate positioning of the volume control is liable to cause undesirable circuit operation; therefore, with the help of several illustrations, let us briefly investigate the problem. Consider the circuit of Fig. 11–9(a). The volume-control setting will affect the ac load line of the first stage and may or may not cause trouble. Circuit frequency response will change with setting and direct collector current in the potentiometer can result in noisy volume variation. The taper of the control must be tailored for the application. For the series control circuit of Fig. 11–9(b) complete attenuation is not possible; however, the control does not pass any dc. The rheostat will be several hundred thousand ohms, but near its low end it may affect the load on stage number one. Frequency effects will be small.

In the circuit of Fig. 11–9(c), consider all resistances including the control to be equal to the nominal input resistance of the following stage. Let us investigate the resistance (R_L) presented by this combination to the preceding stage. K designates the fraction of the variable control tuned in. The load is given by

$$R_L = \frac{R[(1 - K)R]}{R + (1 - K)R} + \frac{RKR}{R + KR}.$$

So

$$R_L = R\left[\frac{1 + 2K - 2K^2}{2 + K - K^2}\right]. \tag{11–42}$$

At each end of the setting, $R_L = 0.5R$, and at the center $R_L = 0.67R$. When we consider that this network will be paralleled by the collector resistor of the preceding stage, this variation in R_L is not too great for many applications.

An effective means of volume control is illustrated in Fig. 11–9(d). This system makes use of two ganged potentiometers to maintain a constant load on the preceding stage. The taper of the pots can be chosen for the desired degree of constancy.

Many other arrangements are possible. In radio receivers, the control is almost always located at the output of the second detector (see Chapter 10). A feedback line oftentimes provides a convenient place for gain control; the amount of feedback is adjusted to determine over-all amplifier gain.

11–4. Shaping the Frequency Response. The designer of an audio amplifier is almost always required to provide frequency-insensitive amplification throughout the audio range, usually considered as 20 to 20,000 cps. While oftentimes the cost of precision components alters this general specification, nevertheless the problem of adequate frequency response is always prevalent. For amplifiers used in control systems a flat response is generally required although the frequency range specification is narrower than for audio circuits.

In addition to the basic flat response requirement, the circuit designer usually must provide a network or series of networks for shaping the frequency-response characteristic to equalize variations that may be due to other devices or circuits or requirements (such as the human ear). In audio-amplifier circuits, it is desirable to provide for manual adjustment of the frequency response (such a circuit is generally termed a tone control). Placement of an adjustment of this type is a more complex problem in a transistor circuit than in a vacuum-tube circuit because the tone-control network is always loaded down by the input resistance of the transistor stage that follows.

One solution to the tone-control location problem is to incorporate a frequency-selective network in a feedback loop. More often it will be found preceding one of the early stages of a cascade amplifier. A statisfactory arrangement is shown in Fig. 11–10. A shunt circuit consisting of a capacitor and an adjustable resistance precedes a stage with emitter feedback. The input resistance of the transistor has been boosted to perhaps 25,000 to 50,000 Ω in order to minimize its loading effect upon the R-C leg. The operation of a circuit of this type may be analyzed by considering the signal current that reaches the transistor base at various frequencies. At low frequencies, the shunt capacitor will present a large reactance to the signal, and so nearly all of the signal will reach the transistor base, but at high frequencies where the reactive effect of the capacitor is negligible, signal current will find an easier path to ground through the R-C network and thus a smaller proportion will reach the base. Such a circuit can be classified as "treble cut" because it serves to attenuate higher frequencies.

Consider a transistor amplifier being fed from a signal source of voltage V_g and internal resistance R_g as shown in Fig. 11-11. It is our desire to investigate

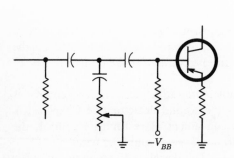

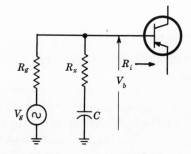

Fig. 11-10. Sample tone-control circuit.　　Fig. 11-11. Equalizing network.

the transfer function V_b/V_g, which represents the ratio of voltage available at the base of the transistor (and consequently base current) to the transducer-voltage output. A solution of the circuit for the required transfer function yields

$$\frac{V_b}{V_g} = \frac{R_i(1 + j\omega C R_x)}{(R_g + R_i) + j\omega C(R_g R_x + R_g R_i + R_x R_i)}. \qquad (11\text{-}43)$$

At very low frequencies (i.e., $\omega \to 0$)

$$\frac{V_b}{V_g} = \frac{R_i}{R_g + R_i}, \qquad (11\text{-}44a)$$

and at very high frequencies (i.e., $\omega \to \infty$)

$$\frac{V_b}{V_g} = \frac{R_i R_x}{R_g R_x + R_g R_i + R_x R_i}. \qquad (11\text{-}44b)$$

The denominator term of Eq. (11-43) will be frequency sensitive at lower values of ω than will the numerator; consequently the equation predicts an increasing attenuation throughout the frequency band from the first "break" that occurs at

$$\omega_{lo} = \frac{R_g + R_i}{C(R_gR_x + R_gR_i + R_xR_i)} \qquad (11\text{--}45)$$

to the high-frequency "break" due to the numerator term that occurs at

$$\omega_{hi} = \frac{1}{CR_x}. \qquad (11\text{--}46)$$

The frequency response of the transfer function V_b/V_g is plotted as Fig. 11–12.

A break frequency results when any term in an equation takes on the form $K \pm jK$. At frequencies below the break, the term is primarily real, above the break, the term is primarily imaginary. Analysis of frequency-variant expressions by means of break frequencies and straight-line diagrams is reserved

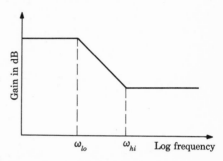

Fig. 11–12. Performance of the network of Fig. 11–11.

for other texts. The reader is referred to any book on feedback control systems for discussion of this method of analysis.

The range of adjustment afforded by variation in R_x can be seen from examination of the break-frequency expressions. If R_x approaches zero ohms, then ω_{lo} increases because the magnitude of the denominator of Eq. (11–45) has been reduced, and ω_{hi} is extended out to infinite frequency. An increase in R_x will have the opposite effects, the low-frequency break will occur at even lower frequencies and the high-frequency break will also occur at a lower ω.

Example. It is desired to design a frequency-selective network to precede the first stage of an audio amplifier; the input resistance of the transistor is 1000 Ω, and the source resistance is 1000 Ω. The network should attenuate frequencies above 1000 cps, and we are not interested in the range above 10,000 cps.

We shall use the circuit of Fig. 11–11. The circuit elements to be determined are C and R_x. If we set $\omega_{lo} = 2\pi(1000)$ rad/sec and $\omega_{hi} = 2\pi(10,000)$ rad/sec, then R_x may be determined by noting that

$$\frac{\omega_{hi}}{\omega_{lo}} = \frac{2\pi(10,000)}{2\pi(1000)} = 10 = \frac{1/CR_x}{(R_g + R_i)/C(R_gR_x + R_gR_i + R_xR_i)}.$$

Therefore, $R_x = 55.6\ \Omega$. Then we may determine C from the formula for ω_{hi}: $C = 0.286\ \mu\text{F}$.

It is interesting to note that the size of R_x is mainly dependent upon R_g and is fairly independent of the network load resistance R_i for small values of R_g. When driven from a current source, i.e., when R_g is large, R_x may take on higher values.

Equalization networks are useful in audio amplifiers to shape the frequency response in accordance with some predetermined specification. An example of a requirement of this type is furnished by the Record Industry Association of America (RIAA); phonograph records that have been cut according to their strandards require, for flat frequency reproduction, an equalizing network within the amplifier whose operation should be as shown in Fig. 11–13. A network to achieve a response of this type will include a shunt leg consisting of R and C in series at the amplifier input.

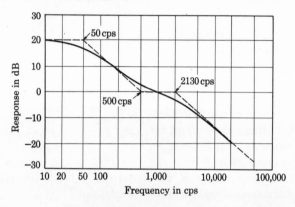

Fig. 11–13. RIAA playback (reproducing) characteristic.

In the field of automatic controls (servomechanisms, etc.), frequency-response shaping is commonplace, and numerous networks have been presented and analyzed by many authors. The voltage-transfer function (ratio of output to input voltage) is usually given for such equalizing networks under the assumption of no loading of the network by the amplifier or circuit that follows. Because of the finite nature of transistor input resistance, transfer functions for unloaded networks must be modified when connected preceding a transistor. A common-collector, degenerative common-emitter, or FET stage is often employed to provide some degree of isolation.

Stereo Amplifier. The schematic of an audio amplifier, one channel of a dual-channel stereo-phonograph system, is shown in Fig. 11–14. This system applies many of the principles previously discussed in this and earlier chapters. Direct voltages measured at the various nodes are noted on the diagram.

Biasing of transistors Q_1, Q_2, and Q_3 is by the self-bias technique, with base current developed from the quiescent collector voltage. A modified form of self-bias is used for Q_2 with the base returned to ground through $R10$. Each of these stages uses unbypassed emitter resistance, primarily to decrease the loading effect upon preceding circuitry. With a pick-up having a capacitive output impedance, increasing the resistance of the bass control causes increased passage of low frequencies and thus a bass boost. The playback characteristic is obtained

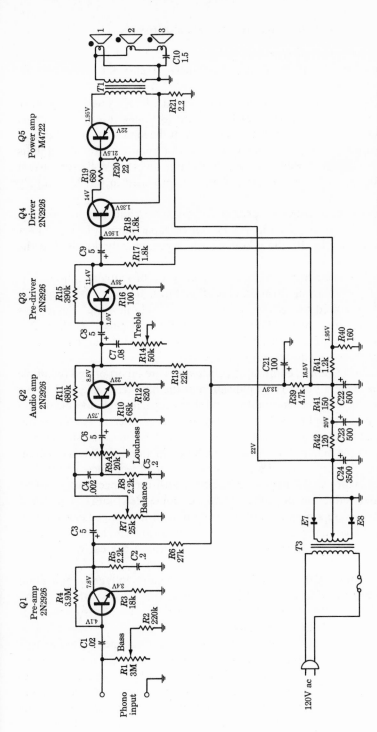

Fig. 11–14. Hi-Fi amplifier (Courtesy Motorola, Inc.). DC voltages noted are measured in absence of input signal.

by the frequency-shaping networks at the outputs of Q_1 and Q_2. The balance control allows equalization of the stereo channels. Treble cut is achieved by adjustment of $R14$.

Base biasing for the driver is obtained by feeding the 1.95-V line through $R18$. The operating point for the driver is at 10 mA and 13 V, and it is direct coupled to the p–n–p power stage. Degenerative feedback of the load signal through $R21$ is used. The output stage is operating Class A with its emitter grounded and its base bias obtained through $R20$. Because of the large quiescent collector-current requirement for the output stage, little filtering is provided in the 22-V supply line.

The load at low frequencies is speaker 1. Speakers 2 and 3 reproduce frequencies high enough to pass the 1.5 μF series capacitance. The amplifier voltage gain is nominally 30, the power gain is approximately 40 dB, and the rated output power level is 2 W.

11–5. The Video Amplifier. A video-frequency or broadband amplifier is one capable of providing uniform amplification throughout a wide frequency range; often the required range is from 30 or 60 cps to about 4 Mc. Sometimes the bandwidth requirement is different from the numbers cited, as they refer to applications in the television field, but in general a video amplifier must exhibit a flat response out to several megacycles.

To achieve a flat response, compensating networks are incorporated to couple stages and to provide a boost in amplification at the high-frequency end of the video spectrum where alpha deterioration and shunt capacitances have maximum effect. Transformer coupling is not used, because of its inherent narrow bandwidth; R-C coupling with associated peaking networks nas become standard.

As discussed in the material of Chapter 6, a falloff in amplification is apparent at low frequencies in a transistor circuit because of the high reactances of coupling or blocking capacitors. At high frequencies, transistor capacitances, wiring capacitance, and reduction in alpha are to be contended with. The shunt capacitances will cause a minimum of difficulty if low input impedance connections (such as the common-base or common-emitter) are employed; however, the rapid reduction in α and β with frequency can cause a great deal of gain reduction.

For circuits employing the common-emitter connection, voltage amplification is satisfactory well beyond $f_{\alpha e}$; nevertheless, unless transistors with very high cutoff frequencies can be afforded, it is necessary to provide some sort of compensation to extend the usable range.

Let us first discuss extension of flat response to low frequencies. Transistors themselves present no problems because parameters are real and constant. Direct-coupled video amplifier stages are possible, and will add no low-frequency operational restrictions, but the problem of drift with direct coupling has, in the past, caused most designers to choose capacitive coupling. The capacitor to be used must be of high value because impedance levels are low;

since biasing potentials are also low (as compared with tube circuits), the physical size of large coupling capacitors is not objectionable for most applications.

It is often desirable to employ a low-frequency compensating network for the purpose of extending flat response. Such a circuit appears in Fig. 11–15. At low frequencies current leaving the collector of the first transistor sees $R_1 - jX_{c2}$ in parallel with $R_i - jX_c$, and at higher frequencies the effective stage load is R_1 paralleled by R_i. It is desired that the current through R_i be independent of frequency at low frequencies, a condition that can be achieved if

$$R_1/R_i = C/C_2. \tag{11-47}$$

R_2 must be a great deal larger than X_{c2} for Eq. (11–47) to be valid. Proof of this criterion is left to the reader (Problem 11–9).

Should a practical size of R_2 cause unsatisfactory performance, improvement may be noted if a resistor in series with a very large capacitor is inserted to shunt C. This shunting resistor across C should match R_2 across C_2.

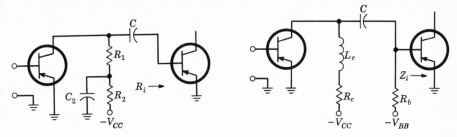

Fig. 11–15. Low-frequency compensating network coupling video amplifier stages.

Fig. 11–16. Shunt peaking circuit for wide-band amplification.

Turning our attention to high-frequency performance, it is usually desired to flatten the amplifier gain frequency curve to several megacycles. Here the problem is to compensate the transistor for its high-frequency limitations; this compensation is achieved in the interstage coupling network or in a transistor emitter leg where signal feedback is affected. The current gain–bandwidth product is given by the transistor parameter f_T. Reduction in gain by employing feedback extends the frequency response of a transistor stage as noted in the preceding chapter. The trading of gain for bandwidth is commonplace.

One means of extending frequency response is to incorporate a frequency-sensitive collector-circuit network that steals a considerable current from the actual circuit load when low-frequency signals are present and transistor amplification is high, but drains little or no current away from the actual circuit load at high frequencies. Such a circuit is the R-L shunt of Fig. 11–16. The shunt inductance is a low reactance at low frequencies, and the transistor collector sees R_c paralleling Z_i. The high reactance of L_c at high frequencies results in an ac circuit load which is essentially Z_i. Extension of response to higher frequencies may be achieved by adding a series "peaking" coil (in series with the coupling capacitor C).

Synthesis of video amplifiers generally proceeds experimentally because of the many complex quantities that are present, and some parameters change value with frequency. Shunt capacitances and reactive loads tend to make mathematical analysis difficult; such studies are available in the literature.[13]

Video amplifiers often feed a high-impedance load, such as a cathode-ray tube, and consequently the final video stage is required to provide a large degree of voltage amplification. Capacitances represent a problem with high-impedance levels; another problem encountered is the required peak-to-peak voltage swing, and thus a high-frequency, high-voltage power transistor is required.

Some additional video amplifier considerations are evident in Sec. 13–3.

11–6. Tuned-Circuit Theory. Before discussing the tuned amplifier a review of the applicable portion of circuit theory will be undertaken.

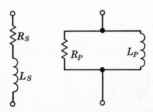

Fig. 11–17. Series and parallel R-L circuits.

Impedance Transformations. First let us investigate the mathematical transformation of series and parallel impedances. Consider the series R-L and the parallel R-L circuits of Fig. 11–17. The impedance of the series circuit is

$$Z_S = R_S + jX_{LS}, \qquad (11\text{–}48)$$

and of the parallel circuit is

$$Z_P = jX_{LP}R_P/(R_P + jX_{LP}). \qquad (11\text{–}49)$$

The S and P subscripts pertain to series and parallel circuits, respectively. If we wish to equate the two impedances, then

$$R_S + jX_{LS} = jX_{LP}R_P/(R_P + jX_{LP}). \qquad (11\text{–}50)$$

Multiplication of both numerator and denominator of the righthand side by the conjugate of the denominator, and separation of real and imaginary terms, gives

$$R_S + jX_{LS} = \frac{X_{LP}{}^2 R_P}{R_P{}^2 + X_{LP}{}^2} + \frac{jX_{LP}R_P{}^2}{R_P{}^2 + X_{LP}{}^2}. \qquad (11\text{–}51)$$

To find the series resistance equivalent to the resistance of the parallel circuit, equate reals; thus

$$R_S = X_{LP}{}^2 R_P/(R_P{}^2 + X_{LP}{}^2), \qquad (11\text{–}52)$$

and the series inductive reactance that can take the place of the parallel circuit reactance is

$$X_{LS} = X_{LP}R_P{}^2/(R_P{}^2 + X_{LP}{}^2). \qquad (11\text{–}53)$$

If the admittances of each type of circuit are equated,

$$R_P = (R_S^2 + X_{LS}^2)/R_S, \tag{11-54}$$

and

$$X_{LP} = (R_S^2 + X_{LS}^2)/X_{LS}. \tag{11-55}$$

Equations (11–52), (11–53), (11–54), and (11–55) provide the tools for conversion from one circuit form to the other. These relationships can be employed when the circuits contain R and C rather than R and L. For this use it is only necessary to replace each X_L in Eqs. (11–52) through (11–55) by X_C.

Let us now define the Q or figure of merit of the series circuit previously considered as the ratio of inductive reactance to resistance

$$Q = X_{LS}/R_S \tag{11-56}$$

at any designated frequency. Equation (11–56) is a practical form of the more general relation,

$$Q = 2\pi \left[\frac{\text{energy stored in electric and magnetic fields per cycle}}{\text{energy dissipated per cycle}} \right].$$

The series definition of Q may be used for a parallel circuit by making use of the proved interrelations, Eqs. (11–52) and (11–53). The division indicated in Eq. (11–56) yields

$$Q = R_P/X_{LP}. \tag{11-57}$$

By equating admittances of the two circuits, the following relationships can be proved:

$$R_P = R_S(1 + Q^2) \tag{11-58}$$

and

$$X_{LP} = X_{LS}(1 + 1/Q^2). \tag{11-59}$$

A single inductance coil is, in reality, a series R-L circuit. Therefore such a coil is often described by its own Q, the ratio of its series reactance to resistance at a specific frequency. The discussion of the preceding paragraphs pertains to complete circuits or to single coils; in the material that follows, Q_C will be used to designate the quality factor of a single coil while the symbol Q will be reserved for use as a measure of over-all circuit selectivity.

The circuit consisting of a parallel combination of capacitance and a practical inductance coil shown in Fig. 11–18(a) can now be replaced mathematically by the parallel R-L-C circuit of Fig. 11–18(b), the value of R being given by Eq. (11–58). As an example consider a coil with a Q_C of 100 and

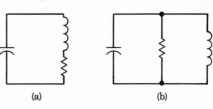

(a)   (b)

Fig. 11–18.   Tuned-circuit equivalence.

R_S of 10 Ω. Equations (11–58) and (11–59) enable us to substitute inductive reactance of 1000 Ω (essentially the same as the series reactance because of the high quality of the coil).

We have, therefore, an undamped or coil quality factor Q_C, and a circuit quality factor Q, the latter being defined by Eq. (11–57) as the ratio of parallel resistance to inductive reactance at the specified or resonant frequency. In the preceding numerical example Q and Q_C were identical, for no additional circuit resistance or inductance was present. Often, in practice, such tuned circuits will be "damped" by parallel resistance and a distinct difference will be observed between Q_C and Q.

Example. The coil with $Q_C = 100$ at 100 kc and $R_S = 10$ Ω is to be used in a tuned circuit to resonate at 100 kc, and the over-all circuit shall exhibit a working Q of 20. Find the necessary parallel capacitance to resonate the entire circuit at the specified frequency, the circuit impedance at resonance, and the value of the additonal parallel damping resistance necessary to provide the the required Q.

At 100 kc, if $X_{CP} = X_{LP}$, the circuit will exhibit its maximum driving-point impedance, total current and voltage will be in phase, and resonance achieved. Therefore

$$\frac{1}{\omega C} = 1000.$$

The required value of shunt capacitance is

$$C = \frac{1}{2\pi(10^5)1000} = 0.0016 \ \mu\text{F}.$$

Q is the ratio of total parallel resistance to X_{LP}, and is given by

$$Q = 20 = \frac{R_a 10^5/(R_a + 10^5)}{1000},$$

so

$$R_a = 25{,}000 \ \Omega.$$

R_a must be inserted in parallel with the coil to achieve the proper degree of damping. The impedance of the composite circuit at the resonant frequency is

$$R_a 10^5/(R_a + 10^5) = 20{,}000 \ \Omega.$$

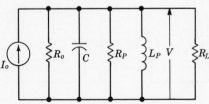

Fig. 11–19. General interstage circuit.

Insertion Loss. The analysis of the tuned circuit will now be extended to the more complete and practical configuration of circuit elements shown in Fig. 11–19. R_o is being used to represent the output resistance of a transistor stage, R_L is the terminating or load resistance, R_P is coil resistance, C is the total parallel capacitance, and L_P the parallel inductance. The current generator I_o is feeding the circuit at the resonant frequency.

To find the insertion loss due to the finite Q_C of the coil in the circuit with an over-all quality of Q we can compare the load power delivered under ideal and actual conditions.

Power to the load with an ideal coil ($R_P = \infty$) is

$$P_L(\text{ideal}) = \frac{V^2}{R_L} = \frac{I_o^2 R^2}{R_L}, \tag{11–60}$$

where R is the parallel combination of R_O and R_L and

$$1/R = G_O + G_L.$$

Power to the load with actual or practical coil having equivalent parallel resistance R_E is given by

$$P_L(\text{actual}) = \frac{V^2}{R_L} = \frac{I_o^2 R'^2}{R_L} \tag{11–61}$$

with

$$1/R' = G_O + G_L + G_P.$$

The ratio of delivered powers is

$$\frac{P_L(\text{actual})}{P_L(\text{ideal})} = \frac{I_o^2 R'^2 / R_L}{I_o^2 R^2 / R_L} = \frac{R'^2}{R^2} = \left(\frac{G_O + G_L}{G_O + G_P + G_L}\right)^2. \tag{11–62}$$

Circuit Q is

$$Q = \frac{R'}{X_P} = \frac{1}{(G_O + G_P + G_L)X_P}. \tag{11–63}$$

After making the substitution that $X_P = R_P/Q_C$ we solve Eq. (11–63) for $G_O + G_L$

$$G_O + G_L = \frac{Q_C - Q}{QR_P}. \tag{11–64}$$

Manipulation of Eqs. (11–63) and (11–64) yields

$$\left(\frac{G_O + G_L}{G_O + G_P + G_L}\right)^2 = \left(\frac{(Q_C - Q)/QR_P}{Q_C/QR_P}\right)^2. \tag{11–65}$$

Therefore the required ratio is given by

$$\frac{P_L(\text{actual})}{P_L(\text{ideal})} = \left(\frac{Q_C - Q}{Q_C}\right)^2, \tag{11–66a}$$

and

$$\text{Insertion loss (in dB)} = 20 \log \frac{Q_C}{Q_C - Q}. \tag{11-66b}$$

Bandwidth. Bandwidth was defined in a preceding chapter as the frequency span between half-power points, and, of course, half-power points are the frequencies where power gain or power transmission has decreased to one-half of its mid-frequency or reference value. The half-points correspond to a reduction in voltage or current ratio to 0.707 or $1/\sqrt{2}$ of the reference value.

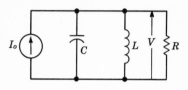

Fig. 11–20.   Composite interstage circuit.

At this stage it is desired to find a relation between bandwidth, resonant frequency, and over-all quality factor. The circuit of Fig. 11–20 uses single R, L, and C elements to represent the composite of output, coupling, and load quantities. It follows that

$$\frac{V}{I_o} = \frac{j\omega LR}{R(1 - \omega^2 LC) + j\omega L}. \tag{11-67}$$

Load current is proportional to V, although the load resistance was not segregated in Fig. 11–20, and at resonance $V/I_o = R$. Therefore, to examine Eq. (11–67) at the half-power points where ω is designated as ω_3, we may write

$$\left| \frac{V}{I_o} \right| = \frac{R}{\sqrt{2}} = \frac{\omega_3 LR}{[R^2(1 - \omega_3^2 LC)^2 + \omega_3^2 L^2]^{1/2}}. \tag{11-68}$$

After making the substitutions that

$$Q = \frac{R}{\omega_r L_P} \quad \text{and} \quad \omega_r = \frac{1}{\sqrt{L_P C}} \tag{11-69}$$

and rearrangement, Eq. (11–68) may be written as

$$\omega_3^4(Q^2/\omega_r^2) - \omega_3^2(1 + 2Q^2) + Q^2\omega_r^2 = 0. \tag{11-70}$$

The solution for ω_3, if negative frequencies are omitted, is

$$\omega_3 = \left[\frac{1 + 2Q^2 \pm (1 + 4Q^2)^{1/2}}{2Q^2/\omega_r^2} \right]^{1/2}. \tag{11-71}$$

Now bandwidth is defined by

$$B = f_h - f_l = (\omega_{3h} - \omega_{3l})/2\pi. \tag{11-72}$$

Substitute Eq. (11–71) in Eq. (11–72) and square to eliminate the radicals.

Finally take the square root of each side of the resulting equation to obtain

$$B = f_r/Q, \qquad (11\text{-}73)$$

the required relationship.

The relations involving B, Q, Q_C, R_o, R_L, R_P, R, and ω_r can be juggled to arrive at a number of useful formulas; several such rearrangements will now be presented. From

$$B = f_r/Q, \quad f_r = 1/(2\pi\sqrt{L_P C}), \quad \text{and} \quad Q = R/\omega_r L_P, \qquad (11\text{-}74)$$

solution for C gives

$$C = 1/\omega_r^2 L_P. \qquad (11\text{-}75)$$

Equation (11–75) can be written as

$$C = Q/\omega_r R \qquad (11\text{-}76)$$

or as

$$C = 1/2\pi BR. \qquad (11\text{-}77)$$

Recall that

$$Q_C = R_P/\omega_r L_P \quad \text{or} \quad R_P = \omega_r L_P Q_C \qquad (11\text{-}78)$$

and that

$$Q = R/\omega_r L_P, \qquad (11\text{-}79)$$

and furthermore that

$$\frac{1}{R} = \frac{1}{R_o} + \frac{1}{R_L} + \frac{1}{\omega_r L_P Q_C}, \qquad (11\text{-}80)$$

to arrive at

$$Q = 1 \Big/ \left[\omega_r L_P \left(\frac{1}{R_o} + \frac{1}{R_L} + \frac{1}{\omega_r L_P Q_C} \right) \right]. \qquad (11\text{-}81)$$

L_P may be obtained from Eq. (11–81). Thus

$$L_P = \frac{R_o R_L (Q_C - Q)}{\omega_r (R_L + R_o) Q Q_C}. \qquad (11\text{-}82)$$

Under matched conditions, $R_o = R_L$ and Eq. (11–82) becomes

$$L_P = R_o(Q_C - Q)/2\omega_r Q Q_C. \qquad (11\text{-}83)$$

11-7. Tuned Amplifiers. When an active circuit is required to amplify a specific band of frequencies and reject signals of higher or lower frequencies, it is commonly referred to as a *tuned* or *narrow-band* amplifier. The word tuned, in this instance, refers to the circuit load that is normally a parallel *L-C* circuit designed to resonate at the carrier frequency (the middle frequency of the band to be passed). Although amplifiers of this type are referred to as narrow-band circuits, the bandwidth that is successfully passed may be many kilocycles or megacycles. Tuned circuits pass a band that is narrow when compared with the magnitude of the carrier frequency.

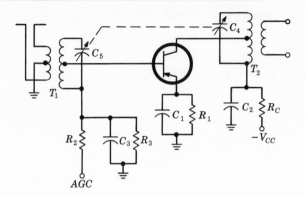

Fig. 11–21.   Typical R.F. amplifying stage.

In communications receiver circuits, composite radio-frequency signals are picked up by the antenna and fed to the *radio-frequency* (R.F.) amplifying stage; a circuit of this type is shown in Fig. 11–21. The antenna transformer is tuned to select the carrier frequency of the station to be received, and the load on the stage is also a tuned circuit. For the AM broadcast band, the R.F. stage is required to amplify signals from 550 to 1600 kc; a comparable FM circuit covers 88 to 108 Mc. For television reception, the R.F. amplifier must be capable of providing gain for signals of 54 to 88 Mc, and 174 to 216 Mc. The u.h.f. band is from 470 to 890 Mc.

R.F. stages are not employed in all equipments, because of cost and design problems. When used their functions are:

1. To provide signal amplification where the signal is at its lowest level with the consequent advantage of increased receiver *sensitivity* (ability to receive weak signals).

2. To provide additional discrimination against signals in adjacent bands (*selectivity*) and improved image frequency rejection.

3. To reduce oscillator reradiation.

A lower gain is to be expected from an R.F. amplifier than can be obtained from other receiver stages because of the high frequencies it is called upon to handle. Because of the low signal levels at this point in a receiver, noise is an important factor.

The *intermediate frequency* (I.F.) amplifier gets its name from the carrier frequency it must amplify, an intermediate value between the high or R.F. and the low or audio spectrums. An I.F. stage always feeds a tuned load; high gain and the desired bandpass are thus obtained. In radio broadcast band receivers the generally accepted intermediate frequency is 455 kc; for TV, radar, FM, and other bands a higher I.F. is necessary. The factors involved in selecting an I.F. are covered in books specifically devoted to communications.

As with R.F. stages, I.F. circuits are biased similarly to the audio amplifiers discussed in preceding chapters, and bypassed emitter resistance is often used for operating-point stability. With high-frequency stages, the coupling and bypass capacitors will be of much smaller value because capacitive reactance decreases with frequency.

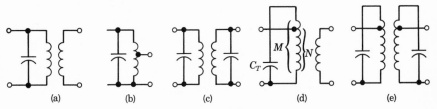

Fig. 11–22. Practical selective coupling networks: (a) single-tuned, two-winding transformer; (b) single-tuned, autotransformer; (c) double-tuned; (d) single-tuned, tapped primary, (e) double-tuned, tapped primary and secondary.

Practical selective coupling networks will take on the forms of Fig. 11–22. In (a) and (b) of the figure a single-tuned two-winding transformer and a single-tuned autotransformer are shown. Since transistor output and input impedance levels are vastly different, the transformer serves to provide impedance matching as well as selectivity. Tuning of both primary and secondary inductances, as in the circuit of Fig. 11–22(c), results in superior performance, a flatter frequency response, and sharper cutoff at the edges of the passband. This network is called a *double-tuned coupling circuit*.

The single and double-tuned circuits of the diagram are modified in (d) and (e) of Fig. 11–22 to provide for a larger winding inductance and a smaller value of tuning capacitance for practical circuits. If N represents the number of turns as indicated on the diagram, M the total number of turns, and C is the required tuning capacitance for the portion of the winding designated by N, then a smaller capacitance C_T can be connected across M according to

$$C_T = \frac{N^2}{M^2} C. \qquad (11\text{–}84)$$

Typical of an I.F. stage is that shown in Fig. 11–23. This circuit bears a great deal of similarity to an audio-frequency transformer-coupled circuit; bypassed emitter resistance R_1 is used for operating-point stability, base bias is achieved by R_2 and R_3 (the method called single-battery bias), and R_3 is bypassed to prevent signal loss in a resistance used for establishing the dc operating point. As previously mentioned, 10 to 50 μF capacitors are not used for bypassing at these frequencies; for 455-kc stages capacitances of 0.05 to 0.1 μF adequately perform the necessary function of presenting low impedance to the ac component of transistor currents. The tuning afforded by C is not exclusive with I.F. amplifiers; indeed, tuning is used in audio circuits to minimize the signal-shunting effects of transformer primary inductance at low frequencies. The need for C in this circuit is, of course, to resonate with L at the carrier frequency, and the required bandpass characteristic is thereby obtained.

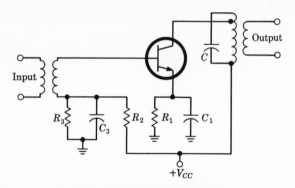

Fig. 11–23. Typical I.F. stage.

11–8. Instability of Tuned Amplifiers. The transistor is a non-unilateral device; its input circuit "senses" the applied load and output characteristics, and its output circuit "senses" the source termination and input-circuit characteristics. At certain frequencies and under certain load conditions, as may be experienced with tuned loads, this sensing or internal feedback may result in the input impedance of a stage exhibiting a negative real part, a condition for self-oscillation. Calculations of conditions for oscillation are complicated by the fact that at high frequencies all parameters of the transistor are complex, the load is complex, and coupling circuits are complex functions of frequency.

If we consider the general h-parameter relationships for input and output impedance, namely,

$$Z_i = h_i - \frac{h_r h_f}{h_o + Y_L} \tag{11–85}$$

and

$$\frac{1}{Z_o} = h_o - \frac{h_r h_f}{h_i + Z_G}, \tag{11–86}$$

it is easy to prove that for certain source and load terminations the real portions of Z_i and Z_o may become negative. Internal freedback as represented by the right-hand members of the above equations may be minimized if $1/Z_L$ and Z_G are very large numbers, so essentially

$$Z_i \cong h_i$$

and

$$Z_o \cong 1/h_o.$$

Another method of minimizing the factors that contribute to instability is to make h_i and h_o more highly resistive. To accomplish this, a resistor may be placed in one of the input leads to the stage, and one may be placed in parallel with h_o across the transistor output terminal pair.

A third method of stabilizing high-frequency tuned amplifiers is by *neutralization*, the process of adding passive circuitry to provide external feedback tending to cancel the internal feedback that fosters instability. Neutralizing circuitry often practically consists of a single capacitor, or a resistance–capacitance parallel combination (or series combination) connected as in Fig. 11–24. The connection is often made from the base of a second transistor to the base of the preceding transistor with the coupling transformer supplying 180° of phase shift (for a typical 455-kc I.F. amplifier, the neutralizing capacitor will be of a value to 250 $\mu\mu$F, depending upon the transformer turns ratio, the transistor used, etc.). The neutralizing scheme of Fig. 11–25 has been employed in radio receiver I.F. strips.

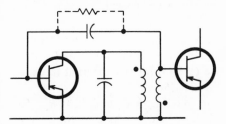

Fig. 11–24. Neutralized common-emitter tuned stage. No biasing is included in the figure.

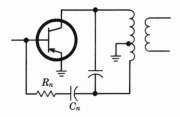

Fig. 11–25. Another neutralizing scheme. Typical values: R_n—3000 to 8000 Ω; C_n—5 to 10 pF. Numbers pertain to broadcast band. No biasing is shown in the figure.

Without neutralization, the non-unilateral aspects of the transistor make alignment of multistage-tuned amplifiers somewhat difficult, any change in the load of one stage affecting the operation of all other cascaded units.

Although one hears "neutralization" and "unilateralization" used interchangeably, actually unilateralization is a special case of neutralization in which the resistive as well as the reactive feedback parameters are balanced out, and therefore unilateralization changes a bilateral network into a unilateral network.

Shea[13] has concluded that potential instability occurs only up to a fraction of the alpha cutoff frequency (f_{ab}) in common-emitter circuits; at higher frequencies this configuration is unconditionally stable (the transistor cannot oscillate, no matter what passive terminations are used). For common-base and common-collector configurations, instability may occur throughout the entire range of frequencies.

11-9. Tuned-Amplifier Design. By making use of the principles discussed in the preceding sections of this chapter it is possible to design a tuned transistor amplifier; a sample design will be forthcoming. The hybrid-π equivalent will be

used as the basis for design procedures even though this circuit is fairly complicated, and the addition of a tuned load and neutralizing elements results in even
greater complexity. Some simplification of the over-all equivalent circuit may
be achieved by converting the hybrid π to a normal π of the type shown in the

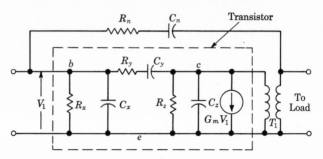

Fig. 11–26.   Normal-π circuit with neutralizing components included.

"boxed" portion of Fig. 11–26. (see Problem 11–16). After making this conversion, the unilateralizing components R_n and C_n linking input and output
and the transformer T_1 providing the phase reversal for this external feedback
are added to the transistor equivalent in Fig. 11–26.

If the transformer turns ratio is 1:1, let us make $C_n = C_y$ and $R_n = R_y$. The
current in the external feedback path will be opposite in phase to the current
through R_y and C_y from base-to-collector, and it can be shown that net signal
transfer from collector-to-base is cancelled. The resulting unilateralized stage
is depicted in Fig. 11–27 and it is obvious that because of the isolation provided
by the external elements, this circuit will be easy to work with.

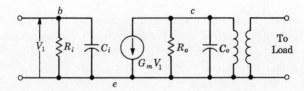

Fig. 11–27.   Unilateralized common-emitter circuit with transformer coupling to load.

Should the turns ratio of the coupling transformer be other than 1:1, let us
say $n:1$, then, for isolation of input from load, and output from source, the
feedback elements must be

$$C_n = nC_y \tag{11-87}$$

and

$$R_n = R_y/n. \tag{11-88}$$

The actual values of C_y and R_y in terms of the original hybrid-π parameters are

$$C_y = \frac{C_{b'c}}{1 + (r_{bb'}/r_{b'e}) - (r_{bb'}/r_{b'c})(C_{b'e}/C_{b'c})} \qquad (11\text{–}89)$$

and

$$R_y = r_{bb'}\left(1 + \frac{C_{b'e}}{C_{b'c}}\right) + \frac{1 + (r_{bb'}/r_{b'e})}{r_{b'c}\omega^2 C_{b'c}{}^2}. \qquad (11\text{–}90)$$

Problem 11–17 may be used to derive these equations.

Solution for the other parameters of the circuit of Fig. 11–27 yields[18]

$$R_i = r_{bb'} + r_{b'e}\left[\frac{r_{b'e} + r_{bb'}}{r_{b'e} + r_{bb'} + \omega^2(C_{b'e} + C_{b'c})^2 r_{b'e}{}^2 r_{bb'}{}^2}\right], \qquad (11\text{–}91)$$

$$C_i = \frac{C_{b'e} + C_{b'c}}{[1 + (r_{bb'}/r_{b'e})]^2 + \omega^2(C_{b'e} + C_{b'c})^2 r_{bb'}{}^2}, \qquad (11\text{–}92)$$

$$\frac{1}{R_o} = g_{ce} + g_{b'c} + g_m\left[\frac{g_{b'c}(g_{bb'} + g_{b'e}) + \omega^2 C_{b'e} C_{b'c}}{(g_{bb'} + g_{b'e})^2 + \omega^2 C_{b'e}{}^2}\right], \qquad (11\text{–}93)$$

$$C_o = C_{b'c}\left[1 + \frac{g_m(g_{bb'} + g_{b'e})}{(g_{bb'} + g_{b'e})^2 + \omega^2 C_{b'e}{}^2}\right], \qquad (11\text{–}94)$$

$$G_m = \frac{g_m}{\{[1 + (r_{bb'}/r_{b'e})]^2 + [r_{bb'}\cdot\omega(C_{b'e} + C_{b'c})]^2\}^{1/2}}. \qquad (11\text{–}95)$$

Conductances have been used in Eqs. (11–93) and (11–94) to somewhat simplify those formulas. Eqs. (11–91) through (11–94) pertain to the unilateralized transistor exlusively; to determine input and output resistances and capacitances for the entire stage, R_n and C_n should be considered as paralleling those terminal pairs (see Problems 11–18 and 11–19).

The load to be fed is often the input impedance of the following stage and it is desired, for maximum power transfer, to reflect the resistive component of this load to the first transistor collector at a level equal to R_o. The interstage transformer performs this function. Input capacitance of the following (load) stage parallels the tuned circuit, and if of significant value must be considered a portion of the over-all tuning capacitance. This composite tuning capacitance (C_T) required to resonate with transformer inductance at the carrier frequency is made up of the parallel elements C_o, reflected load C_i, stray capacitance, and purposely added capacitance.

I.F Amplifier Stage Design Example

Object. To design a single I.F. amplifying stage according to the following specifications:

1. Carrier frequency: 455 kc
2. Bandwidth: 10 kc
3. Load: Z_i of identical unilateralized transistor
4. Power supply available: -9 V

Solution. A suitable transistor is chosen for this service. Let us use a germanium p–n–p alloy junction type having the following small-signal hybrid-π parameters, at an operating point of $V_{CE} = -9$ V, $I_C = -1$ mA:

$$r_{bb'} = 75\ \Omega \qquad\qquad C_{b'e} = 1560\ \text{pF}$$

$$g_{b'e} = 800\ \mu\text{mhos} \qquad\qquad C_{b'c} = 9.5\ \text{pF}$$

$$g_{ce} = 8.6\ \mu\text{mhos} \qquad\qquad g_m = 38{,}600\ \mu\text{mhos}$$

$$g_{b'c} = 0.25\ \mu\text{mho}$$

Preliminary calculations:

$$r_{b'e} = 1/g_{b'e} = 1250\ \Omega, \qquad\qquad g_{bb'} = 1.33 \times 10^{-2}\ \text{mho},$$

$$r_{ce} = 1/g_{ce} = 0.116 \times 10^6\ \Omega, \qquad\qquad \omega_r = 2\pi f_r = 2.86 \times 10^6\ \text{rad/sec},$$

$$r_{b'c} = 1/g_{b'c} = 4 \times 10^6\ \Omega, \qquad\qquad \omega_r^2 = 8.18 \times 10^{12}\ \text{rad}^2/\text{sec}^2.$$

It is necessary to determine the values of the elements of the circuit of Fig. 11–28. The biasing resistances R_2 and R_3 are chosen so that $I_C = 1$ mA, and the

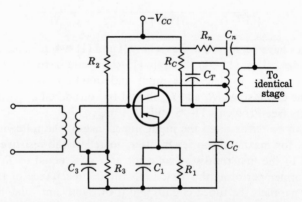

Fig. 11–28. Circuit for I.F. amplifier design example.

reactance of C_3 at 455 kc made much smaller than the resistance of R_3 (if $R_3 = 5$ K, C_3 can be chosen to be 0.05 to 0.1 μF). For bias stability, R_1 will be included; 1000 Ω is typical, bypassed by C_1 of 0.1 μF. The decoupling circuit shall be composed of $R_C = 500\ \Omega$ and $C_C = 0.05\ \mu$F.

Because of the dc potential drops across R_C, R_1, and the winding resistance of the transformer, V_{CE} will not be 9 V, but will have some lesser value. In the absence of parameter correction information for this transistor and because the deviation from 9 V is not too great, the 9-V parameters will be used.

We may calculate feedback elements C_y and R_y by using Eqs. (11–89) and (11–90). From Eq. (11–89)

$$C_y = \frac{9.5 \times 10^{-12}}{1 + (75/1250) - [75/(4 \times 10^6)](1560/9.5)}$$

$$= 9.0 \text{ pF.}$$

From Eq. (11–90)

$$R_y = 75\left(1 + \frac{1560}{9.5}\right) + \frac{1 + (75/1250)}{(8.18 \times 10^{12})(4 \times 10^6)(9.5 \times 10^{-12})^2}$$

$$= 12,760 \ \Omega.$$

Insertion of appropriate external feedback elements will cancel the effects of C_y and R_y and result in a unilateralized stage of the form of Fig. 11–29.

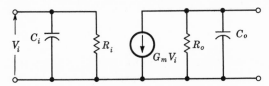

Fig. 11–29.   Unilateralized equivalent circuit.

The five parameters of the circuit of Fig. 11–29 can be calculated. From Eq. (11–91)

$$R_i = 528 \ \Omega.$$

From Eq. (11–92)

$$C_i = 1270 \text{ pF.}$$

From Eq. (11–93)

$$R_o = 32,400 \ \Omega.$$

From Eq. (11–94)

$$C_o = 33.1 \text{ pF.}$$

From Eq. (11–95)

$$G_m = 34.8 \text{ mA/V.}$$

Now to specify the transformer to be used, match R_o to the load resistance, which is R_i of an identical stage.

$$\text{Impedance ratio} = 32,400 : 530.$$

Therefore the turns ratio is

$$n = \left(\frac{32,400}{530}\right)^{1/2} = 7.8 : 1.$$

The feedback elements were given by $R_n = R_y/n$ and $C_n = nC_y$.

$$R_n = \frac{12,760}{7.8} = 1640 \ \Omega$$

and

$$C_n = (7.8)(9.0) = 70 \ \text{pF}.$$

The paralleling effects of these elements upon terminal properties will not be considered here. Problem 11–23 may be used to determine these effects.

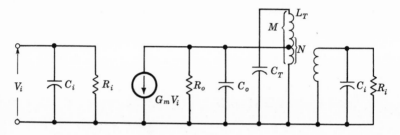

Fig. 11–30.   Coupling and load added to the circuit of Fig. 11–29.

A few other calculations are needed to satisfactorily specify circuit operation and circuit elements. The expected power gain must be predicted, so, from Fig. 11–30,

$$P_i = V_i^2/R_i.$$

$R_L = n^2 R_i = R_o$, and, if load current is symbolized by I_o, then load power is given by

$$P_o = I_o^2 R_L = I_o^2 R_o$$

$$= (G_m V_i/2)^2 R_o.$$

Then

$$G = \frac{P_o}{P_i} = \frac{G_m^2 R_o R_i}{4}$$

$$= \frac{(34.8 \times 10^{-3})^2 (32,400)(528)}{4}$$

$$= 5200, \text{ or } 37.2 \ \text{dB}.$$

This figure assumes a perfect coil. Because an actual coil has losses, less gain will be available. To find the over-all Q required, use Eq. (11–73).

$$Q = \frac{f_r}{B} = \frac{455,000}{10,000}$$

$$= 45.5.$$

If a coil with $Q_C = 100$ is available, then, from Eq. (11–66b),

$$\text{Insertion loss} = 20 \log \frac{Q_C}{Q_C - Q} = 20 \log \frac{100}{100 - 45.5}$$

$$= 5.3 \text{ dB}.$$

The over-all power gain to be expected is, therefore, $37.2 - 5.3$, or 31.9 dB. From Eq. (11–83), a calculation of the coil inductance can be made.

$$L = \frac{R_o(Q_C - Q)}{2\omega_r Q Q_C} = \frac{32,400(100 - 45.5)}{2(2.86 \times 10^6)(45.5)(100)}$$

$$= 68 \ \mu\text{H}.$$

Using the standard equation for parallel resonance permits the determination of parallel capacitance.

$$C = \frac{1}{\omega_r^2 L} = \frac{1}{(8.18 \times 10^{12})(68 \times 10^{-6})}$$

$$= 1800 \ \text{pF}.$$

Of this total required capacitance, C_o makes up 33 pF and reflected C_i of stage two accounts for $1270/(7.8)^2$ or 21 pF. The contribution of a separate tuning capacitor must be 1746 pF.

If a tapped coil is to be used, and if 200 pF of additional tuning capacitance (C_T) is decided upon, then from Fig. 11–30

$$\frac{M}{N} = \left(\frac{1746}{200}\right)^{1/2} = 2.96.$$

The C_o and reflected C_i capacitances amount to 54 pF and are across N turns of the transformer primary. Their contribution to total tuning capacitance is $54/(2.96)^2 = 6.2$ pF. The total primary inductance now is given by

$$L_T = \frac{1}{\omega_r^2 C} = \frac{1}{(8.18 \times 10^{12})(206 \times 10^{-12})}$$

$$= 592 \ \mu\text{H}.$$

Summary. To meet the listed specifications:
Coil requirements:

$$Q_C = 100$$

$$L = 592 \ \mu H$$

$$M/N = 2.96$$

$$32,400 : 530 \ \Omega$$

Circuit elements (refer to Fig. 11–28):

$$C_T = 200 \text{ pF} \qquad R_2 = \text{Approx. } 25,000 \ \Omega \qquad R_1 = 1000 \ \Omega$$

$$R_n = 1640 \ \Omega \qquad R_3 = 5000 \ \Omega \qquad C_1 = 0.1 \ \mu\text{F}$$

$$C_n = 70 \text{ pF} \qquad C_3 = 0.05 \ \mu\text{F} \qquad R_C = 500 \ \Omega$$

$$C_C = 0.05 \ \mu\text{F}$$

Performance:

Power gain = 1550, or 31.9 dB.

PROBLEMS

11–1. Calculate the thermal noise voltage generated by a 500,000 Ω resistor at 100°C. The usable bandwidth is 2 Mc.

11–2. Show that for two resistances R and R_L, connected in series, the thermal noise power transfer from R to R_L is balanced by the power transfer from R_L to R if the resistances are at identical temperatures and their noise voltages are uncorrelated.

11–3. Prove Eq. (11–8) from Eq. (11–7).

11–4. Using the transistor noise model of Fig. 11–3 connected common base, show that the noise figure for this orientation is identical to Eq. (11–27).

11–5. Prove Eq. (11–28) by using Eq. (11–4b) for $\overline{i_c{}^2}$, $\alpha = \alpha_0/(1 + jf/f_{\alpha b})$, and $Z_c = 1/(1/r_c + j\omega C_c)$.

11–6. A transistor with parameters $r_{bb'} = 200$, $r_{e'} = 50$, and $h_{FE} = 100$ is to be connected in a circuit with $R_G = 5000 \ \Omega$. What is the noise figure? What is the minimum noise figure obtainable with this transistor? At what value of R_G is the $F_{\min}$ obtained?

11–7. Derive Eq. (11–33) from Eqs. (11–31) and (11–32).

11–8. For the volume-control arrangement of Fig. 11–9(c), calculate the voltage gain of the interstage network for various control settings and sketch gain vs. K.

11–9. Confirm Eq. (11–47).

11–10. At 800 kc a 200-μH inductor exhibits an equivalent-series R.F. resistance of 8 Ω. Determine:

(a) The series Q_C.

(b) The equivalent parallel inductance at that frequency.

(c) The equivalent parallel resistance at that frequency.

(d) The parallel Q_C.

11–11. Find the insertion loss when using a coil with $Q_C = 52$ in a circuit with half-power points at 600 kc and 612 kc and with the resonant frequency at the center of the band.

11–12. The resonant frequency of the circuit of the figure is 3.1 Mc. Calculate the following:

(a) The over-all circuit Q.

(b) The bandwidth.

(c) The coil (transformer) insertion loss.

(d) The load seen by I at the resonant frequency.

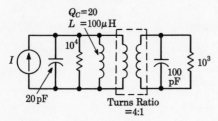

Problem 11–12.

11-13. Derive an expression for the resonant frequency of a circuit with C paralleling a series R-L branch.

11-14. Devise tests to determine the characteristics of an I.F. transformer, i.e., Q_C, ω_r, L, C, and turns ratio, if the assembly is that of Fig. 11-22(a). C may be considered removable if necessary.

11-15. To achieve a wide band, "stagger" tuning is useful. Each I.F. stage is tuned to a different center frequency, and the over-all response of the cascade amplifier is much flatter than the response of a like number of stages single tuned to the center of the passband. If each stage of a two-stage amplifier has a Q of 10, and the center of the band is at 24 Mc, graphically determine the bandwidth of the over-all I.F. strip. Stage No. 1 is tuned to 23 Mc and No. 2 is tuned to 25 Mc.

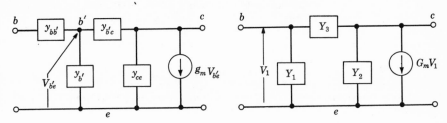

Problem 11-16.

11-16. To convert from the hybrid-π circuit to the normal-π circuit, a simple method involves equating the network y parameters (see Chapter 4) obtained from each of the circuits. Derive expressions for the normal-π parameters in terms of the hybrid-π parameters.

11-17. Y_3 in the circuit of Problem 11-16 may be expressed in terms of hybrid-π admittance parameters thus:

$$Y_3 = \frac{y_{b'c} y_{bb'}}{y_{b'e} + y_{bb'} + y_{b'c}}.$$

Show that separation of the real and imaginary parts of the impedance represented by this expression provides confirmation of Eqs. (11-89) and (11-90). Make the assumptions that $r_{b'c}$ is very large and $C_{b'e} \gg C_{b'c}$.

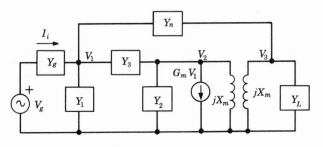

Problem 11-18.

11-18. Consider the normal-π circuit of the figure. The transformer has unity turns ratio but provides phase reversal so $V_3 = -V_2$.

(a) Write the nodal equation at V_1 and show that input impedance ($Z_i = V_1/I_i$) is independent of the load termination provided that $Y_3 = Y_n$.

(b) Write the nodal equations at V_3 and V_1 and show that output impedance is independent of source impedance.

11–19. It has been established in Problem 11–16 that, for the normal-π circuit,

$$Y_1 = \frac{y_{b'e}y_{bb}}{y_{bb'} + y_{b'e} + y_{b'c}}.$$

Problem 11–17 gives Y_3 and the solution to Problem 11–18 provides an expression for Z_i. Using this information confirm Eq. (11–91). Note the statement in the text explaining that Eq. (11–91) does not include the paralleling effects of R_n and C_n. Consider the conductance of the $b'c$ branch to be very small compared to $b'e$ and bb'.

11–20. A unilateralized transistor stage at the carrier frequency of 600 kc exhibits the following terminal properties: $Z_i = 900 - j550$; $Z_o = 20,000 - j14,000$. If the transistor is feeding a load that is an identical stage, a coil $Q_C = 60$ may be assumed, and the required bandwidth is 20 kc, answer the following:

(a) What is the required coil inductance?

(b) With a transformer of the Fig. 11–22(a) type, what impedance ratio should be used?

(c) What is the total required shunt capacitance and how much must be made up by additional capacitance?

(d) What is the gain of the stage including coil losses? Assume that $G_m = 25$ mA/V.

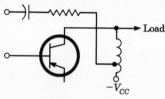

Problem 11–21.

11–21. Design an I.F. stage to meet the following requirements:

1. Carrier frequency: 455 kc
2. Bandwidth: 20 kc
3. Load: 10,000 Ω paralleled by 35 pF
4. Transistor type: use parameters given in Sec. 11–9 example
5. Operating point: -1 mA and -9 V
6. Coupling: inductors available with $Q_C = 70$. Transformers not to be used

7. Unilateralization provided by feedback from inductor tap as shown in diagram. The problem essentially requires determination of coil inductance, additional tuning capacity, and expected gain.

11–22. Discuss the factors involved in choosing an intermediate frequency for a communications receiver. *Theory and Design of Television Receivers*, by S. Deutsch (McGraw-Hill Book Co., Inc., New York, 1951), will be of assistance.

11–23. Alter the text design example by including the paralleling effects of R_n and C_n upon Z_i and Z_o (see Problem 11–19). It is suggested that R_n and C_n first be transformed to equivalent parallel elements to simplify the combination. Compare values obtained with the listed coil requirements, circuit element values, and performance.

REFERENCES

1. Bechtel, N. G., "A Circuit and Noise Model of the Field-Effect Transistor," *Proc. Intern. Solid-State Circuits Conf.*, 1963.
2. DeWitt, D., and Rossoff, A. L., *Transistor Electronics* (McGraw-Hill Book Co., Inc., New York, 1957).
3. Friis, H. T., "Noise Figures of Radio Receivers," *Proc. IRE*, **32** (July, 1944).
4. Gardner, F. M., "Optimum Noise Figure of Transistor Amplifiers," *IEEE Trans. Circuit Theory*, **CT–10**, No. 1 (March, 1963).
5. Hurley, R. B., *Junction Transistor Electronics* (John Wiley & Sons, Inc., New York, 1958).
6. Lo, A. W., *et al.*, *Transistor Electronics* (Prentice-Hall, Inc., Englewood Cliffs, New Jersey, 1955).
7. Martens, N. H., "Notes on Transistor Noise—What It Is and How It is Measured," *Solid-State Design*, **3**, No. 5 (May, 1962).
8. Nielsen, E. G., "Behavior of Noise Figure in Junction Transistors," *Proc. IRE*, **45**, No. 7 (1957).
9. Pettit, J. M., and McWhorter, M. M., *Electronic Amplifier Circuits: Theory and Design* (McGraw-Hill Book Co., Inc., New York, 1961).
10. Rheinfelder, W. A., *Design of Low-Noise Transistor Input Circuits* (Hayden Book Co., Inc., New York, 1964).
11. Riddle, R. L., and Ristenbatt, M. P., *Transistor Physics and Circuits* (Prentice-Hall, Inc., Englewood Cliffs, New Jersey, 1958).
12. Schwartz, M., *Information Transmission, Modulation, and Noise* (McGraw-Hill Book Co., Inc., New York, 1959).
13. Shea, R. F., *Transistor Circuit Engineering* (John Wiley & Sons, Inc., New York, 1957).
14. Staff, Texas Instruments, Inc., *Transistor Circuit Design* (McGraw-Hill Book Co., Inc., New York, 1963).
15. Thornton, R. D., DeWitt, D., Chennette, E. R., and Lin, H. C., *Characteristics and Limitations of Transistors* (John Wiley & Sons, Inc., New York, 1963).
16. van der Ziel, A., *Noise* (Prentice-Hall, Inc., Englewood Cliffs, New Jersey, 1954).
17. van der Ziel, A., "Noise in Junction Transistors," *Proc. IRE*, **46** (June, 1958).
18. Wolfendale, E., *The Junction Transistor and Its Applications* (The Macmillan Co., New York, 1958).

Chapter 12

COMMUNICATIONS CIRCUITS AND SYSTEMS

The discussion up to this point has been centered about signal amplification—the raising of a signal level—with the transistor as the active circuit element. The transistor, however, may be used for purposes other than amplification, and in this chapter, and in the subsequent chapter, such applications will be examined. Because many of the principles thus far considered with reference to amplification apply equally well to the processes of oscillation, modulation, and detection, analysis and synthesis of these new circuits will not appear completely foreign to the transistor-amplifier designer.

12–1. Oscillation. Oscillators are of extreme importance in the communications field, for they are the source of the high-frequency voltages that are generated both in the transmitter and in the receiver portions of a complete system. Actually an oscillator is a power converter in the sense that its only input is the direct-supply potential (and hence supply power) and its output is a time-varying waveform that is usually, but not necessarily, of a frequency well above that which can be generated with rotating equipment. It is therefore customary that no signal input terminal is apparent in the circuit diagram for an oscillator; the output is usually, but not always, taken between transistor collector and ground.

If the generated waveform is basically sinusoidal and the active circuit element is continuously supplying power to the passive circuit elements, the composite is termed a *harmonic oscillator*. Included in this category are *negative-resistance* and *feedback oscillators*. Another broad category among generators includes the *relaxation* types, characterized by nonsinusoidal waveforms (sawtooth, square, etc.) and the switched interchange of energy between active and passive circuit elements. Concern in this section is directed toward the harmonic oscillators, with limited discussion of relaxation oscillators reserved for Chapter 13.

An oscillator may, in some instances, be required to furnish very little power, or, by itself, cannot furnish the power required by the circuit load. However, once the desired time-varying signal is obtained, no matter how weakly, it is then possible to build it up with separate amplifying stages. Because a nonsinusoidal wave or a distorted sinusoidal wave is available from certain oscillator

316

circuits, filtering circuitry can be useful in extracting the fundamental and can help in the attainment of a pure sinusoid if one is required.

A generally quoted "rule of thumb" describes the limiting frequency of oscillation for any transistor as its alpha-cutoff frequency. The treatment here will be concerned with oscillation at frequencies considerably below that limit and will be centered about operation in the audio-frequency band, but the discussion will be useful in analyzing any oscillator when transistor terminal reactances do not play an important part in circuit operation.

From the discussion of feedback in amplifiers presented in Chapter 10 it will be recalled that a unique condition existed when the denominator of the over-all amplification formula equaled zero. Repeated here,

$$A_f = A/(1 - BA) = V_o/V_i. \qquad (12\text{--}1)$$

Thus when $BA \to +1$, $A_f \to \infty$. This represents oscillation, the situation existing when an input signal is unnecessary for the maintenance of an output signal. It is now desired that this generated signal be sinusoidal, and of constant amplitude, and furthermore that its frequency be predictable, and in some cases adjustable.

The loop gain (BA) must actually be greater than unity in all practical feedback oscillators, for if it were precisely unity then aging of circuit components would in all likelihood eventually result in discontinuance of the desired waveform generation, because of gain reduction. When BA is made slightly greater than unity, more signal is being fed back than originally was present, and a buildup in signal level results; this buildup will always be limited by nonlinearities within the transistor (the collector-supply voltage also presents a limit). Such nonlinearities always result in distortion of the output waveform, but in good oscillator designs this distortion may be very slight, and filtering is always possible to improve the waveshape.

Because transistor gain and input and output impedances are so sensitive to ambient temperature, it is mandatory for stable oscillation that the frequency be solely dependent upon high-quality, stable, external tuning elements and not upon the transistor reactances. Elements that determine the frequency of oscillation include R-C networks for phase shifting, resonant L-C pairs, and piezoelectric crystals. In addition, stable biasing is used to keep circuit operation predictable.

A frequency-determining device or circuit is required in all oscillator circuits; inductance–capacitance circuitry can perform this function. It can be recalled from the transient analysis portion of electrical network theory that oscillations are developed in the response of even a simple R-L-C circuit when subjected to a step or suddenly applied dc shock (see Fig. 12–1). The dc transient, however, always decays because of the inescapable damping effect of ever-present resistance.

The current in the simple R-L-C circuit shown can be expressed by

$$i = \frac{V}{L} \frac{e^{-t/T}}{\omega} \sin \omega t. \tag{12-2}$$

The exponential term causing the decay is dictated by $T = 2L/R$. Angular frequency of the sine term is given by

$$\omega = \sqrt{\frac{1}{LC} - \left(\frac{R}{2L}\right)^2}.$$

It is clear that R causes the reduction in amplitude and slightly determines the frequency of oscillation. In the absence of R, never-ending oscillation would exist, because of the interchange of stored energy between inductance and capacitance.

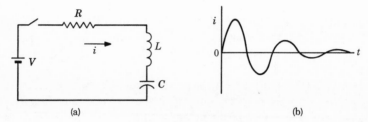

(a)   (b)

Fig. 12–1.   Transient in a simple dc circuit, and the frequency-determining properties of an L-C circuit.

The active element in an oscillator circuit, a transistor in this instance, may be thought of as supplying, to the circuit of Fig. 12–1, or to its parallel counterpart, a negative resistance of sufficient value to overcome the positive resistance R in the figure, and consequently the complete oscillator, including both resonant circuit and negative resistance, when shocked, will oscillate continuously. Oftentimes the only shock needed is the application of power to the circuit.

Oscillators are studied from a negative-resistance standpoint and from a feedback point-of-view, but mathematically there is no rigid division between the two and any particular oscillator may be considered from either approach. In the so-called negative-resistance type of waveform generator, internal positive feedback is present and serves to provide a negative resistance to an external resonant circuit. The so-called feedback-oscillator type employs positive external feedback in order to overcome natural damping.

12–2. Negative-Resistance Oscillators.   One cannot purchase a negative resistance from a components supplier, nor will one see such a device listed in any catalog, so a negative resistance characteristic must be obtained from a common active device when operated in a specific manner, or when used in conjunction with other common circuit elements.

Some transistor types, the point-contact and p–n–p–n hook varieties, for example, possess alphas greater than unity, and it is rather easy to show that negative terminal resistance properties may be forthcoming with these devices (see Problem 12–2).

The tunnel diode is a good example of a two-terminal device capable of providing a variational negative resistance. Its V–I characteristic is referred to as *voltage stable*, for there is only one current that corresponds to each value of

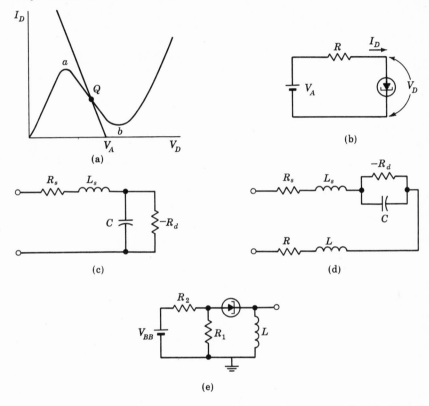

Fig. 12–2. (a) Tunnel diode characteristic with load line; (b) circuit for (a); (c) equivalent circuit of tunnel diode; (d) external elements added for oscillation; (e) series oscillator circuit.

potential difference across the device. The negative resistance region, a to b, is seen in Fig. 12–2(a). Since a negative resistance implies a source of power, and since any physically realizable source can supply only a finite amount of power, a practical device can exhibit negative resistance only within a finite region of its characteristics.

A load line has been drawn that starts at V_A and has a slope dictated by an external series resistance R, as shown in Fig. 12–2(b). If the values of V_A and R

are carefully selected, the load line will intersect the tunnel diode characteristic at only one point, Q. In order to achieve a single intersection, $|R|$ must be smaller than $|-R_d|$, the diode's negative resistance. The net series variational resistance for this circuit is negative, and the circuit will oscillate if reactive conditions are favorable.

A small-signal equivalent circuit for the diode is given in Fig. 12–2(c). Typical values for the parameters are lead inductance $L_s = 10^{-8}$ H; bulk resistance $R_s = 1.0\,\Omega$; junction capacitance $C = 10\,\mathrm{pF}$; variational resistance $-R_d = -100\,\Omega$. Two figures of merit are often quoted for the tunnel diode. The resistive cutoff frequency, f_{ro}, is defined as the frequency at which the real portion of the diode's terminal impedance is zero. It is determined by simply adding the equivalent of $C\|(-R_d)$ to $R_s + j\omega L_s$ and equating the real part to zero. It follows that f_{ro} is obtainable from

$$\omega_{ro}^2 = \frac{|R_d| - R_s}{R_s R_d^2 C^2}.$$

(12–3)

At frequencies above f_{ro} the device is no longer active, for it cannot exhibit negative resistance properties. The self-resonant frequency f_{xo} is obtained by setting the imaginary portion of the driving-point impedance to zero and is available from

$$\omega_{xo}^2 = \frac{1}{L_s C} - \left(\frac{1}{R_d C}\right)^2.$$

(12–4)

For sustained sinusoidal oscillations, it is necessary that the resistive and reactive cutoff frequencies of the driving-point impedance *including external elements* be equal. If $f_{ro} < f_{xo}$, the circuit may be useful as an amplifier; should $f_{ro} > f_{xo}$, nonlinear oscillations are possible.

In Fig. 12–2(d) R and L have been added to the diode equivalent circuit. We shall use $L_T = L_s + L$, $R_T = R_s + R$. The condition for oscillations is obtained by equating Eq. (12–3) with Eq. (12–4), including the external elements. This yields, for the series circuit of Fig. 12–2(d),

$$R_T |R_d| = L_T / C.$$

(12–5)

The corresponding frequency of oscillation is

$$\omega_r^2 = \frac{1 - R_T / |R_d|}{L_T C}.$$

(12–6)

The circuit of Fig. 12–2(e) shows all elements necessary for a simple series oscillator. Elements R_1 and R_2 along with V_{BB} dictate the dc load line and determine the operating point. Because this circuit is rather highly dependent upon $-R_d$ and C of the diode, and these parameters vary with voltage and temperature, this circuit is not as widely accepted as the series–parallel arrangement that uses a tuning capacitor in parallel with L.

12–3. Feedback Oscillators. There is a multiplicity of possible circuit arrangements useful as feedback oscillators. If one starts with a transistor in the common-emitter orientation, 180° of phase shift is inherent between input and output quantities. To feed some of the output signal back to the input in order to provide positive feedback, an additional shift of 180° is required. A transformer can, of course, be used to supply this necessary phase reversal as shown in the circuit of Fig. 12–3. The transformer secondary winding is connected into the transistor base circuit, and the capacitor C is being used to complete the frequency-determining circuit in conjunction with the transformer winding inductance. The element R_e is offering some control over gain and can be used

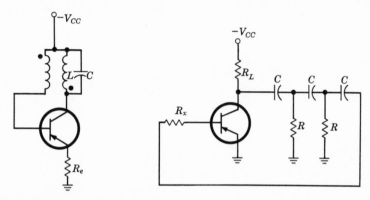

Fig. 12–3. Common-emitter-oriented feed-back oscillator with transformer providing phase reversal.

Fig. 12–4. Phase-shift oscillator. Base biasing not shown.

to keep the waveshape fairly clear of distortion. The circuit shown contains all the elements necessary for oscillation. Frequency is controlled by C and to a minor extent by R_e.

An R-C network can be designed to provide the additional phase shift needed for regeneration. In the circuit of Fig. 12–4, the transistor collector and base are connected through a three-stage phase-shift network; each R-C pair is consequently required to supply about 60° of phase shift. If the loop gain at a particular frequency is greater than unity, with a total phase shift of 360°, oscillations, triggered by noise, will build up. They will reach a steady state because of the always-present nonlinear relation between gain and signal amplitude.

The phase-shifting network of the circuit of Fig. 12–4 is a high-pass filter. Low frequencies are blocked by the C's, so that the loop gain is low. High frequencies easily pass through the capacitance branches, but the phase shift experienced by very high frequencies is less than necessary for oscillation. At one frequency, the loop gain and the phase shift will be correct for oscillation.

The nonlinear relation between A_i and signal amplitude for a typical active device is depicted in Fig. 12–5(a). At low amplitude levels, A_i is shown to be larger than the required steady-state level. Therefore the oscillator waveform will build up until the gain has been reduced to the value necessary to support steady-state oscillation.

To derive a curve such as that shown in Fig. 12–5(a), information such as is given in Fig. 12–5(b) is useful. Shown is a type of transfer characteristic for an active device with abrupt saturation at an I_{out} level of 200 units. At $I_{in} = 1$ unit, $I_{out} = 100$, so the small-signal gain is 100. At $I_{in} = 2$, A_i is still 100. With $I_{in} = 3$, $A_i = 67$; with $I_{in} = 4$, $A_i = 50$. Thus we see the reduction in gain with signal amplitude caused by an abrupt ideal saturation. (A_i may be approximated by

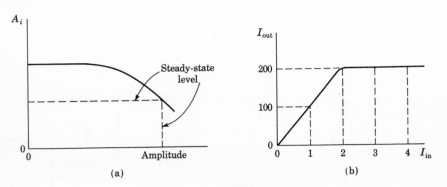

(a)   (b)

Fig. 12–5. Nonlinear gain relations in active elements: (a) typical gain-amplitude curve; (b) idealized transfer characteristic.

h_{fe} at low levels, but with increased signal amplitude, the current gain becomes more nearly equal to h_{FE}.)

Now let us consider an approach to the mathematical analysis of oscillator circuits. Nonlinearities of characteristics impose limits upon waveform magnitude and shape, and because circuit analysis involving nonlinear elements is often to be avoided, on account of the relative complexity, our approach will be to treat the circuit as comprised of linear elements and to predict the frequency of oscillation and the circuit conditions necessary to support oscillation.

Consider an oscillator circuit, with, of course, no driving potential, because no input is specified. If it is assumed that the circuit is oscillating, and further assumed that these oscillations can be represented by sinusoidal circuit quantities, then a normal set of loop (mesh) or nodal equations may be written for steady-state analysis. Such equations were written for the derivation of gain and impedance formulas in Chapter 5, and when solved for circuit currents gave rise to expressions of the form

$$I = f(V_i)/D. \tag{12–7}$$

V_i represents the driving potential and D the circuit determinant. Because $V_i = 0$

in oscillator circuits, Eq. (12–7) may be written as

$$I = 0/D.$$

But I does exist and is not zero as this expression seems to indicate; therefore, the denominator must also be zero. Then

$$I = 0/0$$

and is indeterminate. It is therefore necessary for the circuit determinant D to equal zero for oscillations to exist. It will be recalled that D, when using the loop method of analysis, is composed of functions of both the transistor parameters and the impedances of external elements. This determinant will have a real and an imaginary part, and to equal zero, each part must equal zero. The real part equated to zero yields, upon solution, the necessary conditions for oscillation: a relation between the current-gain parameter h_f and circuit inductances and capacitances. Upon equating the imaginary portion of the determinant to zero, one can solve for the frequency of oscillation, always a function of the circuit parameters, and dependent upon the transistor but essentially determined by the external tuned circuit. In fact, a good approximation to the circuit oscillation frequency is the resonant condition for the L-C combination, when one is used,

$$f = \frac{1}{2\pi\sqrt{LC}}, \tag{12–8}$$

which applies to either series resonant or parallel resonant (anti-resonant) lossless circuits.

Phase-shift oscillator. Now returning in our oscillator discussion to the phase-shift type of Fig. 12–4, let us apply the foregoing treatment to this circuit. A complete ac equivalent using h parameters is shown in Fig. 12–6(a) with R_x being used to bring the total resistance of the input branch up to R in value $(R_x + h_{ie} = R)$. Loop equations will be written after some simplifications are made. If we consider $h_{re}V_o$ as small and $1/h_{oe}$ as very large, those two parameters may be omitted. A source transformation allows us to redraw Fig. 12–6(a) in the form of Fig. 12–6(b). The equations are

$$\left.\begin{aligned}
0 &= I_1(R_L + R - jX_C) - I_2R + I_3h_{fe}R_L, \\
0 &= -I_1R + I_2(2R - jX_C) - I_3R, \\
0 &= 0 - I_2R + I_3(2R - jX_C).
\end{aligned}\right\} \tag{12–9}$$

The numerator of every current expression is zero, and all denominators are equal and will be set to zero. The imaginary part of the determinant provides

$$\omega^2 = \frac{1}{C^2(4RR_L + 6R^2)}. \tag{12–10}$$

Using this value for ω^2 in the real part of the denominator yields

$$h_{fe} = 23 + \frac{29R}{R_L} + \frac{4R_L}{R}. \qquad (12\text{--}11)$$

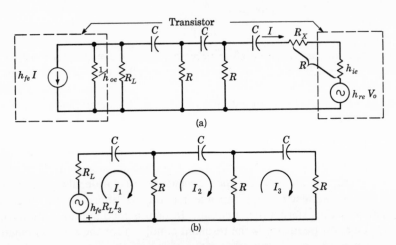

(a)

(b)

Fig. 12–6. AC equivalent of the circuit of Fig. 12–4; (a) current-generator form; (b) simplified voltage-generator form.

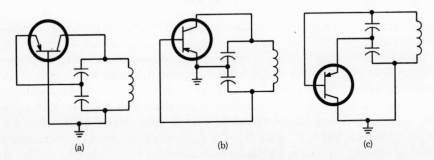

(a)   (b)   (c)

Fig. 12–7. Colpitts-type oscillator: (a) common-base; (b) common-emitter; (c) common-collector.

Equation (12–10) gives us the frequency of oscillation and Eq. (12–11) provides the necessary condition for sustained oscillations. Should $C = 0.1$ μF, $R_L = 10$ kΩ and $R = 2$ kΩ, then the equations predict oscillations at about 160 cps and require h_{fe} to be 49 or larger.

Colpitts oscillator. If a common-base amplifying stage [see Fig. 12–7(a)] is supplying a load that is a tuned circuit and a feedback connection is made from the junction of the split load capacitors to the transistor input (emitter) terminal, and if sufficient positive feedback is available, the circuit is a *Colpitts*-type oscillator. The ac portion of this classical circuit is shown in Fig. 12–7 in the several possible ways in which it can be arranged, for the circuit may be drawn in such a way as to look like a common-base stage, or it can be common-emitter or common-collector oriented.

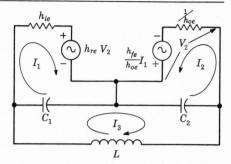

   To perform a linear analysis of the Colpitts oscillator the ac equivalent circuit of Fig. 12–8 has been drawn,

Fig. 12–8. Circuit for analysis of the Colpitts-type oscillator.

with common-emitter h parameters used. For the lower audio frequencies they are real and will be so considered here. Note that

$$V_2 = \frac{I_2}{h_{oe}} - I_1 \frac{h_{fe}}{h_{oe}}.$$

The three loop equations are

$$\left. \begin{aligned}
0 &= I_1\left(h_{ie} - \frac{h_{re}h_{fe}}{h_{oe}} - jX_{C1}\right) + I_2\left(\frac{h_{re}}{h_{oe}}\right) - I_3(-jX_{C1}), \\
0 &= -I_1\left(\frac{h_{fe}}{h_{oe}}\right) + I_2\left(\frac{1}{h_{oe}} - jX_{C2}\right) + I_3(-jX_{C2}), \\
0 &= -I_1(-jX_{C1}) + I_2(-jX_{C2}) + I_3(jX_L - jX_{C1} - jX_{C2}).
\end{aligned} \right\} \qquad (12\text{–}12)$$

Equating the imaginary portion of the circuit determinant to zero allows calculation of the frequency of oscillation. The complete expression is

$$\omega^2 = \frac{h_{oe}}{C_1 C_2 h_{ie}} + \frac{1}{LC_1} + \frac{1}{LC_2}. \qquad (12\text{–}13a)$$

For practical values of the parameters, oscillator angular frequency is

$$\omega^2 = (C_1 + C_2)/LC_1 C_2. \qquad (12\text{–}13b)$$

This expression represents the resonant frequency of a tank circuit with L paralleling a series branch of C_1 and C_2.

   Under the assumptions that $\omega^2 = (C_1 + C_2)/LC_1 C_2$ and $h_{re} \ll 1$, the real portion of the determinant, equated to zero, yields

$$h_{fe}/\Delta^{he} = C_1/C_2, \qquad (12\text{–}14)$$

with

$$\Delta^{he} = h_{ie}h_{oe} - h_{re}h_{fe}.$$

Because h_{fe} may have a value of perhaps 50 and Δ^{he} of perhaps 0.5, it follows that in workable Colpitts-type oscillators a big difference will be observed between the values of C_1 and C_2.

Hartley oscillator. The ac portion of the classical Hartley oscillator, when transistorized, would appear as in Fig. 12–9. The Hartley and Colpitts oscillators are very similar circuits, with just inductance and capacitance interchanged. Therefore the circuit determinant for the Hartley is identical to the determinant previously described, Eq. (12–12), except that for the Hartley circuit jX_{L1} and jX_{L2} must replace $-jX_{C1}$ and $-jX_{C2}$, and $-jX_C$ must replace jX_L. An analysis similar to that made for the Colpitts circuit results in, for the oscillating frequency of the Hartley,

$$\omega^2 = \frac{1}{C(L_1 + L_2) - L_1 L_2 h_{oe}/h_{ie}}. \tag{12–15}$$

The condition for oscillation is

$$h_{fe} = \frac{L_1}{L_2} + \Delta^{h_e}\frac{L_2}{L_1}. \tag{12–16}$$

If the L_2/L_1 term is considered as a variable z, then $h_{fe} = 1/z + \Delta^{h_e}z$, and solution for z yields, with $h_{fe}^2 \gg 4\Delta^{h_e}$,

$$\frac{h_{fe}}{\Delta^{h_e}} \cong \frac{L_2}{L_1} \tag{12–17}$$

as the desired relationship.

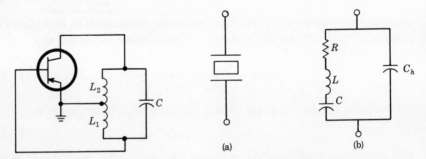

Fig. 12–9. AC portion of the Hartley-type oscillator, common-emitter oriented.

Fig. 12–10. Piezoelectric crystal: (a) circuit diagram symbol; (b) equivalent electrical circuit.

Mutual inductance may be present between the two inductive elements, resulting in expressions for ω and h_{fe} that also include M (see Problem 12–8). Some have found that the drawing of a more-or-less universal equivalent circuit similar to the figure of Problem 12–9 but using generalized Z elements and including mutual impedance (between Z_1 and Z_2 in that figure) can provide a basis for the derivation of formulas for the Colpitts, Hartley, and Clapp circuits, and for any variations of the basic circuit.

Stability Considerations.   Drifting of the frequency of oscillation is an important engineering problem, for certain types of oscillator applications require a very great degree of frequency stability. It has already been noted that in good design the oscillation frequency should be solely dependent upon high-quality external tuning elements and not upon the transistor reactances, for the latter are subject to aging and climatic conditions as well as power-supply variations. The R, L, and C external parameters also will show a tendency to vary with temperature excursions and on occasion, if compensatory circuits and highest quality components do not suffice, the elements of importance may be located in a constant-temperature bath.

Clapp's modification of the Colpitts oscillator type can result in greater frequency stability, and is accomplished by insertion of an additional capacitor in series with the tuning inductance of the Colpitts circuit.[1] The Wien bridge oscillator enjoys excellent frequency stability; further discussion is reserved for the literature.[6]

A piezoelectric crystal can be used as the prime tuning element and will provide exceptionally stable oscillation. A vibrating electromechanical system is formed within such a crystal (quartz, for instance) when a potential is applied to its opposite faces and the device is properly excited. The frequency of the resulting oscillations depends upon crystal dimensions, mounting, and cut, and units are available that resonate at from several kilocycles to frequencies in the lower megacycle range.

A circuit diagram symbol and the electrical equivalent circuit for a crystal are shown in Fig. 12–10. R, L, and C are electrical equivalents of the mechanical parameters, while C_h represents electrical capacitance of the crystal between electrodes. The crystal represents a very high Q circuit, with values of Q in the thousands; if we therefore omit R from the determination of resonant frequency, no significant error is introduced. Also because C_h may be 100 or more times larger than C, it can be shown that the resonant frequency of the crystal may be approximated by

$$f = \frac{1}{2\pi\sqrt{LC}}.$$

A crystal may be substituted for an L-C resonant circuit in order to improve the stability of oscillation frequency.

Bias Considerations.   Oscillators as discussed in this section may be biased Class A by the methods previously considered for amplifiers. For higher efficiency Class-B or Class-C operation may be chosen. Starting generally requires that the circuit be initially self-biased somewhere in the active region unless some auxiliary starting means is included.

Bypassed emitter resistance permits Class-C transistor operation in a manner somewhat similar to the grid-leak method used with vacuum-tube oscillators. An average voltage builds up across the emitter $R\text{-}C$ combination that provides reverse bias for the emitter diode. With an initial operating point near cutoff, rising oscillations will first result in clipping at the low-current end of the load line, and eventually the buildup will be limited by nonlinearities at the high-current end. The operating point will eventually lie in the cutoff region.

Radio-Frequency Oscillators. Because of the requirement for multichannel reception, adjustable-frequency waveform generation at frequencies well above the audio is necessary in the superheterodyne type of communications receiver. Transistor reactances, temperature excursions, and power-supply variations must be contended with, but the basic principles of oscillation previously discussed naturally pertain. Of course, as in any design, economic considerations are also of great importance.

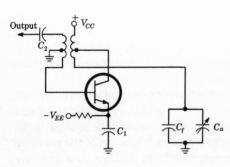

Fig. 12–11. Transistor local oscillator.

A practical local oscillator for broadcast-band radio receiver circuits is shown in Fig. 12–11. The circuit employs $L\text{-}C$ resonance, and might be called a phase-shift type of harmonic oscillator, for the transformer provides the required shift and C_a and C_f resonate with transformer inductance. Capacitor C_1 is ac grounding the emitter terminal of the transistor, and emitter bias is being used. Quiescent base current is returned to ground through part of the transformer's base circuit winding. Typical values for the blocking capacitors C_1 and C_2 are 0.01 to 0.05 μF.

12–4. Modulation. If the output of an oscillator is connected to an antenna, some of the output is radiated into space and a fraction of the radiated signal may be intercepted by a receiving antenna. This, then, is a communications system, but to convey intelligence some characteristic of the radiated signal must be varied with time. If the phase or frequency of carrier oscillation changes as a result of coded intelligence, the method is called frequency modulation (FM). Changing carrier amplitude in accordance with intelligence yields amplitude modulation (AM), and pulse modulation (PM) results from on–off control of the carrier.

Modulation, therefore, is the process of producing a composite waveform, some characteristic of which varies in accordance with the instantaneous value of another wave, called the modulating wave (the signal).

Amplitude Modulation. The process of amplitude modulation may be illustrated by first considering the mathematical relations. The carrier wave may be described by the standard sinusoidal waveform equation

$$v_c = V_{cm} \cos \omega_c t, \qquad (12\text{–}18)$$

and will generally be of high frequency. The modulating signal, if a simple sinusoidal function of time, may be described by

$$v_m = V_{mm} \cos \omega_m t, \tag{12-19}$$

a low-frequency signal.

If the magnitude of the carrier is changed in proportion (K_a) to v_m so that

$$v = (V_{cm} + K_a V_{mm} \cos \omega_m t) \cos \omega_c t, \tag{12-20a}$$

then this equation describes amplitude modulation. In a slightly different form, Eq. (12–20a) becomes

$$v = V_{cm}\left(1 + \frac{K_a V_{mm}}{V_{cm}} \cos \omega_m t\right) \cos \omega_c t \tag{12-20b}$$

or

$$v = V_{cm}(1 + m_a \cos \omega_m t) \cos \omega_c t. \tag{12-20c}$$

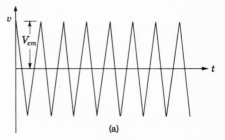

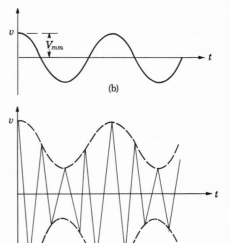

m_a is proportional to the ratio of maximum amplitudes of the component waves and is called the *modulation factor* or *modulation index*. Figure 12–12 illustrates the waveforms of interest. Should m_a exceed unity, distortion is introduced. All of the intelligence given by Eq. (12–19) is contained in the envelope of the composite waveform, for the envelope [the dashed curve joining peaks in Fig. 12–12(c)] can be described by

$$V_{cm}(1 + m_a \cos \omega_m t).$$

Its time-varying component is

$$V_{mm} \cos \omega_m t,$$

which is Eq. (12–19).

Should the composite waveform relationship given by Eq. (12–20c) be expanded trigonometrically, we obtain

Fig. 12–12. Amplitude modulation: (a) unmodulated carrier (sinusoidal shape not used, in order to simplify the diagram); (b) modulation signal; (c) modulated wave $m_a = 0.5$.

$$v = V_{cm} \cos \omega_c t + \tfrac{1}{2} m_a V_{cm} \cos(\omega_c + \omega_m)t + \tfrac{1}{2} m_a V_{cm} \cos(\omega_c - \omega_m)t. \tag{12-21}$$

Equation (12–21) represents the sum of three waveforms, one of the carrier frequency, one higher and another lower than the carrier frequency. The higher frequency is part of the *upper sideband*, while the lower-frequency portion lies in the *lower sideband*. Should the modulating signal contain waves of many frequencies, as one would find in broadcasting, the sidebands too would be made up of many different frequencies.

The amplitude-modulation process can occasionally be useful for frequency shifting. Should ω_m and ω_c be supplied to a modulator, the frequencies ω_c, $\omega_c - \omega_m$, and $\omega_c + \omega_m$ are available from a perfect process. Not only is the low- or audio-frequency signal shifted to a higher level in the spectrum as evidenced by the second and third terms of Eq. (12–21), but the carrier frequency is also shifted higher and lower according to those same terms.

The AM Amplifier. A method for amplitude-modulating a carrier is to feed the carrier through an amplifying stage whose gain varies in accordance with the frequency of the modulating signal. We have already seen that the gain of transistor stage is highly dependent upon quiescent emitter current. Suppose that total emitter current is caused to follow the instantaneous modulating wave as in

$$i_E = I_E + K'V_{mm}\cos\omega_m t. \tag{12–22}$$

Amplitude modulation will result provided that the maximum signal amplitude V_{mm} is smaller than the direct emitter current I_E. If gain is a function of total emitter current, and, more specifically if

$$A_v = K''i_E,$$

then voltage amplification is

$$A_v = K''(I_E + K'V_{mm}\cos\omega_m t). \tag{12–23}$$

Output voltage may be given by

$$v_o = A_v v_c. \tag{12–24}$$

Substitution of Eqs. (12–18) and (12–23) into Eq. (12–24) yields

$$v_o = K''(I_E + K'V_{mm}\cos\omega_m t)(V_{cm}\cos\omega_c t). \tag{12–25a}$$

This may be written as

$$v_o = K''I_E V_{cm}\cos\omega_c t$$
$$+ \tfrac{1}{2}(K'K''V_{mm}V_{cm})[\cos(\omega_c + \omega_m)t + \cos(\omega_c - \omega_m)t]. \tag{12–25b}$$

Thus

$$v_o = K\{V_{cm}\cos\omega_c t + \tfrac{1}{2}(m_a V_{cm})[\cos(\omega_c + \omega_m)t + \cos(\omega_c - \omega_m)t]\}. \tag{12–25c}$$

This represents an amplitude-modulated wave as described by Eq. (12–21). The modulation factor m_a in the above equation equals $K'V_{mm}/I_E$.

Because a perfectly proportional relationship between gain and bias was previously assumed, the expression for v_o contained no harmonics or signals of unwanted frequencies. Undesirable signals always result from practical modulation techniques, and a tuned circuit is used in the collector of the modulator stage to provide the necessary frequency selectivity. Naturally the bandpass characteristic of such a circuit must include the carrier and sidebands.

The modulating signal may be injected into a carrier-amplifying stage as base signal, emitter signal, or collector signal. Because the frequency of the carrier

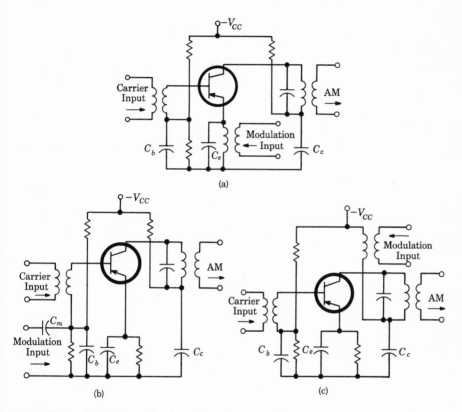

Fig. 12–13. Modulator circuits: (a) emitter modulation; (b) base modulation; (c) collector modulation.

is always much higher than the modulating frequency, capacitors and transformers may be used to maintain separation of signals. Thus the capacitor across the modulation input in each circuit, C_e, C_b, and C_c in a, b, and c of Fig. 12–13, respectively, is chosen as a short-circuit for the carrier only; one would naturally not want to ground the modulation at its input. C_m in Fig. 12–13(b) blocks dc; the remaining capacitors in each circuit are useful in bypassing all ac from the parallel dc path.

Base and emitter modulation are very similar; both methods represent a sort of "low-level modulation," because operation is limited to the most linear portion of the gain vs. i_E curve. Shea[10] has shown almost perfect linearity using emitter injection up to 92% modulation, with base injection resulting in more distortion.

Collector modulation causes collector-to-emitter voltage to vary with the modulation voltage. The most linear region of the gain vs. v_{CE} curve is at low levels of potential; therefore, collector injection will also be limited to low signal levels.

Frequency Modulation. A frequency-modulated wave results when the instantaneous deviation in frequency from the carrier is proportional to the instantaneous value of the modulating signal. Thus the angular frequency of the FM wave is described by

$$\omega = \omega_c + K_f V_{mm} \cos \omega_m t. \tag{12-26}$$

Total phase angle $\phi = \omega t$, so that, if ω is variable,

$$\phi = \int_o^t \omega \, dt = \int_o^t (\omega_c + K_f V_{mm} \cos \omega_m t) \, dt.$$

Therefore

$$\phi = \omega_c t + (K_f V_{mm}/\omega_m) \sin \omega_m t, \tag{12-27a}$$

or

$$\phi = \omega_c t + m_f \sin \omega_m t. \tag{12-27b}$$

The *modulation index* is m_f. Substitution of Eq. (12-27b) into the carrier equation, $v = V_{cm} \cos \phi$, yields

$$v = V_{cm} \cos (\omega_c t + m_f \sin \omega_m t). \tag{12-28}$$

This is the general equation for a frequency-modulated wave. Phase modulation results in a similar voltage equation.

FM Methods. A simple method for producing an FM wave is to vary the capacitance or inductance of the tank circuit used for determining the frequency of an oscillator. Mechanical motion of a capacitor plate or of an inductor slug is possible. A more satisfactory method for producing an FM wave is to vary the reactance of a transistor paralleling an oscillator tank in accordance with the modulating signal. This varying reactance will in turn vary the frequency of oscillation. The analogous vacuum-tube circuit is referred to as a "reactance-tube modulator."

A Colpitts oscillator with an additional transistor connected across the inductance can generate an FM wave. If the transistor's collector and base terminals are connected across the tuned circuit, then C_{ob} is the important parameter. Because the value of C_{ob} is dependent upon collector voltage and emitter current as evidenced by Fig. 4–13, C_{ob} will vary at the modulating frequency when that voltage or current is made to change in accordance with the modulating signal. Hence the oscillator frequency will be modulated.

A "Miller-effect modulator" is shown in Fig. 12–14. The input capacitance of TR1 varies with the modulation frequency. This input capacitance is coupled through C to the tank of the Colpitts oscillator. Capacitance variations caused by the modulation cause the oscillator frequency to vary.

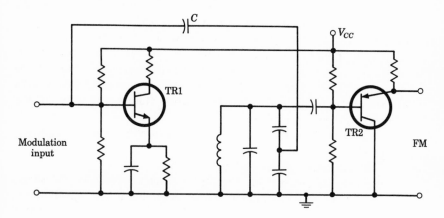

Fig. 12–14.   Miller-effect modulator.

12–5. Detection.   It is, of course, necessary to separate the modulated wave into its components, carrier and signal, in order to retrieve the intelligence in a communications system. The process of separation of information from the carrier and sidebands is called *detection* or *demodulation*. The carrier can be looked at as a tool for the successful transmission of electromagnetic radiations; it is discarded at the receiver after its purpose has been served.

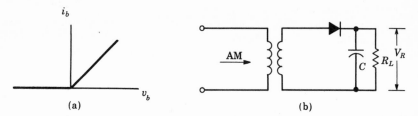

Fig. 12–15.   Left, idealized diode characteristic; right, simple diode detector circuit with filter and load.

Diode Detection.   Two-electrode devices, the semiconductor diode in particular, are very popular elements for detection. The volt–ampere characteristic of the diode, even when idealized as in Fig. 12–15(a), is nonlinear in the sense that it will pass only signals of a particular polarity, and it can be shown that a nonlinear characteristic is essential for both the modulation and the demodulation processes.

The ideal diode characteristic is given mathematically by

$$i_b = v_b/r_p \text{ for } v_b > 0$$

and

$$i_b = 0 \text{ for } v_b < 0.$$

i_b and v_b are the instantaneous plate current and plate-to-cathode voltage, respectively, and r_p the dynamic plate resistance (forward diode resistance).

For an analysis of diode detection, we shall consider only the popular circuit of Fig. 12–15(b), operating so as to perform what is commonly referred to as *envelope detection* or *linear detection*. In appearance this is merely a rectifier type of circuit with capacitor input filter, so rectification studies will prove helpful in analyzing such an envelope detector.

The waveform available to the circuit is that of an amplitude-modulated wave, with a high-frequency carrier and a low-frequency envelope usually varying according to audio-frequency modulation. The diode slices off negative-going portions of the composite waveform. The capacitor may be thought of as shorting all of the carrier to ground, or, alternatively, providing a low impedance to the carrier so that most of the carrier voltage will drop across r_p. The capacitor charges up to the peak of the composite wave through the fairly low r_p, and then, on negative half-cycles of the carrier, tries to discharge through the relatively high-resistance load R_L. Because the capacitor is chosen so that this discharge is very slight in the time available between carrier half-cycles, the voltage available at R_L is simply the audio-frequency modulation superimposed upon a constant level, that level resulting from the rectification process.

An average or direct voltage exists across the load during all periods when the circuit is in operation, and that potential will alter the preceding idealized discussion, for the diode operating point, in the presence of signal, will be at $-V_R$ volts along the v_b axis instead of 0. Although, in reality, V_R is not a constant-valued quantity, it will herein be assumed constant in order to simplify the analysis. The instantaneous potential applied to the diode can now be written as

$$v_b = V_{cm}(1 + m_a \cos \omega_m t) \cos \omega_c t - V_R. \qquad (12\text{–}29a)$$

In a further quest for simplicity, this equation will be written as

$$v_b = V' \cos \theta - V_R, \qquad (12\text{–}29b)$$

with $V' = V_{cm}(1 + m_a \cos \omega_m t)$. V' will be treated as a constant when only a few cycles of the carrier are being investigated. Over a single cycle of the carrier the average of the load current is given by an integration of the current waveform. Thus

$$I_R = \frac{1}{2\pi} \int_{-\pi}^{\pi} \frac{v_b}{r_p} \, d\theta. \qquad (12\text{–}30)$$

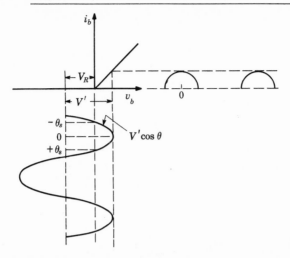

Fig. 12–16.   Operation of diode detector during a cycle of the carrier.

Because there is conduction between $-\theta_s$ and $+\theta_s$, as shown in Fig. 12–16, the integration limits in Eq. (12–30) may be changed. Substitution of Eq. (12–29(b)) into the integral and evaluation yields

$$I_R = \frac{1}{\pi r_p} (V' \sin \theta_s - V_R \theta_s).$$
(12–31)

Recall that $V_R = I_R R_L$ if $R_L \gg 1/\omega_c C$. Observation of Fig. 12–16 shows $\cos \theta_s = V_R / V'$, and therefore

$$V_R = \frac{V' R_L}{\pi r_p} (\sin \theta_s - \theta_s \cos \theta_s).$$
(12–32)

Removal of V' gives

$$V_R = \frac{V_{cm} R_L}{\pi r_p} (\sin \theta_s - \theta_s \cos \theta_s) + \frac{V_{mm} R_L}{\pi r_p} (\sin \theta_s - \theta_s \cos \theta_s) \cos \omega_m t.$$
(12–33)

Equation (12–33) indicates that a substantial direct voltage is present across the load, and that it is highly dependent upon carrier magnitude. The second term shows that the modulating frequency has been recovered without distortion.

Practically, distortion is evident in most demodulators because of curvature in the diode characteristic, and because for some modulation frequencies the capacitor cannot discharge at the same rate as the modulation envelope decreases. An empirically derived relation for designers indicates that distortion is not excessive if

$$\frac{1}{R_L C} \geq m_a \omega_m.$$
(12–34)

Transistor Detectors. The transistor is used occasionally as a detector. It is capable of detection because of the diode-like characteristic of its emitter–base input circuit. When operated at a very low quiescent emitter current (less than 50 μA), the detection performance of a transistor is good; it provides signal gain and therefore may be used to play the dual roles of detector and first audio amplifier. Where AGC is used, more control power is available with a transistor detector.

As we have seen in Chapter 6, low emitter current results in low gain, and therefore the gain provided by a transistor detector will not be as great as that of a regular audio amplifier. A simple transistor detector stage is illustrated in

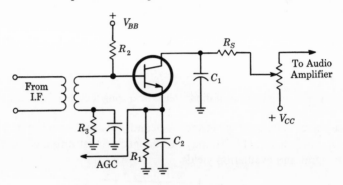

Fig. 12–17.   Transistor detector.

Fig. 12–17. A small base-bias is provided by R_2 and R_3; the dc level at the emitter, after detection, is fed back for AGC purposes. Capacitors C_1 and C_2 are of 0.01 μF, a size consistent with the requirement for low I.F. impedance in broadcast receiver operation, but they do not effectively short the audio modulation. R_S helps to maintain a direct collector potential that is fairly constant, and therefore not too seriously affected by volume-control setting.

FM Demodulation. An FM detector must be capable of changing variations in frequency into variations in amplitude. Because it is desired that amplitude variations caused by noise and unwanted signals not be reproduced in the loud-speaker, the FM receiver sometimes includes an amplitude-limiting circuit. This *limiter* precedes the detector and provides the detector with a substantially constant amplitude signal above a certain low level. Limiting action is possible through use of the saturation and cutoff regions of transistor characteristics. When a *ratio detector* is being used, the translation from FM to AM can be accomplished without external limiting, for the ratio detector circuit is insensitive to amplitude variations. Because ratio detectors are primarily diode circuits and because analysis is fairly involved, no description of such circuits will be attempted. The reader is referred to the excellent treatment available in other texts.[9]

12–6. Conversion and Mixing. In the superheterodyne receiver, the incoming modulated carrier (R.F.) is combined with a locally generated waveform to produce a new frequency, the I.F., which is also modulated and is at lower frequency than the original carrier. This combining of waveforms may be accomplished in a *mixer stage,* or the local oscillator and mixing functions may be combined in a single stage. When this latter procedure is used the process is described as *frequency conversion* and the stage is said to be a frequency converter. The two possible methods for producing the amplitude-modulated I.F. are shown in Fig. 12–18 in block form.

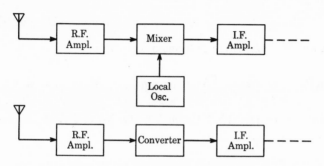

Fig. 12–18. Block diagrams of receiver front end—local oscillator and converter systems for obtaining the I.F.

Some choose to view frequency conversion as a modulation process because the amplitude of one signal is made to follow the variations of another signal. The local oscillator output corresponds to the waveform to be modulated and the R.F. wave is the modulating signal. Others feel that frequency conversion is detection, and the converter is frequently called the "first detector" because a frequency shifting from the R.F. level to I.F. level is accomplished.

The mixing of two waveforms in a linear device does not result in the generation of waveforms of new frequencies. Therefore, again, a nonlinear characteristic will be necessary. A square-law characteristic such as

$$i_c = Kv_b{}^2 \tag{12-35}$$

satisfies the requirements. Consider the amplitude-modulated waveform mathematically described by

$$v_1 = V_{cm}\cos\omega_c t + \frac{m_a V_{cm}}{2}\cos(\omega_c - \omega_m)t + \frac{m_a V_{cm}}{2}\cos(\omega_c + \omega_m)t. \tag{12-36}$$

The local oscillator voltage is given by

$$v_2 = V_{xm}\cos\omega_x t. \tag{12-37}$$

Addition of these two voltages to give v_b and squaring their sum as indicated by

Eq. (12–35) results in a host of terms; those involving ω_c, ω_x, $\omega_c + \omega_x$, and $\omega_c + \omega_x \pm \omega_m$ and their harmonics will be discarded because it is desired that ω_i, the intermediate frequency, be lower than the carrier, ω_c, and that tuned coupling to the following stage will pass only those frequencies in the neighborhood of the I.F. Thus, the angular I.F. will be

$$\omega_i = \omega_c - \omega_x. \tag{12–38}$$

The terms of interest are

$$i_c = KV_{xm}V_{cm}[\cos(\omega_c - \omega_x)t + (m_a/2)\cos(\omega_c - \omega_x + \omega_m)t$$
$$+ (m_a/2)\cos(\omega_c - \omega_x - \omega_m)t]. \tag{12–39}$$

This equation may be written in terms of the I.F.

$$i_c = KV_{xm}V_{cm}\left[\cos\omega_i t + \frac{m_a}{2}\cos(\omega_i + \omega_m)t + \frac{m_a}{2}\cos(\omega_i - \omega_m)t\right]. \tag{12–40}$$

A comparison of Eq. (12–40) with Eq. (12–36) clearly shows the frequency translation that has taken place.

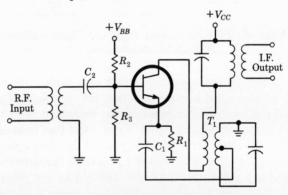

Fig. 12–19.   Transistor converter stage.

A typical converter stage is shown in Fig. 12–19. Emitter injection of the oscillator coil (T_1) signal is used to minimize interaction between the oscillator and R.F. sections. Resistors R_1, R_2, and R_3 provide and maintain the operating point, with C_2 blocking dc from the input transformer secondary.

12–7. The AM Receiver.   The preceding material will now be integrated in order to briefly study the complete superheterodyne AM receiver. A general block diagram of this type of receiver is shown in Fig. 12–20. In operation only the R.F. stage and the local oscillator are tuned to receive a specific station. All other portions of the set are pretuned at the factory or in service alignment. The I.F. stages must handle only the intermediate frequency (455 or 262 kc, for example) and sidebands; the audio stages just amplify the modulation frequencies. Thus each incoming signal is converted to the same I.F. and amplified by high-gain, fixed-tuned stages designed for the required selectivity.

The frequencies at various points within the receiver are shown in the diagram with the following abbreviations:

$$f_c = \text{carrier frequency,}$$
$$f_m = \text{modulation frequency (audio),}$$
$$f_o = \text{local oscillator frequency,}$$
$$f_i = \text{intermediate frequency.}$$

Deviations from the general block diagram are common. The R.F. stage may be omitted in certain receiver designs, because of economic considerations; the

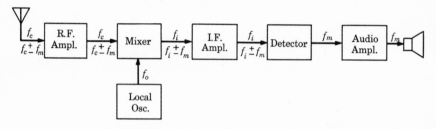

Fig. 12–20. Block diagram for complete AM receiver.

functions of separate local oscillator and mixer circuits may be performed by a single converter stage; and AGC may be shown on the diagram connecting the appropriate blocks. The number of transistors used in the I.F. portion may differ among designs.

Naturally, the receiver takes on the form dictated by design specifications regarding sensitivity, output power, frequency response, distortion, costs, etc.

In our brief study of the AM receiver, attention will be focused upon the complete radio schematic shown in Fig. 12–21. Because this circuit offers a number of interesting features, it was selected to be included here. A discussion of these features follows.

Upon first examination, notice that both p–n–p and n–p–n types are used with a single 9-V supply, negative grounded. The common-emitter orientation is used throughout. The n–p–n transistors use $+9$ V as their collector supply; p–n–p units have their collectors at dc ground with the $+9$ V supplied to their emitters. Notice that base-bias resistors are more or less opposites when using different transistor conductivity types; this is apparent when the converter stage is compared with the second I.F. stage.

The AGC line is from the plate of the detector diode to the base of the first I.F. stage. Base bias for that stage is obtained from the AGC line, and in the absence of signal there is a quiescent base current because of the connection

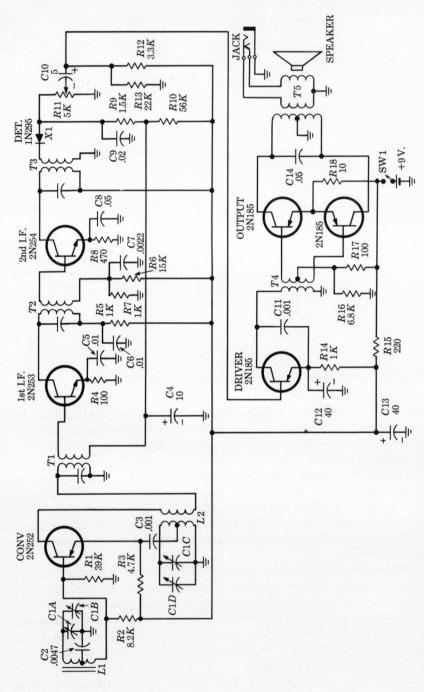

Fig. 12-21. Typical battery-powered AM receiver. All capacitors are in microfarads and resistors are in ohms. (Courtesy Westinghouse

through R_{10} to the supply. The output pair is conventional Class-B push–pull with some base bias for the elimination of crossover distortion. Bypassed emitter resistance is used in all Class-A stages and what we have called single-battery bias is used throughout except where AGC feedback is introduced.

The ac path commences with signal pickup in the antenna coil L_1. For the frequency for which C_1 is adjusted, series resonance results in the greater portion of the signal being available at the base of the converter. Unwanted signals (off resonance) find C_1 part of a high reactance and drop across the untuned L-C series combination, leaving little signal at the relatively low-impedance converter input.

Collector-to-emitter coupling through the oscillator coil L_2 provides the adjustable locally generated frequency. The I.F., formed from signal mixing in the converter, is transformer coupled to the first I.F. stage. The I.F. stages are unneutralized. Detection is accomplished with a diode in the conventional manner; the driver and output pair are also conventional.

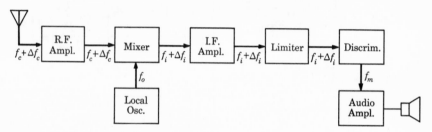

Fig. 12–22.   Block diagram for complete FM receiver.

12–8. The FM Receiver.   FM receivers use the superheterodyne principle, and in Fig. 12–22 a block diagram of such a system is shown. The frequencies at various points within the receiver are shown and the following abbreviations are used:

$$f_c = \text{carrier frequency},$$
$$\Delta f_c = \text{carrier variation due to modulation},$$
$$f_o = \text{local oscillator frequency},$$
$$f_i = \text{intermediate frequency},$$
$$\Delta f_i = \text{I.F. variation due to modulation},$$
$$f_m = \text{modulation frequency (audio)}.$$

Because high-frequency audio signals are accentuated by a *pre-emphasis* network in the FM transmitter in order to improve the signal strength relative to noise, the FM receiver must include a response-shaping network (*de-emphasis*) to reduce the highs.

The application of transistors to FM circuits proceeded rather slowly because of the poor performance of early production types at FM frequencies (88 to

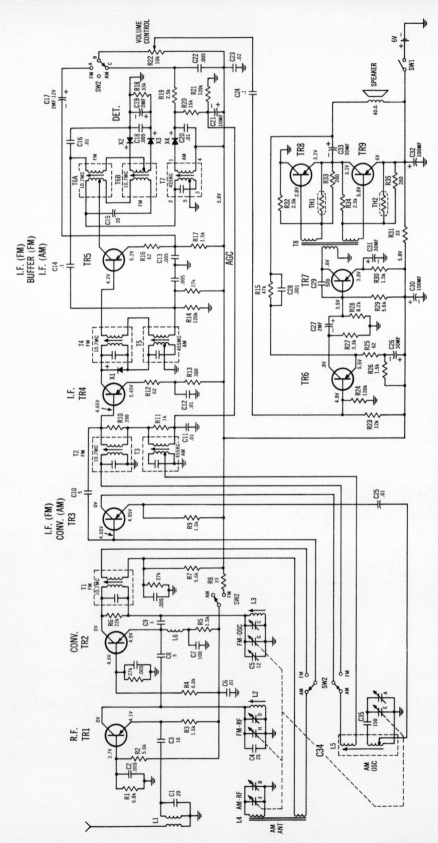

Fig. 12-23. Battery-operated AM–FM receiver. (Courtesy Westinghouse Electric Corporation.)

108 Mc. The advent of modern high-frequency types such as the drift, mesa, and planar transistors surmounted the frequency obstacle.

The complete schematic diagram of an all-transistor battery-operated AM–FM receiver is shown in Fig. 12–23. Nine transistors, four semiconductor diodes, and two thermistors are used in addition to the normal complement of passive circuit elements. This circuit will be discussed because it makes use of many of the aforementioned electronic principles and deviates from convention in several ways.

The receiver is physically extremely small. It operates from a self-contained 6-V supply consisting of four penlight cells. Maximum power output is 150 mW. The no-signal current drain is 13 mA on AM and 15 mA when FM is selected.

FM Operation. To analyze the operation of the receiver, we first note that the signal picked up by the FM antenna is coupled to the emitter of TR1. $L1$ and $C1$, loaded by the input resistance of that transistor, broadly tune the FM band. TR1 is serving as an R.F. amplifier and is common-base connected. This orientation provides the highest output resistance thus resulting in a more favorable Q for the tuned collector load, $L2$-$C4$. The stage is biased at 1.2 mA to provide a good balance between signal-to-noise ratio and gain. $C4$ is adjustable to the frequency being received. The R.F. signal is fed into the emitter of TR2, the converter, also common-base connected. TR2 oscillates at a frequency dependent upon the value of capacitance selected through adjustment of $C5$, 10.7 Mc above the R.F.. The feedback from collector to emitter is made through the 3 pF capacitor $C9$. $L6$ keeps the emitter above ac ground, and $R5$ stabilizes the quiescent emitter current at 0.6 mA.

Transformer $T1$ is tuned to the I.F., 10.7 Mc. $R6$ shapes the frequency response by loading down the primary of the tank. With switch SW2 in the FM position, the I.F. goes directly to the base of TR3, the first I.F. amplifier. TR3 is operated at 0.5 mA by the 5.6 and 27 kΩ base-biasing elements and is stabilized by $R9$ bypassed by $C25$. The tuned coil $T2$ forms the load on this stage; $T3$ is tuned to 455 kc and is not a significant impedance at 10.7 Mc. Neutralization of this stage is accomplished by $C10$.

TR4, the second I.F. stage, is unneutralized, and is base-biased by the potential on the AGC line. Although no AM signal will be present in $T7$ when the receiver is operating in the FM option, the detector diode $X4$ passes direct current from the 5.8-V line to the voltage divider $R20$-$R21$. The necessary base current for operation of TR4 is derived from the junction of these resistors. Diode $X1$ at the collector tank limits signal amplitude at that point.

Emitter resistances $R12$ and $R16$ in the second and third I.F. amplifiers desensitize those stages to parameter changes caused by unit-to-unit variations. Base bias for TR5 is derived from the 5.8-V line, $R14$ and the 27 kΩ resistance. (0.005 μF elements are essentially short circuits at the I.F.) TR5 feeds the FM discriminator coils $T6A$ and $T6B$. These coils, $X2$, $X3$, and associated elements form a modified *ratio detector*. The audio output is available at the junction of $C14$ and

$C16$ and is fed back to the base of TR5. TR5 now acts as an emitter-follower for the audio.

The signal is fed through $C17$ and the volume control to the first audio amplifier, TR6, a conventional stage capacitively coupled to the audio driver, TR7. Negative feedback for reducing high frequencies is apparent from the location of $C29$. Transformer coupling is used between the driver and the Class-B push–pull output pair. TR8 is operating common-collector, and TR9 is common-emitter. This circuit eliminates the need for an output transformer; it uses a 40-Ω loudspeaker. Thermistors TH1 and TH2 provide temperature stabilization. The load signal is fed back to the emitter of TR6 for gain stability and filtering.

AM Operation. For receiving AM, TR1, and TR2 are de-energized. Signals picked up by $L4$, the AM antenna, are fed to TR3 which is now being used as a converter instead of an I.F. amplifier. TR4 and TR5 are the I.F. amplifiers for AM signals. The detector output at $X4$ is filtered by $C21$ and fed back as AGC to the base of TR4. The audio level is adjusted by the volume control $R22$. Further audio amplification is identical to that previously discussed.

12–9. The TV Receiver. The television receiver also uses the superheterodyne principle. Because it is required to perform a variety of functions necessary for picture reproduction, it is considerably more complex than the AM and FM receivers previously considered. Space limitations make it impossible to completely describe the operation of this system here. We shall present a summary of some of the more important principles; for a more detailed treatment, the reader is referred to books specifically devoted to TV.

The composite television signal contains sound information which is frequency modulated, picture information which is amplitude modulated, and synchronizing and blanking pulses. The synchronizing (sync) pulses are used to synchronize horizontal and vertical sweep oscillators located in the receiver with those of the broadcasting station. In the U.S.A., each channel is alloted a 6-Mc bandwidth, with the sound carrier 4.5 Mc above the video carrier. The video carrier is located at 55.25 Mc for channel 2; the alloted band for that channel extends from 54 to 60 Mc.

Figure 12–24 is a block diagram of a typical monochrome receiver. Audio and video signals are picked up by the antenna, amplified by the R.F. stage tuned to the appropriate channel, and converted to an I.F. in the mixer. The I.F. chain, typically centered at 45 Mc, uses stagger-tuned stages to pass the rather wide band required. At the video detector, the intermediate frequency is removed.

In the video amplifier chain, synchronizing pulses and sound are separated from the video information. The latter is fed to a grid of the picture tube to control the intensity of the electron beam. The separated audio signal, modulating the 4.5 Mc sound carrier, is amplified, detected, and further amplified before reaching the loudspeaker. Sync separation is accomplished by clipping off the large amplitude synchronizing pulses at the output of the video detector, and feeding the 60 cps sync pulses to the vertical oscillator while the 17,500 cps horizontal sync pulses are forwarded to the horizontal oscillator. The horizontal output, a sawtooth waveform, is applied to the horizontal deflection coils to move the beam from left to right across the face of the picture or *cathode-ray tube* (C.R.T.). A sawtooth wave from the vertical oscillator is supplied to the vertical deflection coils, to move the electron beam from top to bottom of the C.R.T.

Movement of the beam across the face of the picture tube is referred to as *scanning*. Let us consider that the beam starts at the upper left-hand edge of the screen at $t = 0$. It is driven toward the right by the horizontal deflection system,

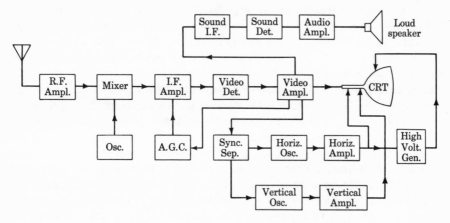

Fig. 12–24.   Typical TV receiver block diagram.

and, at the same time, downward by the vertical deflection voltage. During its traverse, the intensity of the beam, the factor controlling picture detail, is varied by the video signal applied to the control grid. When the beam reaches the right hand side of the tube, it has completed one line of the 525 lines that make up a complete picture. It ends its first line displaced slightly below the vertical position at which it started, because the vertical deflection voltage is now slightly different from its value at $t = 0$. The beam now rapidly jumps to the left-hand side of the screen, and, slightly displaced vertically, repeats the process noted above.

The slow-rising portion of the sawtooth used for horizontal scanning moves the beam relatively slowly, compared to the rapid rate of amplitude reduction after reaching its peak. The high-slope portion of the sawtooth is used for *retrace*, returning the beam to its starting place at the left side of the picture, or, in the case of vertical deflection, to the top of the screen. Blanking signals, used to prohibit the electron beam from reaching the screen during retrace intervals, are of large amplitude and are broadcast along with the sync signals. Upon reaching the C.R.T. they cut off the beam when it is merely moving into position for the next scanning run. With the type of transmission used in the U.S., large signals are analogous with black screen color. Thus blanking, and extraneous noise pulses as well, are not seen by the eye.

A fundamental rate of 30 images or *frames* per second is used, but because of *interlaced scanning*, a process that samples every other line at the studio camera, the effective rate is 60 frames per second. If the downward or vertical scanning rate is 60 cps, every even line will be scanned in 1/60 of a second. The same is true for the odd lines. The entire image is made up of 525 horizontal lines, $262\frac{1}{2}$ scanned during each frame. Thus the horizontal oscillator must operate at $262\frac{1}{2}$ times the vertical rate, or at 15,750 cps.

Let us study the reason for the large bandwidth used in the transmission of video information. Consider each line to be composed of 700 separate picture elements, with a picture element simply a dot or a location that can be excited ideally with a beam of high intensity to cause it to be white, or with a low-intensity beam for a black spot. Thus, in one second, $700 \times 15,750 = 11,025,000$ picture elements are sent. In terms of frequency, this requires a 5.5 Mc signal. In practice a 4-Mc bandwidth is allowed for picture detail on the larger tubes; this dictates the response of the video amplifier stages. With regular methods of AM, picture detail would require a channel allocation of 8 Mc, ± 4 Mc about the carrier. To reduce the required channel bandwidth, *vestigial-sideband* operation is used, with one sideband removed at the transmitter by filtering. We know that all of AM information is contained in either sideband; consequently, this procedure is valid. Each channel is alloted 6 Mc; 4 Mc for the picture, 50 kc for the audio, and much of the remainder of the band contains unused remnants of the undesired sideband. (The picture carrier is 1.25 Mc above the lower frequency limit of the channel.)

The picture tube requires a high anode potential, 5 to 30 kV, in order to satisfactorily accelerate the electron beam. In most TV receivers, this voltage is generated from the large di/dt present during retrace in a transformer located in the horizontal deflection system. The inductive "kick," or "fly-back" is rectified and filtered to provide the necessary high voltage.

As an example of a portion of the circuitry employed in a TV receiver, consider Fig. 12–25. Several points previously discussed may be appreciated from a study of that diagram.

Transistor $Q1$, the first video amplifier, is connected emitter-follower to furnish the power necessary to drive the second video amplifier, as well as the clipper and AGC circuits. To remove the sound signal centered about its 4.5 Mc carrier, an audio take-off or trap $T1$ is used to present a low series impedance for the sound signal.

The video signal is amplified by $Q2$. Element $C3$ blocks dc, while $R2$ and $R3$ base bias this second video amplifier. $R4$ is the collector load for this stage. The video signal is applied to the first or control grid of the C.R.T. through $L1$ and $C4$ which provide series peaking in order to extend the bandwidth of the stage.

$R5$ is a leakage path for the control grid. Emitter peaking is accomplished by $C5$, $R6$, and $R7$. The gain of the stage, referred to as *contrast*, is controlled by adjustment of $R8$, which affects the emitter-base bias voltage.

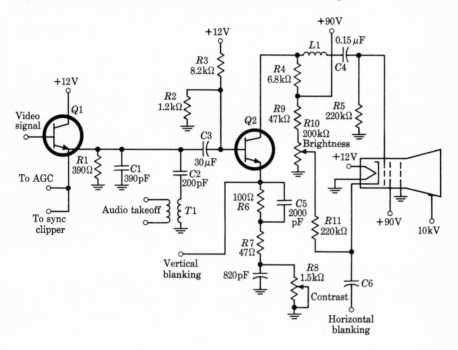

Fig. 12–25.   Portion of TV receiver.

Positive-going horizontal blanking signals are supplied through $C6$ to the cathode of the C.R.T. Elements $R9$, $R10$, and $R11$ provide a positive bias for the tube and thus serve to set the *brightness* of the picture. Vertical blanking signals are inserted into the emitter circuit of $Q2$.

PROBLEMS

12–1. Solve for the expression of the instantaneous current in the series $R\text{-}L\text{-}C$ circuit of Fig. 12–1 suddenly supplied with a direct voltage of V volts. The circuit has been at rest for some time prior to switching. Express the frequency of this oscillation in terms of the circuit parameters.

12–2. Consider a common-emitter transistor stage with unbypassed emitter resistance R_e. Show that, if $\alpha > 1$, the necessary condition for negative input resistance is

$$R_e > [r_b(\alpha - 1) - r_e].$$

A point-contact transistor may have $\alpha > 1$.

12–3. A tunnel diode has the following parameters: $L_s = 10^{-9}$ H, $C = 1$ pF, $-R_d = -50$ Ω, $R_s = 1$ Ω.

(a) Determine f_{ro} and f_{xo}.

(b) What is the frequency of oscillation of a simple series circuit employing this diode if $R_T = 25$ Ω? How large is the external inductance?

12–4. For a series–parallel tunnel-diode oscillator, derive the relation for oscillation frequency,

$$\omega_0{}^2 = \frac{1}{L(C - C_1)} - \frac{1}{R_d{}^2 C(C - C_1)}$$

and the relation for R_T

$$R_T = G_d/(\omega_0{}^2 C^2 + G_d{}^2).$$

Neglect L_s and consider that C parallels R_d and C_1 parallels the external inductance L.

12–5. Confirm Eqs. (12–10) and (12–11) for the phase-shift oscillator.

12–6. Confirm Eqs. (12–13) and (12–14) for the Colpitts-type oscillator.

12–7. Confirm Eqs. (12–15) and (12–16) for the Hartley-type oscillator.

12–8. Include mutual inductance in the derivations for starting conditions and frequency of oscillation for a Hartley-type oscillator.

12–9. Write the circuit determinant for the generalized oscillator shown in the accompanying diagram.

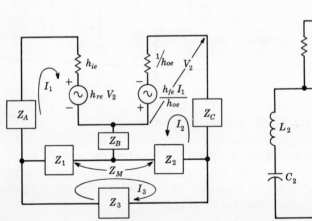

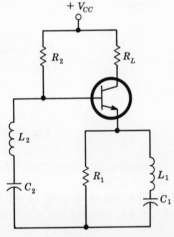

Problem 12–9.   Problem 12–12.

12–10. Can you find a relationship among external elements, from the solution to Problem 12–9, that will result in the frequency of oscillation being completely independent of the transistor parameters?

12–11. A quartz crystal has the following equivalent parameters: $L = 10$ H, $C = 0.04$ pF, $R = 5000$ Ω, $C_h = 3$ pF.

(a) Determine the resonant frequency of the series portion of the circuit.

(b) Determine the Q of the series branch.

(c) Determine the resonant frequency of the entire parallel circuit (neglect R but include C_h).

(d) By what percent does the parallel resonant frequency differ from the series resonant frequency?

12–12. In the tuned-emitter, tuned-base oscillator of the accompanying diagram, R_1 and R_2 are large-valued resistances useful for biasing. Prove that the frequency of oscillation for this circuit is given by

$$\omega^2 \cong \frac{C_1 + h_{fe}C_2}{C_1 C_2 (L_2 + h_{fe}L_1)}.$$

12–13. Discuss the crystal oscillator of the accompanying figure.

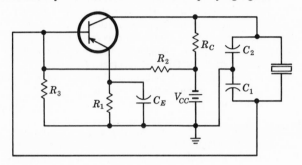

Problem 12–13.

12–14. So-called *square-law* or *small-signal* modulation is produced when a device with a nonlinear transfer characteristic, for example one of the form

$$i_c = K_1 v_b + K_2 v_b^2,$$

is excited with a base voltage that is the sum of modulation and carrier-frequency terms as

$$v_b = V_{mm} \cos \omega_m t + V_{cm} \cos \omega_c t.$$

(a) Show that the resulting expression for collector current contains terms involving ω_c, ω_m, $(\omega_c + \omega_m)$, $(\omega_c - \omega_m)$, and harmonics of the two input frequencies.

(b) Derive the expression for i_c that contains only terms in ω_c, $(\omega_c + \omega_m)$, and $(\omega_c - \omega_m)$ by assuming that a frequency-selective network eleminates all terms not in the vicinity of ω_c.

(c) Prove that the modulation index may be given by $m_a = 2K_2 V_{mm}/K_1$.

12–15. For a modulated wave given by

$$v = 100(1 + 0.4 \cos 2000t) \sin 10^6 t,$$

find the three frequencies contained in the wave and the peak amplitude of each.

12–16. Derive an expression for the sideband power as a percentage of carrier power in terms of the modulation factor m_a. 5000 W of 30% amplitude-modulated R.F. power contains how much sideband power?

12–17. Square-law detection depends upon a voltage–current characteristic of the form

$$i_b = K v_b^2.$$

If an amplitude-modulated wave

$$v_b = V_{cm}(1 + m_a \cos \omega_m t) \cos \omega_c t$$

is impressed upon a device with a characteristic as given above, show that i_b will contain terms in ω_m, $2\omega_m$, $2\omega_c$, and in the sum and difference of harmonics of the carrier and modulating frequency. Find the coefficients for each term of the expansion.

12–18. For the square-law detector of Problem 12–17, determine the highest allowable modulation index in order for second-harmonic distortion to be limited to 10% of the fundamental (ω_m).

12–19. Show that a circuit element with a square-law characteristic (see Problem 12–17) can be used as a frequency multiplier when $v = V_{max} \sin \omega t$ is applied.

12–20. A superheterodyne AM receiver contains an R.F. amplifier, separate oscillator, three I.F. amplifiers, and a Class-B audio-amplifier pair. The I.F. is 455 kc, and the receiver is tuned to a station at 1050 kc, modulated at 1000 cps.

(a) Draw a block diagram clearly showing all necessary functions.

(b) On the diagram indicate the frequencies present in each stage.

12–21. Draw a block diagram for the AM receiver of Fig. 12–21.

12–22. Describe the function of each resistor in the circuit of Fig. 12–21.

12–23. Describe the function of each capacitor in the circuit of Fig. 12–21.

12–24. Describe the function of each inductor and transformer in the circuit of Fig. 12–21.

12–25. For the circuit of Fig. 12–21, compare the reactance of emitter bypass capacitors with the resistance they bypass for the audio and I.F. stages. The I.F. is 455 kc.

12–26. In the circuit of Fig. 12–21, what approximate direct voltages would be measured from base-to-ground and collector-to-ground for the I.F. and audio stages? Consider that the I.F. stages each operate at 1 mA, the driver at 2 mA, and the output pair at 0 mA.

12–27. Redraw the circuit of Fig. 12–21 showing only those components that make up the dc portions of the circuit; in other words, the components affecting the operating points.

12–28. Redraw the circuit of Fig. 12–21 showing only those components that make up the ac portions of the circuit; in other words, the components affecting the signal.

12–29. Repeat Problem 12–27 for the FM circuit of Fig. 12–23.

12–30. Repeat Problem 12–28 for the FM circuit of Fig. 12–23.

12–31. For the circuit of Fig. 12–23, draw a complete block diagram. Include the AGC path.

REFERENCES

1. Clapp, J. K., "An Inductance-Capacitance Oscillator of Unusual Frequency Stability," *Proc. IRE*, **36** (March, 1948).
2. Cunningham, W. J., *Introduction to Nonlinear Analysis* (McGraw-Hill Book Co., Inc., New York, 1958).
3. DeWitt, D., and Rossoff, A. L., *Transistor Electronics* (McGraw-Hill Book Co., Inc., New York, 1957).
4. Glasford, G. M., *Fundamentals of Television Engineering* (McGraw-Hill Book Co., Inc., New York, 1955).
5. Hurley, R. B., *Junction Transistor Electronics* (John Wiley & Sons, Inc., New York, 1958).
6. Millman, J., *Vacuum-Tube and Semiconductor Electronics* (McGraw-Hill, Book Co., Inc., New York, 1958).
7. Reich, H. J., *Functional Circuits and Oscillators* (D. Van Nostrand Co., Inc., Princeton, New Jersey, 1961).

8. Riddle, R. L., and Ristenbatt, M. P., *Transistor Physics and Circuits* (Prentice-Hall, Inc., Englewood Cliffs, New Jersey, 1958).
9. Ryder, J. D., *Electronic Fundamentals and Applications* (Prentice-Hall, Inc., Englewood Cliffs, New Jersey, 1964), 3rd ed.
10. Shea, R. F., *Transistor Circuit Engineering* (John Wiley & Sons, Inc., New York, 1957).
11. Terman, F. E., and Pettit, J. M., *Electronic Measurements* (McGraw-Hill Book Co., Inc., New York, 1952).
12. Towers, T. D., *Transistor Television Receivers* (John F. Rider Publisher, Inc., New York, 1963).
13. Wolfendale, E., *The Junction Transistor and Its Applications* (The Macmillan Co., New York, 1958).

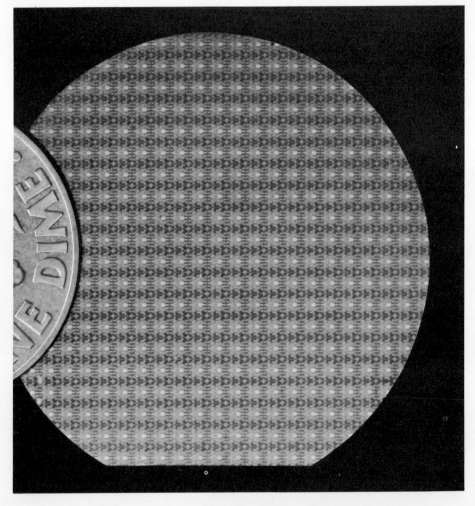

A silicon slice, 1-in. diam, containing about 350 semiconductor networks. Each network has been triple diffused to form 56 components. The components are interconnected, using a gold deposition pattern, to make four NAND gates. Subsequently the slice is scribed, broken apart, and the networks mounted in separate packages (Photo Courtesy Texas Instruments, Incorporated).

Chapter 13

PULSE CIRCUITS

Continuous and generally sinusoidal currents and voltages were considered in the foregoing chapters. There are a great many applications where discontinuous and nonsinusoidal waveforms play an important role, and consequently this chapter will be devoted to *pulse* and *switching circuits*, those circuits wherein abrupt and often large changes in the important quantities occur. Changes of this sort often result from the presence or absence of an input drive, and faithful reproduction of the input waveform is sometimes not a requirement. Switching circuits are not conveniently analyzed by steady-state methods because operation involves the saturation and cutoff regions as well as the active region of the transistor characteristics.

Pulse circuits are required to perform certain functions; these functions may be summarized as follows:

1. Generation of pulse waveforms
2. Amplification of pulse waveforms
3. Shaping of pulse waveforms
4. Storage of digital information
5. Switching and gating.

Generation and storage will be described in the section of this chapter devoted to multivibrators; item 2, the amplification of nonsinusoidal waveshapes, will be given some further attention and may also be classified under the video amplifier heading of Chapter 11. Item 3 will not be discussed here as it is primarily a passive-device function, but general switching theory, item 5, does warrant some attention here, and our discussion will proceed with the considerations involved.

13–1. Switching. The resistive load R_L shown in Fig. 13–1(a) is connected in a series circuit with a switch and a dc supply. The resistor is to be supplied with current, and hence power, from the supply when the switch is closed. The generalized switch of the figure may take on one of many forms. For instance, it may be an electromechanical, a purely mechanical, or a purely electrical device. Often the power available to control the switch (to change its state from ON to OFF or vice versa) is small, and therefore the switch may also be required to provide amplification, for then, from a small-signal command, it can control a great deal of load power by completing the R_L-V circuit.

An electromechanical switch, the relay for example, combines amplification with control. A small signal of either polarity (or even ac) supplied to the relay coil will close the switch and complete the R_L-V circuit as shown in Fig. 13–1(b). The signal applied must be more than a specified minimum in order for the relay to actuate and close the contacts; the relay will "drop out" and the contacts will open when the voltage V_1 decreases below a specified level.

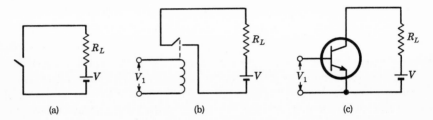

(a)   (b)   (c)

Fig. 13–1. Switching: (a) general circuit; (b) the relay as a switch; (c) the transistor as a switch.

The transistor may be used as a switch. In the circuit of Fig. 13–1(c) a transistor takes the place of the relay of the preceding figure. The low-power n–p–n transistor depicted requires, for the full ON condition, a potential V_1 of several hundred millivolts, or, alternatively, a base current of several hundred microamperes of the correct polarity. The full ON condition exists when the transistor is in saturation, and consequently the resistance of the collector-to-emitter branch is very low. Various ON conditions are possible and correspond to operation within the active region of the collector characteristics, but for the time being let us concern ourselves with full ON. To turn the transistor OFF, opening of the base lead may not suffice, for I_{CEO} is the resulting collector-to-emitter current. The full OFF condition is attained when a small negative potential is applied to the input terminal pair to reverse-bias the emitter junction. The resulting load current is I_{CO} and may be just a few nanoamperes in a high-quality silicon unit.

Let us now examine the advantages and disadvantages of the transistor in relation to the relay as a switching device. One measure of comparison is the ratio of open- to closed-circuit resistance introduced into the load circuit by the switching device. An ideal switch has infinite resistance when open, zero resistance when closed, and therefore an infinite resistance ratio. The relay approaches this ratio. However, the transistor when full ON or saturated does have a finite collector–emitter resistance, and when full OFF does pass some leakage current, so a finite resistance ratio is apparent. For a typical low-power germanium transistor, the saturation resistance may be of the order of 4 Ω and I_{CO} may be 5 μA at $V_{CE} = 10$ V. These figures indicate an OFF-to-ON resistance ratio of 0.5×10^6. A silicon transistor for the same job may have a saturation resistance of 10 Ω, and I_{CO} may be 0.01 μA at $V_{CE} = 10$ V. These numbers yield a ratio of 100×10^6. Higher-power transistors have lower saturation resistance but more leakage current.

The transistor is, as we have seen, inferior to an electromechanical switch in the aspect discussed above, but the devices, may be compared on other counts. Because the transistor has no moving parts and therefore lacks mechanical contacts that are subject to wear, the semiconductor device is far more reliable. The transistor as a switch is smaller, quieter, more efficient electrically, and costs less than a relay. A great advantage in electronic switching is the speed of that operation. Operating time is reduced by a factor of more than 1000 when the transistor is compared with a mechanical device. Where applicable, then, it may be concluded that electronic switching provides many advantages.

A brief discussion regarding transistor orientation is always appropriate when new uses for the device are considered. If switching were to be accomplished with a common-base oriented transistor, about as much input current (i_E) would be required as load current (i_C) to be controlled. With the common-emitter configuration a small base current can control a much larger collector current, and because of this internal amplification this configuration is the most widely used in switching circuits.

13–2. Semiconductor Switches. The common-emitter collector characteristics for a low-power transistor are illustrated in Fig. 13–2. A 2500-Ω load line has been drawn linking $V_{CC} = 15$ V with $V_{CC}/R_L = 6$ mA. Point A represents the upper limit of the OFF region and point B represents saturation or full ON. Switching as previously discussed could occur between these extremes and should base current assume values of 125 μA or greater to drive collector current to point B, the transistor would be called a *saturating switch*. A *nonsaturating switch* is one in which base current variations cause operation between the region of point A and a point such as C. C represents the ON condition, and is located somewhere in the active region of the characteristics.

A saturating switch requires more base current "drive" and longer switching time, but results in a much lower ON resistance than does the nonsaturating type. With respect to collector dissipation the saturating type of switch has advantages. Both types exhibit low dissipation in the standby or OFF condition, but when ON the saturating switch has a much lower V_{CE}-I_C product. Should the load line as shown in Fig. 13–2 cut across the maximum-dissipation contour, it is possible that the maximum allowable junction temperature of the transistor will not be exceeded, provided that the switching time is fast. Therefore, because their average dissipation is low, switching transistors can handle large voltages and currents without exceeding the rated maximum dissipation.

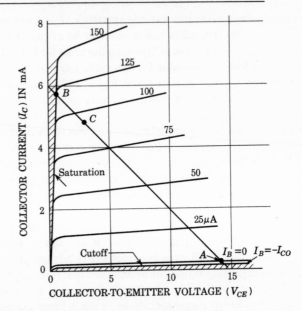

Fig. 13–2.　Load line on collector characteristics with points of interest noted.

A nonsaturating switch with a load line intersecting the maximum-dissipation contour must be carefully designed in order not to exceed the junction temperature limit; the duty cycle and tolerances must be accurately known.

In order to investigate more clearly the transistor operated in a switching mode, the common-emitter input characteristics for a typical low-power unit are illustrated in Fig. 13–3.

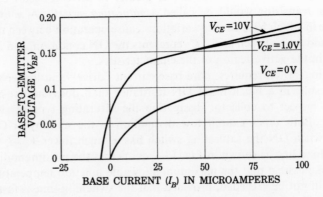

Fig. 13–3.　Input characteristics for a typical low-power transistor, common-emitter connected.

There are several possible OFF conditions for the common-emitter connected transistor, three of which are shown in Fig. 13–4. In (a) of the figure, zero base-to-emitter voltage is available because of the obvious short circuit across the input terminal pair; the resulting collector current is often given the symbol I_{CES}. When the base terminal is open, as in Fig. 13–4(b), no base current can

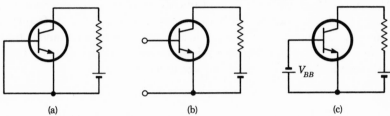

(a)   (b)   (c)

Fig. 13–4. OFF conditions for common-emitter-connected transistor: (a) zero input voltage; (b) zero input current; (c) restraining input voltage.

exist, and collector current is symbolized by the familiar I_{CEO}. Collector current I_{CEO} is two or more times greater than I_{CES}. A third method of turning OFF the transistor is by applying a restraining input voltage to reverse-bias the base–emitter diode. By choosing a suitable reverse bias the collector current can be most efficiently turned OFF; I_{CO}, the inevitable leakage, is then the remaining collector current.

To summarize switching states, it may be concluded that in the OFF condition input and output resistances are high, small leakage currents are apparent, and collector voltage approaches the supply voltage V_{CC}. The saturated ON condition results in $I_C \cong V_{CC}/R_L$, $V_{CE} = I_C R_{CS} < 1$ V, and a fairly low input resistance, with several hundred millivolts needed to supply the input terminal pair with the base current necessary for the saturation of low-power transistor.

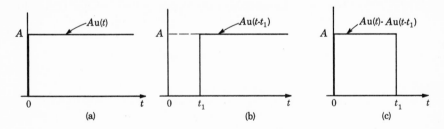

Fig. 13–5. Step functions.

Drive. A universal test for transistors used as switches is their response to a *step* input function. A step function $Au(t)$ is a voltage current or that at $t = 0$ rises immediately and instantaneously from a value of zero to a value A and remains at that level afterwards. (A unit step function has a plateau value, A, of unity.) A plot of $Au(t)$ is shown in Fig. 13–5(a). Mathematically, if the step function does not start at $t = 0$ but rather at some other time t_1, the function can be described by $Au(t - t_1)$. Should a rectangular pulse be considered that rises at $t = 0$, and falls at $t = t_1$, then an addition of the two functions $u(t)$ and $-u(t - t_1)$ can describe the pulse. Thus, for Fig. 13–5(c), $A[u(t) - u(t - t_1)]$ describes the resultant function.

Naturally, the ideal step function can only be approached in practice, for the ideal pulse, if described by a Fourier series, contains terms of frequencies to infinity. A device that would pass an ideal pulse must have an infinite frequency response. The transistor does not follow an ideal rectangular pulse because of transit time and minority-carrier storage in its base.

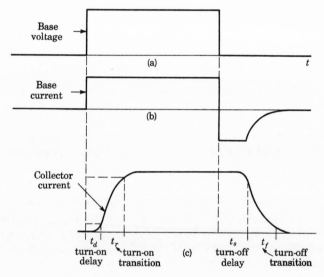

Fig. 13–6. Transistor step-function response: (a) step of base voltage; (b) resulting base current; (c) resulting collector current.

The base current produced by a given base-to-emitter voltage will vary because of production tolerances and consequently a constant current source is generally used to provide a controlled value of I_B in saturating switching circuits.

Turn-on and Turn-off. Consider an ideal step function of voltage shown in Fig. 13–6(a) applied between base and emitter of an n–p–n transistor. The transistor was in the OFF condition and the pulse is turning it ON. Base current is immediately evident, as in (b) of the figure, but collector current does not instantaneously respond. Electrons from the emitter must travel across the p-type base, and a finite time is required for their travel. This time is shown in (c) of the diagram as "turn-on delay." Electrons arriving at the collector travel by various paths; some paths are longer than others and consequently a finite time is again required before normal operation is achieved. This effect, wherein faster electrons traveling shorter paths arrive at their destination ahead of the less-energetic and dispersed carriers, is referred to in the diagram as "turn-on transition." Delay time is generally measured from the beginning of the input pulse to the 10% point on the output waveform. Transition or rise time has, for its limits, the 10% and 90% marks.

When the transistor is driven into saturation, the collector junction is forward-biased, and the collector then emits electrons into the base (for n–p–n). This causes an excess of minority carriers in the base region. A saturated transistor cannot be effectively turned OFF until this "stored base charge" is reduced. Therefore the high current level in the collector is supported by this charge

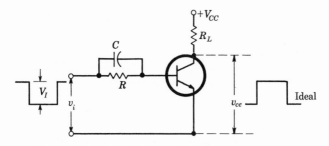

Fig. 13–7. Turn-off of a transistor with a voltage pulse. A speed-up capacitor is included, and ideal v_{ce} is shown.

during the time interval immediately after the OFF command is given to the input terminals. *Minority-carrier storage effect* is the name given to the "turn-off delay" encountered. The "turn-off transition" results from different velocities and path lengths that affect the arrival time of the last electrons to reach the collector. Note that the base current suffers a reversal in direction when the base-driving voltage is removed; stored charge accounts for this base current.

To measure stored base charge a voltage pulse is applied to a circuit such as Fig. 13–7. If the pulse saturates the transistor, and the output (v_{CE}) waveform is observed for various test values of C, a "clean" or best turn-off will be observed with a particular value of C. In this instance clean means that v_{CE} will be straight-sided. The amount of stored base charge is then given by

$$Q_s = CV_I.$$

The capacitor, C, is often referred to as a "speed-up" capacitor. In circuit design, knowledge of Q_s from given data or from a test such as just described can be combined with information concerning the voltage amplitude of the pulse and base current required for saturation (I_B''). Then R can be determined from

$$R = V_I/I_B''.$$

It is of course desirable to minimize the total time required for a switching operation to be performed. Turn-on delay may be reduced by driving the base with a high current, for this provides a greater number of available carriers in that region. The rise time t_r is dependent in part upon the frequency-response characteristics of the device, but can be reduced by application of transient circuit theory.

A speed-up in the switching time required to turn a transistor ON (t_r) can be accomplished by overdriving, supplying the base with a current pulse of sufficient amplitude to drive the transistor deep into saturation, rather than just to V_{CC}/R_L. Transistor performance can be approximated by the differential equations given in Problem 13–4 and derived in Problem 13–5, namely,

$$\frac{di_c}{dt} + \omega_{hfe}i_c = \beta_o\omega_{hfe}i_b. \tag{13-1}$$

The solution of Eq. (13–1), for a step function base current of Δ_B, is

$$i_c = \beta_o\Delta_B(1 - e^{-t/T}) \tag{13-2}$$

with the time constant T equal to $1/\omega_{hfe}$. This expression predicts an exponential rise in collector current with time, as would be found in the current response of a series R-L circuit to a suddenly applied direct potential.

The time constant is the value of t that causes the exponential term to assume the form e^{-1}, and represents the time required for 63.2% of the total transient change to occur. It would appear that a speed-up in i_c could be accomplished only by a reduction in T; however, it is to be remembered that we are dealing with a quantity, i_c, that will enter the saturation region of the collector characteristics, and saturation will end the transient, for collector current can be no larger than its saturated value. Consequently, to speed-up switching times we wish to get to saturation as rapidly as possible.

Figure 13–8 shows the collector-current response to three input pulses. The A curve rises to a value of V_{CC}/R_L, or just to saturation. Curves B and C would rise (dotted lines) to twice and thrice the saturation collector current, respectively, were it not for saturation which prevents their complete rise. It is obvious from examination of the figure that curve C has the shortest transient time (t_3), and curve A has the longest (t_1).

Although the transition times are measured from 10% of the final value of the changing quantity to 90% of the final value, the regular network theory rules also apply here—95% of the total change occurs in time equal to three time constants and the transient is over in four time constants, for 98% of the total change has then occurred.

When turning OFF a transistor that has been in the ON state, the base region must be swept clean of minority carriers before collector current can cease. The turn-off period (t_f) is characterized by the same parameters as dictated turn-on, except that an initial collector current is apparent, which shall be designated as I_C'. If we consider that i_c will fall to zero, then

$$i_c = I_C'(e^{-t/T}).\qquad(13\text{--}3)$$

But if a base-current drive is to be used to reduce the time required to reach cutoff,

$$i_c = I_C'e^{-t/T} - \beta_o\Delta_B(1 - e^{-t/T})\qquad(13\text{--}4)$$

more clearly describes the process. Just as overdriving can speed up the turn-on operation, so it can also be used, in the opposite sense, to turn off a transistor quickly.

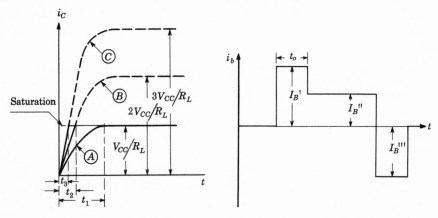

Fig. 13–8. Collector-current response to   Fig. 13–9. Ideal base-current drive for a
            input pulses.   saturating switch.

Overdriving, when used to saturate or cut off a transistor, may tend to cause a higher input-junction dissipation than is apparent for normal operation, and consideration must often be given to this additional power conversion. An ideal base-current waveform for fast turn-on and turn-off is shown in Fig. 13–9. This waveform results in a speed-up of the drive into saturation, levels off at a value just necessary for saturation so that storage effects will be minimized, and over-drives into the cutoff region when shutoff is required.

A waveform approaching this ideal can be achieved when the speed-up capacitor previously discussed is incorporated into the input circuit of a switching transistor. If, again as in Fig. 13–9, the saturated base-current level is designated as I_B'' and the entire pulse height as I_B', then it is desired that the overdrive, represented by $I_B' - I_B''$, be supplied by the capacitive branch during the transient. The duration of time, designated as t_o, during which an overdrive is required need only be as long as is necessary for the collector current to reach saturation.

Consider the circuit of Fig. 13–10. What appears to be base bias, namely the $V_{BB} - R_2$ branch, also seems at first glance to be backwards, for V_{BB} is a negative potential and the circuit uses an n-p-n transistor. The function of V_{BB} and R_2 is to provide a base bias at cutoff; that is, to reverse-bias the input junction. This reverse bias on the emitter–base diode will allow only I_{co} as the collector current.

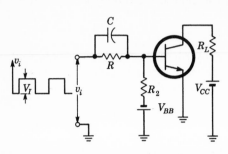

Fig. 13–10. Switching circuit.

Now, turning our attention to the C-R branch, we recall that the instantaneous current through a capacitor is given by

$$i = C \frac{dv}{dt}.$$

For the present problem the increment of voltage is V_I; the signal is going to change, from 0 to $+V_I$ volts. The desired capacitive current as previously stated, amounts to $I_B{'} - I_B{''}$, and if the switching-time increment necessary and desired is designated as t_o, then the capacitance may be determined from

$$C = \frac{(I_B{'} - I_B{''})t_o}{V_I}. \tag{13–5}$$

A numerical example may be of assistance. Suppose that V_I is to step between 0 and $+10$ V and a 1 μsec rise and fall time is allowed for v_{ce}. The transistor used has a 2500 Ω load, $V_{CC} = 15$ V and therefore the saturation collector current is 6 mA. The worst leakage current (I_{co}) to be expected is 40 μA. Available $V_{BB} = 5$ V, and consider that Figs. 13–2 and 13–3 apply.

For the circuit of Fig. 13–10, R_2 may be calculated from $V_{BB}/I_{co} = 5/40 \times 10^{-6} = 125{,}000$ Ω. To drive the transistor represented by the average curve (Fig. 13–2) just into saturation requires 125 μA of base current, so $I_B{''} = 125$ μA. From Fig. 13–3, the V_{BE} drop is found to be, for $V_{CE} = 0$, about 0.1 V. Therefore, to determine R

$$R = \frac{V_I - 0.1}{I_B{''} + I_{co}} = \frac{9.9}{165 \times 10^{-6}} = 60{,}000 \ \Omega.$$

The reason that the denominator of the above fraction takes on the form shown is clear when one realizes that base current, for the turn-on operation, starts at $-I_{co}$ and must rise to $+I_B{''}$; therefore its total excursion is $I_B{''} + I_{co}$.

Because the capacitor should handle a current pulse considerably greater than the saturation requirement, and because 1 μsec has been allotted as the rise time for this example, a transient study can be made to determine the base-current overdrive needed to reach collector-current saturation in 1 μsec. For a transistor with $f_{hfb} = 5$ Mc, from Eq. (13–2),

$$6 \times 10^{-3} = 50\Delta_B \left\{ 1 - \exp\left[-\left(\frac{10^{-6}}{1/[1 - 50/51][5 \times 10^{+6}][2\pi]} \right) \right] \right\},$$

so

$$\Delta_B = 257 \ \mu A.$$

Because the resistive branch will supply the base with the plateau value of 125 μA, the remaining 132 μA must come thru C:

$$132 \times 10^{-6} = C \frac{10}{10^{-6}}.$$

So $C = 13.2$ pF is the required value for the speed-up capacitor.

A nonsaturated switch with its ON levels in the active region of the collector characteristics can provide faster operation because storage time t_s will be extremely short. Many circuits have been proposed to "clamp" collector voltage at an unsaturated value. The reader is referred to the literature.

Diode Switch. A semiconductor diode may be used as a switch since it has two states, ON corresponding to its characteristic when forward biased, and OFF representing diode behavior when reverse biased. When switching the diode with a voltage source from ON to OFF, a transient caused by minority-carrier storage is observed. A large reverse current similar to the base-current waveform noted in Fig. 13–6 is evident. This large reverse current is supported until all minority carriers return to regions from whence they came, or enter into recombination with majority carriers.

13–3. Pulse Amplifiers. Often it is necessary to amplify pulse waveforms. to raise the amplitude level of a sharply rising pulse requires an amplifying stage having an extremely wide bandwidth. Should the amplifier bandwidth be too narrow, the rise time of the output pulse may be severely lengthened in comparison to the input. The specifications of a pulse amplifier are very similar to those of the video amplifier, briefly discussed in Chapter 11.

Transient response information is usually obtainable for pulse amplifiers. A rule for converting step-function response to frequency response may be obtained for use with low-pass amplifiers (as opposed to bandpass networks) without excessive overshoot. To simulate a wide-band amplifier we shall use a simple R-L series circuit. The time constant of this model is of course simply L/R. The 10% to 90% rise time T of this simple circuit occurs in about 2.2 time constants. Using steady-state analysis on the same model we find that the current will decline to 0.707 of its low-frequency value when $f = R/2\pi L$. This frequency will be called B, the bandwidth. Then it follows that the product of T and B is

$$TB = \left(\frac{2.2L}{R}\right)\left(\frac{R}{2\pi L}\right) = \frac{1.1}{\pi}.$$

Because a wide-band amplifier is not a simple R-L circuit, it is convenient to generalize this equation, as has been done in the literature[9]:

$$TB = 0.35 \text{ to } 0.45. \tag{13-6}$$

Equation (13–6) is of value in estimating the bandwidth of an amplifier when its rise time is known, or its rise time when bandwidth is given.

Another type of pulse amplifier will be considered under the *monostable* multivibrator heading that follows.

13–4. Multivibrators. The multivibrator circuit is important from both a classical and a practical point of view. Three classes of multivibrators are common: The *astable* or free-running circuit is a square-wave oscillator; the *monostable* or one-shot circuit is useful as a regenerative pulse amplifier; and the *bistable* or flip-flop can store information. The term "multivibrator" suggests the abundance of harmonics present in the associated nonsinusoidal waveshapes.

Astable. The astable circuit is an oscillator in the sense that it exhibits characteristics similar to oscillators as set forth in the earlier discussion of Chapter 12, namely that a time-varying waveform is generated although no input other than the dc supply is necessary, and that feedback is evident. In one aspect it differs from a true oscillator. The circuit possesses two conditions of stable equilibrium, and generally the active element switches from its conducting to its nonconducting state and vice versa because of a timing transient determined by external circuit elements. Thus a particular transistor in an astable multivibrator is OFF part of the time and ON during the remainder of its period. Although its ON period may be a saturated or unsaturated condition, it will be assumed in the discussion of this chapter that a saturating switch will always be considered because saturation provides certain advantages.

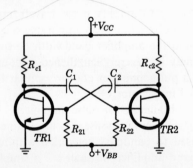

Fig. 13–11. Sample astable multivibrator.

A typical astable multivibrator circuit is shown in Fig. 13–11. V_{CC} is available to the transistor collectors through R_{c1} and R_{c2}, and V_{BB} supplies the bases through R_{21} and R_{22}, although the bases could utilize the collector supply if conditions so warrant. Capacitor C_1 joins the collector of TR1 with the base of TR2, so it is through this element that the signal will come to change the state of TR2. The circuit is symmetrical with C_2 joining the TR2 collector to the TR1 base.

If the transistors are to be operated between saturation and cutoff, then the aforementioned simplified conditions prevail. Repeated here, for a saturated *n–p–n* transistor,

$$v_c \cong 0$$
$$v_b = +$$
$$i_c \cong V_{CC}/R_c$$

and for a cutoff unit

$$v_c \cong V_{CC}$$

$$v_b = -$$

$$i_c \cong 0$$

Operation is dictated by the fact that the charge on a capacitor and hence the voltage across its plates cannot change instantaneously. Each capacitor in the figure is tied to points in the circuit where the potential will vary between wide limits when switching states change. Although only positive direct voltages are supplied to this circuit, the switching action will actually result in voltages that are negative with respect to ground.

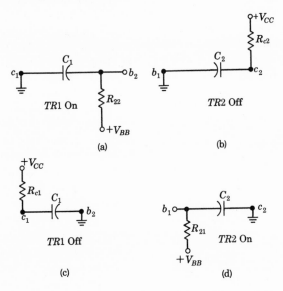

Fig. 13–12.   Portions of Fig. 13–11 used for analysis.

When supply voltage is initially applied, currents flow in the various circuit branches and the capacitors build up charge. Because the two halves of the circuit are similar, currents will be alike at first, but even the slightest unbalance will result in a cumulative difference in the two collector currents. This unbalance, no matter how slight, will result in the saturation of one transistor and cutoff of the other. The starting requirements are, therefore, that a dissymmetry exist—this is unescapable—and that the other conditions to be presently introduced be satisfied.

To analyze the operation of switching circuits, such as the astable multivibrator, simplified circuit diagrams of the Fig. 13–12 type give an indication of the ultimate capacitor potentials if the circuit would allow complete buildup to take place. From (a) and (c) of the figure it can be noted that C_1 would tend to go through an excursion of $V_{CC} + V_{BB}$ because with TR1 ON it will try to charge to V_{BB} volts, positive on the right, and with TR1 OFF it will try to charge to the V_{CC} potential magnitude, positive on the left. Actually, from (a) of the figure, C_1 will not charge up to V_{BB}, for when the voltage on b_2 gets slightly positive, switching occurs.

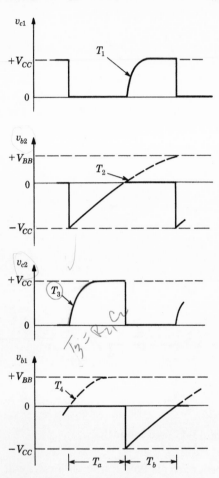

If the time constants $R_{c1}C_1$ and $R_{c2}C_2$ are made short (compared with the firing time constants $R_{22}C_1$ and $R_{21}C_2$), collector potentials v_{c1} and v_{c2} will reach their ultimate or steady-state values rapidly, and therefore collector potentials during the OFF periods can be described by a simple exponential expression obtained from Fig. 13–12(a) and (c). For example,

$$v_{c1} = V_{CC}(1 - e^{-t/T_1}) \qquad (13\text{–}7)$$

with

$$T_1 = R_{c1}C_1.$$

This expression assumes that collector voltage is zero during the ON or saturated condition.

At the instant that TR1 is turned ON by the voltage on its base terminal, the capacitor C_1 holds accumulated charge which is positive on its left hand or c_1 terminal because of its previous history; but that terminal is switched to approximately ground potential when TR1 is turned ON, and b_2, which is directly attached to the other terminal of the capacitor, must become $-V_{CC}$ volts with respect to ground potential because of the switching just described. For an expression for the voltage on b_2, with this initial condition included, we have

$$v_{b2} = (V_{BB} + V_{CC})(1 - e^{-t/T_2}) - V_{CC}, \qquad (13\text{–}8)$$

where

$$T_2 = R_{22}C_1.$$

Fig. 13–13. Waveforms for the astable multivibrator.

This transient never reaches the ultimate value mathematically predicted because when v_{b2} becomes only slightly positive the transistor saturates.

If we set Eq. (13–8) for v_{b2} equal to zero and solve for the time period (T_a) necessary for that voltage to build up to zero and hence turn ON transistor No. 2, we find

$$0 = (V_{BB} + V_{CC})(1 - e^{-T_a/T_2}) - V_{CC},$$

so

$$T_a = -T_2 \ln\left(\frac{V_{BB}}{V_{BB} + V_{CC}}\right). \tag{13–9}$$

This, then, is the OFF period for TR1. Expressions for the other transistor are similar, with $T_3 = R_{c2}C_2$ and $T_4 = R_{21}C_2$:

$$v_{c2} = V_{CC}(1 - e^{-t/T_3}),$$

$$v_{b1} = (V_{BB} + V_{CC})(1 - e^{-t/T_4}) - V_{CC},$$

$$T_b = -T_4 \ln\left[\frac{V_{BB}}{V_{BB} + V_{CC}}\right]. \tag{13–10}$$

The frequency of oscillation is given by

$$f = 1/(T_a + T_b).$$

It is obvious from this discussion that the designer is free to control the duration of each half cycle, and has good control over the frequency of oscillation. He must also select component sizes to assure transistor saturation and to control performance by external elements rather than transistor reactances.

Monostable. The monostable multivibrator circuit, when triggered by a small pulse, generates a larger pulse, the width of which is under the control of the circuit designer.

In the monostable circuit of Fig. 13–14, transistor TR1 is biased so that its collector current is in saturation, and TR2 is biased normally at cutoff. A negative-going pulse on the base of TR1 will turn OFF that transistor, and an interesting sequence of circuit activity follows.

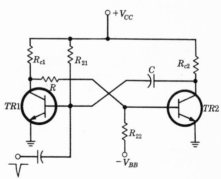

Fig. 13–14. Sample monostable multivibrator.

Because the capacitor C determines the timing of the operation, it will be studied in detail with the aid of Fig. 13–15. In part (a) of that figure, the simplified circuit is shown with TR2 OFF and TR1 ON. It can be seen that C will charge through R_{c2} to V_{CC}, positive on the right. When TR1 is turned OFF by

the incoming pulse TR2 turns ON because of the change in TR1 collector voltage, and the circuit with C in it switches to the form of Fig. 13–15(b). Consequently, TR1 will remain OFF until the capacitor loses its charge and b_1 goes
slightly positive. An equation describing the performance of this portion of the
monostable multivibrator can be written from observation by noting that the

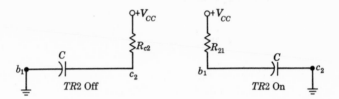

Fig. 13–15.   Simplified version of Fig. 13–14 showing timing circuitry.

capacitor potential starts at V_{CC} and would eventually charge to V_{CC} of the opposite polarity if it were not for switching occurring when v_b goes positive.   Therefore

$$v_{b1} = 2V_{CC}(1 - e^{-t/T_1}) - V_{CC}, \qquad (13\text{–}11)$$

with

$$T_1 = R_{21}C.$$

This transient never reaches its ultimate predicted by Eq. (13–11) because TR1
saturates when v_{b1} reaches a slightly positive value.

The sequence of operation will now be summarized.   An externally generated
pulse, applied to the base of the ON transistor, turns TR1 OFF and TR2 ON.
TR2 remains ON during the time interval determined by the discharge of capacitor C. TR1 is then switched ON and TR2 returns to the OFF state (Problem
13–19).

Bistable.   The basic multivibrator circuit of the preceding discussion can be
altered to provide us with a circuit with two stable states, capable of remaining
in either state indefinitely until triggered by an external signal.   The circuit that
exhibits this type of operation has been given the name of *bistable multivibrator*
but is more commonly known as a *flip-flop.*   This sort of operation indicates
that the flip-flop has a memory—it will remember the last signal received until
another signal is forthcoming.

One form of the bistable multivibrator is the emitter-coupled circuit of Fig.
13–16.   Capacitors are for speed-up and not for timing.   Input signals are fed to
the transistor bases in this diagram and outputs are taken at the collectors.

If it is assumed that TR1 is conducting and TR2 cut off, then the base bias for
the conducting transistor is provided by the divider action of resistors R_{c2}, R_{21},
and R_{31} on V_{CC}. TR1 may or may not be saturated by this bias circuit, which
effectively provides a base-to-emitter potential of $V_{B1} - V_E$; the latter voltage,
V_E, is equal to $I_{E1}R_e$.

The OFF transistor stays in that state because its base-to-emitter potential is essentially

$$(V_{CE1} + V_E) \frac{R_{32}}{R_{22} + R_{32}} - V_E.$$

This results, for practical component values, in the input junction being reverse-biased.

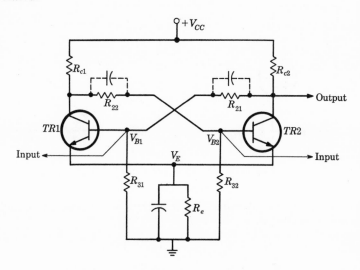

Fig. 13–16. Typical bistable multivibrator.

Assume that a signal pulse of positive polarity and of sufficient amplitude and width is supplied to the base of the OFF transistor. It immediately turns ON, lowering its collector voltage because of the $I_{C2}R_{C2}$ drop. When v_{c2} does decrease, the biasing that originally dictated that TR1 be ON is now nonexistent, and TR1 must switch to an OFF condition, to be held OFF by $I_{E2}R_e$.

The output waveshape obtained from either collector will be a constant potential with a magnitude of nearly V_{CC} at certain times, and of approximately $I_E R_e$ at other times, depending upon the history of supplied pulses.

13–5. Waveform Generators. Two common and interesting circuits useful for generating special waveforms will now be considered.

Unijunction Relaxation Oscillator. A simple yet effective relaxation oscillator can be made with just three passive elements and a unijunction transistor, as shown in the diagram of Fig. 13–17. Refer to Sec. 2–11 for definitions of the parameters of this device.

In order to analyze the operation of this circuit, consider initially that the transistor is in its OFF state. Upon application of V_{BB}, capacitance C will charge through R_1. When the voltage across its terminals reaches $\eta K V_{BB}$, the transistor will fire, and the capacitor will rapidly discharge through the forward-biased transistor junction. The constant K represents voltage division in the base circuit and equals $R_{BB}/(R_{BB} + R_2)$. If the maximum value of emitter current supported by V_{BB} is less than the valley current I_v, the device will revert back to

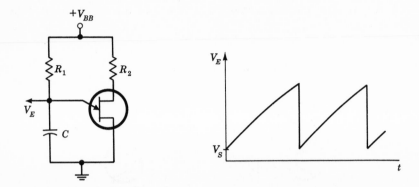

Fig. 13–17.   Unijunction relaxation oscillator, and emitter waveform.

the OFF state, and the aforementioned process will repeat periodically. The conditions for oscillation are

$$\frac{V_{BB} - V_p}{R_1} > I_p, \qquad \frac{V_{BB} - V_v}{R_1} < I_v.$$

The frequency of oscillation is given by

$$f \cong 1 \bigg/ \left[R_1 C \ln \left(\frac{V_{BB} - V_s}{V_{BB} - \eta K V_{BB}} \right) \right]. \tag{13–12}$$

This relation may be derived by the method of the preceding section. The sawtooth output is picked off at the emitter; if a sharp pulse is desired, it may be obtained from base 2.

The oscillation frequency is liable to vary because of changes in the emitter diode characteristic and the interbase resistance with temperature. These effects tend to partially cancel. If the resistance R_2 is several hundred ohms, it serves to compensate such variations by equalizing the effective temperature rate of change of R_{BB} with that of the diode. It can be shown that the optimum value of R_2 is given by

$$R_2 = \frac{0.312 R_{BBO}}{\eta V_{BB}}, \tag{13–13}$$

where R_{BBO} is the 25°C-value of interbase resistance (Problem 13–20). Circuits have been constructed in which the oscillation frequency varies by less than 2% over the range from $-55°$ to $+100°$ C.

Schmitt Trigger. The Schmitt trigger is a valuable addition to the family of nonlinear circuits that may be used for the purpose of generating a square wave or for increasing the rise time of a waveform. It generates an extremely fast-rising pulse when triggered. Consider Fig. 13–18. Transistor Q_1 will be initially

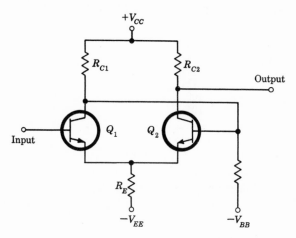

Fig. 13–18. A form of Schmitt trigger.

considered OFF and Q_2 ON; the latter transistor is held in that state by the large positive collector voltage of Q_1. A positive-going voltage applied to the base of Q_1 will initiate conduction of that transistor; its collector voltage declines, thus starting to turn OFF Q_2. As Q_2 turns OFF, the drop across R_E reduces, thus further turning ON Q_1. The action proceeds rapidly until the change of state is completed. It is necessary for the input signal to Q_1 to drop below the critical value in order to restore the circuit to its original state.

13–6. Binary Arithmetic and Boolean Algebra. To perform the mathematical manipulations necessary in modern high-speed electronic computing systems, the transistor switch is used with great effectiveness. It is rugged, fast, consumes little power, and is inexpensive. In order to understand the application of this device to processes such as counting and addition, we begin by discussing the type of algebra applicable to switching networks.

Binary Addition. Because most types of realizable switching devices can be in only one of two *states*, ON or OFF, computation using such devices is generally limited to use of the *binary* number system. The binary system consists of two symbols, typically 0 and 1, and makes use of these digits to symbolize any decimal number. A *binary digit* is often referred to as a *bit*.

A binary number is made up of bits that represent powers of 2. Thus the number 1010 in binary represents the decimal number *ten*, for reading 1010 from right to left, we find $0 \times 2^0 + 1 \times 2^1 + 0 \times 2^2 + 1 \times 2^3$, and their decimal sum is ten.

In Table 13–1, we note the equivalence of some decimal and binary numbers.

TABLE 13–1

Decimal	Binary	Decimal	Binary
0	0	6	110
1	1	7	111
2	10	8	1000
3	11	9	1001
4	100	10	1010
5	101	11	1011

It is immediately obvious from the table that rules for the addition of two binary numbers are quite simple. Thus to add the bits 1 and 1, we obtain 0 and carry 1 to the next left-hand column. Some examples of binary addition follow:

$$
\begin{array}{cc}
101 & 5 \\
101 & +5 \\
\hline
1010 & 10
\end{array}
\qquad
\begin{array}{cc}
11 & 3 \\
01 & +1 \\
\hline
100 & 4
\end{array}
\qquad
\begin{array}{cc}
1010 & 10 \\
1111 & +15 \\
\hline
11001 & 25
\end{array}
$$

Boolean Algebra. The branch of mathematics called Boolean Algebra is especially applicable to electronic computing, for it is based upon only two values or states, often represented by 0 and 1. In switching terms, 0 state could represent an open contact or circuit, while 1 could represent a closed connection. When a Boolean variable is discussed, it exists in either of the two possible states.

Because Boolean Algebra differs in many ways from conventional mathematics, the symbolism differs too. For the operation of addition we shall use the + symbol. Boolean addition is usually referred to as "OR." Thus $A + B$ means "variable A or variable B." The multiplication operation will be symbolized by juxtaposition; thus AB means the Boolean product of variable A and variable B, and is usually referred to as A "and" B. Where needed for clarity, a product dot may be useful to indicate multiplication. Complementation, a third basic operation, is referred to as "NOT," and symbolized by a bar above the variable. Thus $\bar{A}$ is "not A." For two states represented by 0 and 1, $\bar{0} = 1$ and $\bar{1} = 0$.

To interpret the three Boolean algebra operations noted in the preceding paragraph, the following discussion may be of assistance. In terms of switches, complimentation of a closed switch represented by 1 is $\bar{1} = 0$, and 0 is an open switch. The addition operation for two variables, $A + B$, can represent two *parallel* switches. If either A or B close, continuity will result. Thus $1 + 1 = 1$,

$0 + 1 = 1$, $1 + 0 = 1$. Multiplication can be envisioned as *series*-connected switches. All must close before continuity exists. Thus $1 \cdot 0 = 0$, $0 \cdot 1 = 0$, $1 \cdot 1 = 1$.

In addition to the three operations, addition, multiplication and complimentation, certain laws for the manipulation of Boolean algebraic expressions are valuable. The applicable relations are given here:

Commutative Laws	$A + B = B + A$	$AB = BA$
Associative Laws	$A + (B + C) = (A + B) + C$	$A(BC) = (AB)C$
Distributive Laws	$A(B + C) = AB + AC$	$A + BC = (A + B)(A + C)$
Indempotent Laws	$A + A = A$	$AA = A$
Unit and Zero Laws	$0 + A = A$	$1 \cdot A = A$
	$0 \cdot A = 0$	$1 + A = 1$
Complementarity Laws	$A\bar{A} = 0$	$A + \bar{A} = 1$
Involution Law	$\overline{(\bar{A})} = A$	
Dualization Laws (deMorgan's Theorems)	$\overline{AB} = \bar{A} + \bar{B}$	$\overline{A + B} = \bar{A}\bar{B}$

Truth Table. To determine the Boolean function that describes the behavior of several variables, consider the following example. Three variables are present. We desire the function that describes the case when any two are in the high or 1 state. A truth table can be filled out, and the various combinations of variables assigned.

Variables

A	B	C	f
0	0	0	0
0	0	1	0
0	1	0	0
0	1	1	1
1	0	0	0
1	0	1	1
1	1	0	1
1	1	1	1

Ones are noted in the f or function column when two variables are in the 1 state. Thus, from the table,

$$f = \bar{A}BC + A\bar{B}C + AB\bar{C} + ABC.$$

Using the distributive law, this may be somewhat simplified to

$$f = \bar{A}BC + A\bar{B}C + AB.$$

To generate this function, electronic gates may be employed.

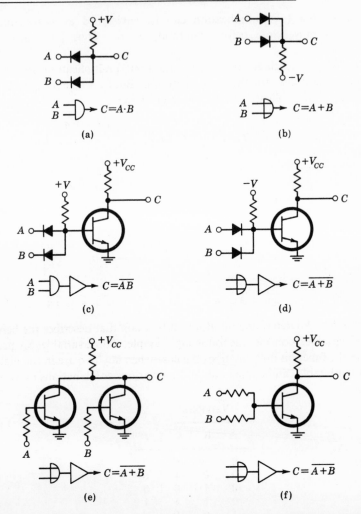

Fig. 13–19. (a) AND gate and symbol (DL); (b) OR gate (DL); (c) NAND gate (DTL); (d) NOR gate (DTL); (e) NOR gate (DCTL); (f) NOR gate (TRL).

13–7. Gating. To realize binary operations involving two or more variables, electronic *gates* are employed. AND, OR, NAND (not AND), and NOR (not OR) gates are available and form the basis for digital computations. We are concerned with voltage-mode logic, wherein the state of a device is represented by the voltage level at its output; generally a high voltage corresponds to the 1 or ON state, low voltage to the 0 or OFF state.

An AND gate using diodes is shown in Fig. 13–19(a), along with a block-diagram symbol for the gate useful to simplify complex diagrams of circuits performing a multitude of logical operations. In the absence of signals on the

A and *B* lines (consider ground potential), the diodes are forward biased by $+V$ and the available output is essentially ground or 0 volts. When a positive pulse of sufficient amplitude to reverse bias a diode is available on either input line, that diode conducts but the output remains at the zero volt level because the other diode is still ON. Both diodes must simultaneously be fed positive pulses in order for the output level at *C* to change from 0 to 1, where 1 corresponds to $+V$ volts. Thus the circuit is an AND gate.

A diode OR gate is illustrated in Fig. 13–19(b). With no signal on lines *A* and *B*, both diodes are reverse biased by $-V$. A positive pulse of sufficient amplitude on either line will cause the corresponding diode to conduct, and the pulse will therefore appear at *C*. Thus operation of this gate provides the OR function.

Diode Logic (DL) as discussed in the preceding paragraphs has the disadvantage that with the propagation of information through a chain of gates, severe power attenuation will eventually limit the number of passive gates that can be used to perform a given operation. Consequently, transistor gates are often employed because they provide the power amplification needed in complex applications. Diode Transistor Logic (DTL) is a simple extension of the aforementioned principles. Transistors are added at the outputs of simple diode gates. Because of the signal inversion caused by a common-emitter amplifying stage, the simple diode AND gate becomes a NAND gate, as in Fig. 13–19(c), and the OR gate becomes a NOR when a transistor is used as in Fig. 13–19(d).

Direct-Coupled Transistor Logic (DCTL) is exemplified by the NOR gate shown in Fig. 13–19(e). Both transistors share a common load resistance. A NAND operation is possible if the transistors are connected in series rather than the parallel arrangement shown. Transistor Resistor Logic (TRL) uses no diodes, just resistances connected so that current addition is possible as in Fig. 13–19(f). The sum of the input currents is then made available to a transistor base. The inverted pulse is available at the transistor collector.

Inverters and Buffers. To provide isolation between logic circuits, as well as to amplify voltage waveforms, simple inverting and buffering circuits occasionally may be required. A single common-emitter stage may qualify as an inverter because its output is the complement of its input.

Two inverters in cascade would qualify as a buffer, for the net phase shift is zero. A single emitter follower is generally preferable.

13–8. Worst-Case Design. The design of logic circuitry usually proceeds under a "worst-case" philosophy, in which the worst conditons to be expected in application are included in the mathematical design procedure. Particular constraints on gate design include the *fan-out* factor, N, which represents the number of identical gates loading the stage under consideration, and the *fan-in* factor, M, which represents the number of gates contributing to the base current of that stage. Naturally, the dc beta of the transistor, h_{FE}, plays an important role in determining whether a stage will reach saturation with a given input current drive.

As an example of a worst-case design procedure, consider an RTL NOR circuit, with fan-in M and fan-out N. Figure 13–20(a) is useful for studying the worst case for turn-on of Q_1; for studying turn-off we use Figure 13–20(b). To simplify the analysis, silicon transistors will be assumed. This allows us to omit the collector current of an OFF transistor, and also to consider that $V_{BE} = 0$ will keep a transistor OFF.

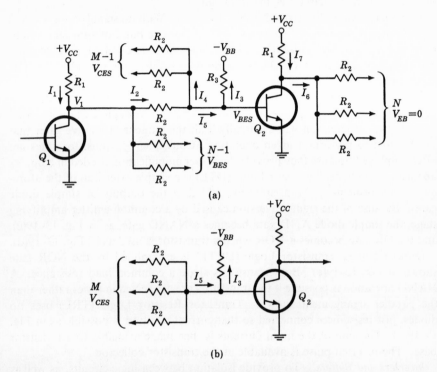

(a)

(b)

Fig. 13–20. NOR circuit for worst-case discussion.

To include the tolerances on circuit elements, symbols will be underscored to represent the minimum value of a quantity, while overscoring will be used to represent a maximum value. The subscript S will be used to represent a quantity related to saturation; thus I_{BS} is the base current for a saturated transistor.

With Q_1 OFF, Q_2 ON, the currents in Fig. 13–20(a) are

$$I_1 = \frac{V_{CC} - V_1}{R_1}, \qquad I_2 = \frac{V_1 - V_{BES}}{R_2}, \qquad I_3 = \frac{V_{BES} + V_{BB}}{R_3},$$

$$I_4 = (M - 1)\left(\frac{V_{BES} - V_{CES}}{R_2}\right), \qquad I_6 = \frac{N V_{CES}}{R_2}, \qquad I_7 = \frac{V_{CC} - V_{CES}}{R_1}. \tag{13–14}$$

We recognize that $I_1 = NI_2$. I_2 may be rewritten to eliminate V_1. Thus

$$I_2 = \frac{V_{CC} - V_{BES}}{R_2 + NR_1}. \tag{13-15}$$

The maximum value of h_{FE} for Q_2 is related to the circuit currents as follows:

$$\overline{h_{FE}} = \frac{\overline{I_{CS}}}{\underline{I_{BS}}} = \frac{\overline{I_7} - I_6}{\underline{I_2} - \overline{I_4} - \overline{I_3}}. \tag{13-16}$$

To assure that Q_2 will be OFF when all drivers are ON, we may determine from Fig. 13-20(b) that

$$I_3 = \overline{I_5} \quad \text{or} \quad \frac{V_{BB}}{\underline{R_3}} = \frac{\overline{V_{CES}}}{\underline{R_2/M}}. \tag{13-17}$$

Equation (13-17) may be used to modify the expression for I_3 previously given. Let $\phi \overline{R_3} = \underline{R_3}$. Then we may write

$$\overline{I_3} = \frac{M(\overline{V_{BES}} + \overline{V_{BB}})\overline{V_{CES}}}{\phi \underline{V_{BB} R_2}}. \tag{13-18}$$

Using Eqs. (13-14), (13-15), and (13-18) in Eq. (13-16) yields

$$\overline{h_{FE}} = \frac{\dfrac{\overline{V_{CC}} - V_{CES}}{\underline{R_1}} - \dfrac{N V_{CES}}{\overline{R_2}}}{\dfrac{\overline{V_{CC}} - \overline{V_{BES}}}{\underline{R_2} + N\overline{R_1}} - (M-1)\left(\dfrac{\overline{V_{BES}} - V_{CES}}{\underline{R_2}}\right) - \dfrac{M\overline{V_{CES}}}{\phi \underline{R_2}}\left(\dfrac{\overline{V_{BES}} + \overline{V_{BB}}}{\underline{V_{BB}}}\right)}. \tag{13-19}$$

For $\overline{V_{CC}} = \overline{V_{BB}} = 10$, $\underline{V_{CC}} = \underline{V_{BB}} = 9.9$, $M = N = 5$, $\overline{V_{CES}} = 0.3$, $\underline{V_{CES}} = 0.2$, $\overline{V_{BES}} = 0.5$, $R_1 = 1$ kΩ, $R_2 = 5$ kΩ, $R_3 = 50$ kΩ, $\pm 10\%$ tolerances, Eq. (13-19) predicts $\overline{h_{FE}} = 67.2$. In order to assure that the requirements are satisfied, the minimum value of h_{FE} for the transistor to be used in this application is 68.

This analysis can be extended. Suppose that R_1 and R_2 were to be determined, rather than having known values as in the preceding numerical example. Equation (13-19) can be written in terms of a variable θ, where $\theta = R_2/R_1$, and minimized by setting $d\overline{h_{FE}}/d\theta = 0$. The resulting value of θ, employed in Eq. (13-19), could then predict $\overline{h_{FE}}$. Equation (13-19) can also be solved for M as a function of N. Generally, it may be concluded that transistors with higher h_{FE} will support increased fan-in and fan-out. M and N also increase with V_{CC}.

13-9. An Application of Logic Circuitry. An example of the use of gating circuits to perform an arithmetic operation will now be treated. Consider that we wish to develop a computer to perform arithmetic operations. Computing is most easily done using binary numbers. Therefore decimal-to-binary and binary-to-decimal conversion circuits can be used at input and output stages of the computer. The problem will be limited to addition of two numbers. It is necessary then to develop a binary adding circuit.

The *half-adder* accepts two inputs x and y, and provides two output lines, s for sum, and c for carry. The corresponding truth table is

x	y	s	c
0	0	0	0
0	1	1	0
1	0	1	0
1	1	0	1

The sum is given by

$$s = \bar{x}y + \bar{y}x$$

and carry by

$$c = xy.$$

To generate these functions it is only necessary to arrange logic gates as shown in Fig. 13–21(a). That circuit makes use of AND, OR, and INVERT blocks. The half-adder function could also be performed using NAND or NOR blocks.

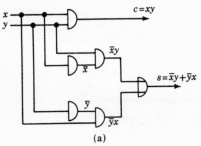

(a)

A *full-adder* must be capable of accepting two variables plus the carry from a preceding stage c_i. The corresponding truth table is given here.

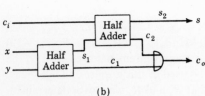

(b)

Fig. 13–21. (a) Half-adder; (b) full adder.

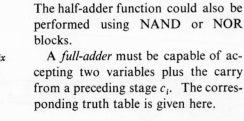

x	y	c_i	s	c_o
0	0	0	0	0
0	0	1	1	0
0	1	0	1	0
0	1	1	0	1
1	0	0	1	0
1	0	1	0	1
1	1	0	0	1
1	1	1	1	1

The sum is

$$s = \bar{x}\bar{y}c_i + \bar{x}y\bar{c}_i + x\bar{y}\bar{c}_i + xyc_i.$$

Simplified, the carry is

$$c_0 = xc_i + xy + yc_i.$$

The full-adder operation may be accomplished using two half-adders as noted in

Fig. 13–21. Proof is left to the reader (Problem 13–25). It is possible to extend this discussion to more extensive circuitry capable of adding many digits of binary information.

PROBLEMS

13–1. A power transistor with a spread in h_{FE} of 30 to 100 is to be used as a saturating switch. R_{CS} has a spread of 0.1 to 0.3 Ω. If the load resistance is 5 Ω, V_{CC} is 10 V, and the switching circuit is designed for a constant base current drive, calculate the value of base current to assure that all units will be driven into saturation.

13–2. A saturating transistor switch has a cutoff at $V_{CE} = 20$ V and $I_{CO} = 10$ μA and saturation at $V_{CE} = 1$ V and $I_C = 20$ mA. Allow 10% for losses in the base circuit.

(a) Compute the OFF dissipation.

(b) Compute the ON dissipation.

(c) If the duty cycle is 0.5 msec ON and 1.0 OFF, and the switching time is 10 μsec, compute the average dissipation.

13–3. For the transistor whose collector characteristics are depicted in Fig. 13–2, with the load as drawn, it is required that a switching circuit be designed to handle an ideal input voltage pulse of 5 V. The circuit of Fig. 13–7 will be used.

(a) Determine R for a saturation base current of 400 μA. Use Fig. 13–3 to estimate the transistor input resistance.

(b) The stored base charge is known to be 750 $\mu\mu$coulombs. Find C.

13–4. The differential equation for common-base operation is given as

$$\frac{di_c}{dt} + \omega_{hfb} i_c = \omega_{hfb} \alpha_o i_e,$$

and for common-emitter operation as

$$\frac{di_c}{dt} + \omega_{hfe} i_c = \omega_{hfe} \beta_o i_b.$$

(a) Derive the equation for i_c of a common-base-connected transistor subjected to a step-input disturbance ($i_e = \Delta_1$).

(b) Derive the equation for i_c of common-emitter-connected transistor subjected to a step-input disturbance ($i_b = \Delta_2$).

(c) Should $\Delta_1 = \Delta_2$, show that the initial rate of rise of i_c (di_c/dt at $t = 0$) for each of the above connections may be expressed by the same relationship.

13–5. The differential equations of the preceding problem may be derived from the knowledge that

$$\alpha = \frac{\alpha_o}{1 + j\omega/\omega_{hfb}},$$

and

$$\alpha = i_c/i_e.$$

Make use of the Laplace transform, recalling that $s = j\omega = d/dt$, to derive the two equations referred to.

13–6. For typical transient of the form

$$i = K(1 - e^{-t/T})$$

with T the time constant, and K the steady-state value of the quantity i, make a listing of the percentage of total change occurring in times of $T/2$, T, $2T$, $3T$, $4T$, and $5T$.

13–7. From your solution to Problem 13–4, and considering a common-emitter-connected transistor with $f_{hfb} = 5\text{Mc}$, and $\beta_o = 50$, make a plot of i_c vs t for values of t from 0 to $5T$. Consider Δ_B equal to 1 mA.

13–8. Compare the time required for an exponential transient to build up from 10% of its final value to 90% of that value with the time required for 0 to 90% and 0 to 95%. Express your results in terms of the circuit time constant T.

13–9. Derive a mathematical expression for a current transient that rises from zero to a value of I_s, a value somewhat lower than its steady-state value, I_{ss}, and then remains at I_s for all values of time after t_s. The expression will explain the saturating curves of Fig. 13–8.

13–10. Figures 13–2 and 13–3 apply to a transistor to be used in the circuit of Fig. 13–10. A voltage pulse of 5 V will trigger the circuit, which has $R_L = 2000\ \Omega$, $V_{CC} = 10$ V, and $V_{BB} = 10$ V. It is possible that with temperature variations I_{CO} will reach 50 μA. Determine R, R_2, and C for a turn-on time of 0.5 μsec. Consider f_{hfb} to equal 4 Mc.

13–11. If the turn-on time specification listed in Problem 13–10 was tightened to become 0.4 μsec, which circuit elements need be changed, and what new values must they take on?

13–12. Consider that the resistors and capacitors used in the circuit of problem 13–10 have a tolerance of $\pm 10\%$ of their nominal value, and h_{FE} can vary $\pm 20\%$ from unit to unit. Discuss the operation of this circuit by considering the poorest operation that may be encountered.

13–13. Mathematically determine the base current waveshape when a voltage step function is applied to the parallel combination of speed-up capacitance C_1 and R_1, in series with the base input of a transistor. Let the transistor be represented by $C_t \| R_t$. Show that the current in this network is composed of three components, an impulse, a decaying exponential, and a rising exponential.

13–14. Redraw the astable multivibrator circuit of Fig. 13–11 as a two-stage feedback amplifier.

13–15. An astable multivibrator of the form of Fig. 13–11 is to be designed to generate a 400 cps waveform with symmetrical half periods. $V_{CC} = V_{BB} = 10$ V. Determine the values of all circuit elements in your design.

13–16. What effect would a $\pm 20\%$ tolerance on the nominal values of all passive circuit elements have upon the frequency of oscillation of the circuit designed in Problem 13–15?

13–17. What effect would a $\pm 10\%$ variation in V_{CC} and V_{BB} have upon the frequency of oscillation of the circuit designed in Problem 13–15?

13–18. Instead of considering that collector current in the OFF state is zero, consider it to be I_{CO}, and consider base voltage and collector voltage for saturated ON periods to be V_{BE}', and V_{CE}' rather than zero. Derive equations that include I_{CO}, V_{CE}', and V_{BE}' to predict the effect of these quantities upon the frequency of oscillation of the circuit of Problem 13–15. If these quantities have values to 10 μA, 0.2 V, and 0.2 V, respectively, predict the frequency of oscillation.

13–19. For a monostable multivibrator of the Fig. 13–14 form, draw the portion of the circuit that affects the turn-on and turn-off of TR2 and describe the cause of this switching.

13–20. Consider that the firing voltage necessary for a unijunction relaxation oscillator is given by

$$V_P = V_D + \eta K V_{BB}.$$

V_D is the drop across the diode and $dV_D/dT = -2.5 \times 10^{-3}$ V/°C. K represents the voltage division between R_2 and R_{BB}. Set dV_P/dT equal to zero, consider that $R_{BB} = R_{BBo}[1 + 0.008(T - 25°\ C)]$, and show that near 25° C the optimum value for R_2 is given by Eq. (13–13). The assumption $R_{BB} \gg R_2$ must be used to verify that equation.

13–21. Derive Eq. (13–13) for the frequency of oscillation of a unijunction relaxation oscillator. What assumptions are being made in that equation?

13–22. Boolean variables A and B are available. Use only NOR gates to generate the "exclusive OR" function, $A\bar{B} + \bar{A}B$.

13–23. Show that

$$xyz + xy\bar{z} + x\bar{y}z + x\bar{y}\bar{z} + \bar{x}yz = x + yz$$

by using the theorems given in the text.

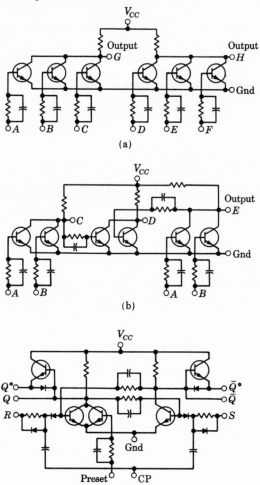

(a)

(b)

(c)

Problem 13–26.

13–24. It is desired to require a minimum value of $\overline{h_{FE}}$ for the circuit of Sec. 13–8. Use values as given in the example, letting $\theta = R_2/R_1$, an unknown. Find θ by setting $\overline{dh_{FE}}/d\theta = 0$.

13–25. Prove that the network of Fig. 13–21(b) does in fact satisfy the full-adder equations.

13–26. The three networks shown are microelectronic assemblies.

(a) What is the function of circuit (a)? Draw a logic diagram for this network.

(b) What operation will circuit (b) perform upon inputs A, $\overline{A}$, B, $\overline{B}$? Draw a logic diagram and truth tables for output lines C, D, E.

(c) Circuit (c) is an R-S fiip-flop. Inputs are R and S, and a clock pulse may be present on CP. Describe operation of this circuit.

REFERENCES

1. Bright, R. L., "Junction Transistors Used as Switches," *Trans. AIEE, Communications and Electronics*, **74** (March, 1955).

2. Ebers, J. J., and Moll, J. L., "Large-Signal Behavior of Junction Transistors," *Proc. IRE*, **42** (December, 1954).

3. Harris, J. N., *Digital Transistor Circuits* (John Wiley & Sons, Inc., New York, 1964).

4. Hurley, R. B., *Transistor Logic Circuits* (John Wiley & Sons, Inc., New York, 1961).

5. Hurley, R. B., *Junction Transistor Electronics* (John Wiley & Sons, Inc., New York, 1958).

6. Ivy, W., "Some Comments on Frequency and Transient Response," *Device-circuit Notes* No. A-58-9, Texas Instruments, Inc.

7. Pressman, A. I., *Design of Transistorized Circuits for Digital Computers* (John F. Rider Publisher, Inc., New York, 1959).

8. Staff, *Switching Transistor Handbook*, Motorola, Inc., Phoenix, Arizona, 1963.

9. Valley, G. E., Jr., and Wallman, H., *Vacuum-Tube Amplifiers* (McGraw-Hill Book Co., Inc., New York, 1948).

10. Von Tersch, L. W., and Swago, A. W., *Recurrent Electrical Transients* (Prentice-Hall, Inc., Englewood Cliffs, New Jersey, 1953).

Appendix I

SELECTED TRANSISTOR DATA

The following pages contain data as supplied by the various manufacturers on three commercial transistor types. This information is useful in solving the end-of-chapter problems. It can be noted that some of the symbols and conventions used here differ among manufacturers and differ from those of the text. The types selected are:

2N2614 Germanium p–n–p alloy-junction
2N3242 Silicon n–p–n planar
2N539 Germanium p–n–p junction

RCA TYPE 2N2614 *P–N–P* GERMANIUM ALLOY-JUNCTION TRANSISTOR

RCA 2N2614 is an alloy-junction transistor of the germanium *p–n–p* type intended primarily for use in small-signal and other low-power stages of high-quality audio-frequency amplifier equipment.

Because of its excellent beta linearity, the 2N2614 can provide high gain over its entire operating current range.

In driver applications, the 2N2614 when used with a typical heat sink having a thermal resistance of 50° C/W can dissipate 225 mW and deliver a maximum power output of 100 mW. This amount of power is sufficient to drive to full output a 25-W output stage having a power gain of 24 dB.

MAXIMUM RATINGS, ABSOLUTE-MAXIMUM VALUES

Collector-to-base
  voltage (V_{CBO}) ... ... -40 max. volts
Collector-to-emitter voltage (V_{CER}) $R_{BE} = 10,000\ \Omega$ ... -35 max. volts
Emitter-to-base voltage (V_{EBO}) ... ... -25 max. volts
Collector current (I_C) ... ... -50 max. mA
Emitter current (I_E) ... ... 50 max. mA
Transistor Dissipation (P_T):
  In free air at T_{FA}
    up to 55° C ... ... 120 max. mW
    Derating factor ... ... 2.6 mW/° C
  With infinite heat sink
    at T_C up to 55° C ... ... 300 max. mW
    Derating factor ... ... 6.67 mW/° C
  With typical heat sink
    ($\theta = 50°$ C/w) at
    T_C up to 55° C ... ... 225 max. mW
    Derating factor ... ... 5 mW/° C
Temperature:
  Storage (Free-air) ... ... -65 to $+100$ ° C
  Operating (Junction) ... ... $+100$ max. ° C
  Leads—At distances not less than 1/32 in. from
    seating surface for 10 sec. max. (during solder-
    ing) ... ... $+225$ max. ° C

ELECTRICAL CHARACTERISTICS, AT A FREE-AIR TEMPERATURE (T_{FA}) OF 25° C

Characteristics	Symbols	Test conditions						Limits			Units
		DC collector-to-base voltage V_{CB} (V)	DC collector-to-emitter voltage V_{CE} (V)	DC Emitter-to-base voltage V_{EB} (V)	DC emitter current I_E (ma)	DC collector current I_C (ma)	External Base-Emitter Resistance R_{BE} (Ω)	min.	typ.	max.	
Collector-cutoff current	I_{CBO}	−20			0					−5	μA
Emitter-cutoff current	I_{EBO}			−20		0				−7.5	μA
Collector-to-emitter break-down voltage	BV_{CER}		−6			−1	10,000	−35			V
Collector-to-base breakdown voltage	BV_{CBV}			−2		−0.05		−40			V
Emitter-to-base breakdown voltage	BV_{EBO}				−0.05	0		−25			V
Small-signal forward-current transfer ratio (measured at 1 kc)	h_{fe}		−6			−1		100	160		
Small-signal forward-current transfer-ratio cutoff frequency	f_{hfb}		−6			−1			10		Mc
Extrinsic base-lead resistance measured at 20 Mc	$r_{bb'}$		−6			−1			300		Ω
Collector-to-base feedback capacitance	$C_{b'c}$		−6			−1			9		pF

$V_{ce} = -6$ V
$I_c = -1$ mA
$r_{bb'} = 300$ Ω

$g_{b'e} = 250$ μmhos
$g_{b'c} = 0.35$ μmho
$g_{ce} = 6$ μmhos

$C_{b'e} = 750$ pF
$C_{b'c} = 9$ pF
$g_m = 38,500$ μmhos

NOTE: The approximate frequency f for unity power amplification based on this equivalent circuit is given by:

$$f = \frac{1}{4\pi}\left(\frac{g_m}{r_{bb'}C_{b'c}C_{b'e}}\right)^{1/2}$$

Typical variations in the parameters of type 2N2614 are given in Fig. 8–11.

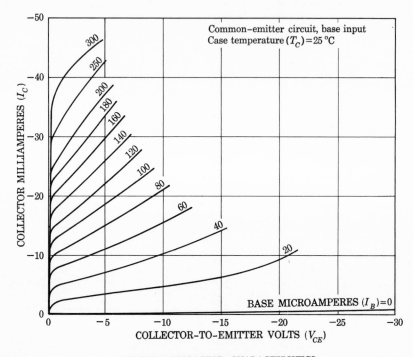

TYPICAL COLLECTOR CHARACTERISTICS.

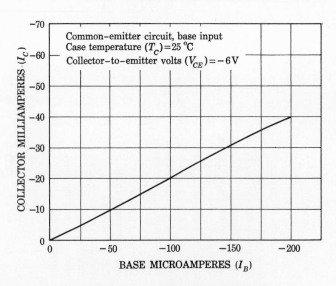

TYPICAL TRANSFER CHARACTERISTIC.

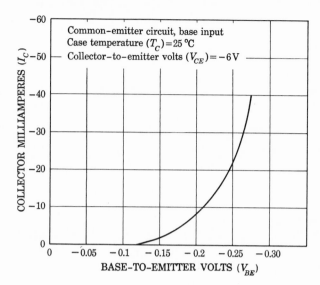

TYPICAL TRANSFER CHARACTERISTIC.

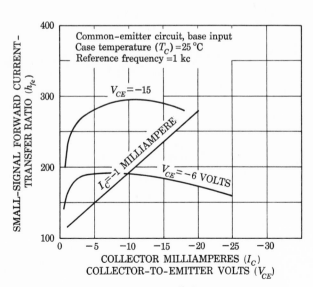

TYPICAL SMALL-SIGNAL BETA (h_{fe}) CHARACTERISTICS.

DIMENSIONAL OUTLINE
JEDEC No. TO-1
Dimensions in inches

.240 max.
dia.

.410
max.

Seating plane

1.5
min.

3 leads
.019
.016 dia.
(see note)

.081
.061 dia.

Note: The specified lead diameter applies in zone between 0.050 and 0.250 in. from the seating plane. Between 0.250 and 1.5 in. a maximum diameter of 0.021 in. is held. Outside of these zones, the lead diameter is not controlled.

TERMINAL DIAGRAM

Lead 1 – Emitter
Lead 2 – Base
Lead 3 – Collector

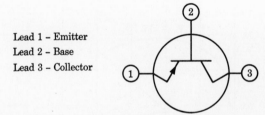

RCA TYPE 2N3242 *N–P–N* SILICON PLANAR TRANSISTOR

RCA 2N3242 is a planar transistor of the silicon *n–p–n* type suitable for use in amplifier and other applications requiring high small-signal beta, excellent linearity of characteristics, low noise, low leakage, and high temperature capability. This transistor utilizes a hermetically sealed, three-lead package which features an internal connection between collector and case for effective heat transfer.

The 2N3242 is particularly desirable for use in high-gain, high input-impedance, direct-coupled amplifier stages.

MAXIMUM RATINGS, ABSOLUTE-MAXIMUM VALUES

Collector-to-emitter voltage, V_{CEO} ... ... 25 max. V
Collector-to-base voltage, V_{CBV} ($V_{EB} = 1$ V) ... ... 30 max. V
Emitter-to-base voltage, V_{EBO} ... ... 5 max. V
Collector current, I_C ... ... 200 max. mA
Emitter current, I_E ... ... 200 max. mA
Transistor dissipation, P_T:
   For free-air temperatures up to 25° C ... ... 500 max. mW
   For free-air temperatures above 25° C ... ... See Fig. 1
   For case temperatures[a] up to 75° C ... ... 2 max. W
   For case temperatures[a] above 75° C. ... ... See Fig. 1
Temperature range:
   Storage and operating (Junction) ... ... −65 to +175 °C
Lead temperature
   (During soldering):
     At distances not closer than 1/32 in. to seating surface
     for 10 sec. max. ... ... 255 max. °C

[a] Measured on case perimeter at junction with seating surface.

ELECTRICAL CHARACTERISTICS

Characteristics	Symbols	Test conditions								Limits			Units
		Free-air temperature T_{FA} (°C)	Frequency f (kc)	DC collector-to-base voltage V_{CB} (V)	DC collector-to-emitter voltage V_{CE} (V)	DC emitter-to-base voltage V_{EB} (V)	DC emitter current I_E (mA)	DC collector current I_C (mA)	DC base current I_B (mA)	min.	typ.	max.	
Collector-cutoff current	I_{CBO}	25		25								10	nA
		150		25								10	μa
Emitter-cutoff current	I_{EBO}	25				2.5		0				10	nA
Collector-to-base breakdown voltage	BV_{CBV}	25				1		0.05		30			V
Collector-to-emitter breakdown voltage	BV_{CEO}	25						10	0	25			V
Emitter-to-base breakdown voltage	BV_{EBO}	25					0.05	0		5			V
Collector-to-emitter saturation voltage	V_{CE}(sat)	25						50	2.5		0.5	1	V
Base-to-emitter saturation voltage	V_{BE}(sat)	25						50	2.5		0.8		V
DC forward current-transfer ratio	h_{FE}	25			12			10		75	150		
Gain-bandwidth product	f_T	25	10*		6			1			60		Mc
Noise figure	NF	25	1*		6			0.1			2		dB
					6			0.5			4	6	dB

*Bandwidth of measurement circuit = 1 cps; source resistance (R_g) = 1000 Ω.

ELECTRICAL CHARACTERISTICS

Characteristics	Symbols	Test conditions									Limits			Units
		Free-air tempera-ture T_{FA}	Fre-quency f	DC collec-tor-to-base voltage V_{CB}	DC collec-tor-to-emitter voltage V_{CE}	DC emit-ter-to-base voltage V_{EB}	DC emit-ter cur-rent I_E	DC collec-tor cur-rent I_C	DC base current I_B		min.	typ.	max.	
		(°C)	(kc)	(V)	(V)	(V)	(mA)	(mA)	(mA)					
Small-signal forward current-transfer ratio	h_{fe}	25	1		12			10			100	175	375	
Small-signal input impedance	h_{ie}	25	1		12			10				600		Ω
Small-signal output admittance	h_{oe}	25	1		12			10				75		μmhos
Small-signal reverse voltage-transfer ratio	h_{re}	25	1		12			10				125×10^{-6}		
Open-circuit, common-base-output capacitance	C_{ob}	25	1	6				0				22		pF
Extrinsic base-lead resistance	$r_{bb'}$	25	100Mc		6			1				20		Ω
Thermal resistance: junction to free air	θ_{J-a}	25											300	°C/W
Thermal resistance: junction to case	θ_{J-c}												50	°C/W

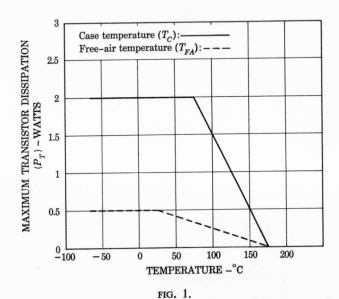

FIG. 1.

FIG. 2.   TYPICAL COLLECTOR CHARACTERISTICS.

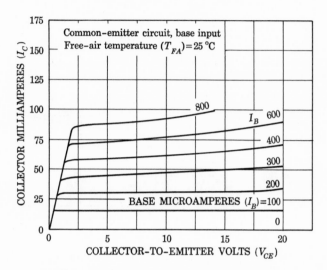

FIG. 3. TYPICAL COLLECTOR CHARACTERISTICS.

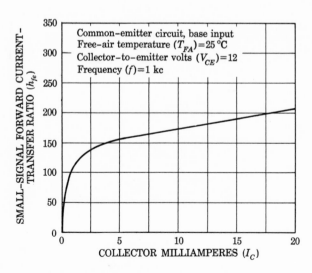

FIG. 4. TYPICAL SMALL-SIGNAL BETA CHARACTERISTIC.

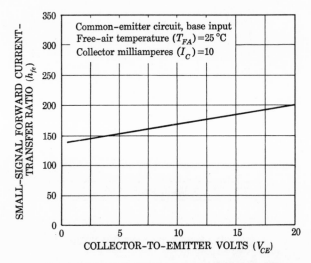

FIG. 5. TYPICAL SMALL-SIGNAL BETA CHARACTERISTIC.

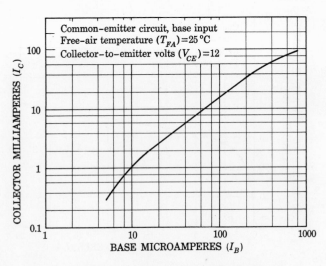

FIG. 6. TYPICAL DC FORWARD CURRENT-TRANSFER.

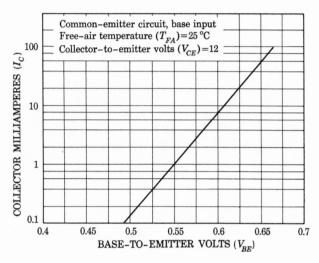

FIG. 7. TYPICAL TRANSFER CHARACTERISTIC.

DIMENSIONAL OUTLINE
Dimensions in inches

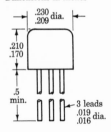

TERMINAL DIAGRAM

Lead 1 – Emitter
Lead 2 – Base
Lead 3 – Collector, case
      (identified by
      color dot on case)

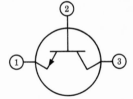

HONEYWELL TYPE 2N539 *P–N–P* GERMANIUM
JUNCTION TRANSISTOR

The Honeywell 2N539 is a rugged, hermetically sealed germanium *p–n–p* transistor designed for a variety of uses including servo amplifiers, power conversion, voltage regulation, switching, etc. It is capable of carrying currents in excess of 3 A and of dissipating 10 W of power at a case temperature of 71° C. *It is dynamically tested to ensure 80-V collector diode and reach-through (punch-through) ratings and a 55-V α = 1 rating.* Limits of current gain and transconductance are the same as those for the former Honeywell type H6. The exact replacement for the H6, however, is the 2N539A which is unilaterally interchangeable with the 2N539 but, in addition, is characterized by power conductance and input resistance limits.

DESIGN LIMITS

Junction temperature, T_J ... ...   95° C max.
Thermal resistance, junctions to mounting base, θ ... ...   2.2° C/W max.
Collector-to-base voltage, V_{CB} ... ...   −80 V max.
Collector-to-emitter voltage V_{CE}
    Active region (emitter forward biased) ... ...   −55 V max.
    Cutoff region (emitter reverse biased) ... ...   −80 V max.
Emitter-to-base voltage, V_{EB} ... ...   −28 V max.
Emitter current, rms, I_E ... ...   −3.5 A max.
Base current, rms, I_B ... ...   −0.5 A max.

ELECTRICAL CHARACTERISTICS

Performance specifications, $T_{MB} = 25° \pm 3°$ C ($\pm 3\%$ tolerance applies to all electrical measurements).

Characteristics	Symbol	Test conditions	min.	typ.	max.	Units
Current gain, common emitter	h_{FE}	$I_C = -2$ A, $V_{CE} = -2$ V	30	43	75	
Base-to-emitter voltage	V_{BE}	$I_C = -2$ A, $V_{CE} = -2$ V	-1.0	-1.7	-2.5	V
*Power conductance, common emitter	G_P	$I_C = -2$ A, $V_{CE} = -2$ V	35	51	105	mho
*Input resistance, common emitter	H_{IE}	$I_C = -2$ A, $V_{CE} = -2$ V	27	37	54	Ω
Thermal resistance, junctions to mounting base	θ			1.7	2.2	°C/W
Time response of junction temperature	τ		10	30		msec
Collector junction leakage current	I_{CBO}	$I_E = 0$, $V_{CB} = -2$ V -28 V -80 V		-0.04 -0.1	-0.1 -1.0 -2.0	mA
Alpha = 1 voltage, collector junction	$V_{\alpha=1}$		-55			V
Emitter floating potential	V_{EBF}	$R_{EB} = 10$ Ω, $V_{CB} = -60$ V -80 V		-0.1 	-0.3 -0.5	V
Emitter junction leakage current	I_{EBO}	$I_C = 0$, $V_{EB} = -2$ V $= -28$ V		-0.03 -0.15	-0.15 -2.0	mA
Collector saturation voltage	V_S	$I_C = -2$ A, $I_B = -200$ mA		-0.15	-0.6	V
Gain bandwidth product ($\sim f_{aco}$)	$h_{fe}f_{ae}$	$I_C = -100$ mA, $V_{CE} = -4$ V $I_b = -1$ mA	200			kc

*Applies to 2N539A only.

ALPHA = 1 VOLTAGE TEST

The voltage limit of a transistor in the active region is determined by the voltage at which $\alpha = 1$. The normal α, being less than unity, results in a current flow out of the base, and therefore a negative slope on an oscilloscope connected as shown in the circuit below. If the collector voltage is such that $\alpha = 1$, I_b will be zero and the slope of the oscilloscope trace will also be zero. If the voltage is such that $\alpha > 1$, the base current will reverse resulting in a positive slope of the trace.

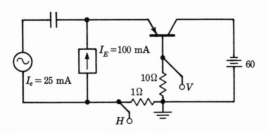

TYPICAL CHARACTERISTICS, $T_{MB} = 25^\circ$C

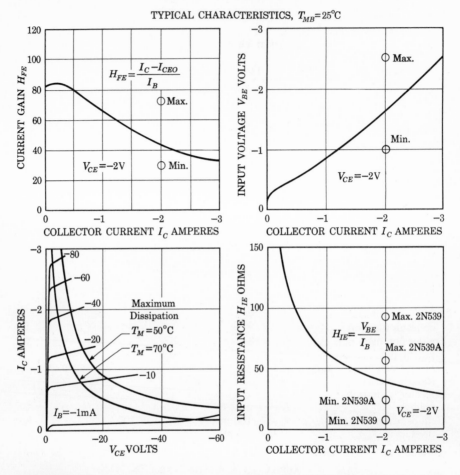

MOUNTING

It is very important that a power transistor be provided with a good heat dissipating facility. The surface to which the transistor is attached must be flat and free from burrs. The nut must be tightened securely (150 inch-ounce torque limit when used against a metal chassis or the bushing supplied, provided that all parts are clean and dry).

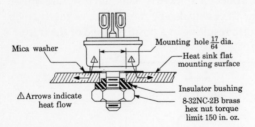

DIMENSIONS AND CONNECTIONS

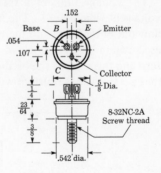

Appendix II

MATRIX ANALYSIS

A. Rules of Matrix Algebra

1. *Matrix Equality.* Two matrices [a] and [b] are equal when each element in [a] is equal to the corresponding element in [b]. If

$$[a] = [b],$$

then

$$a_{11} = b_{11}, a_{12} = b_{12}, \text{ etc.}$$

2. *Matrix Addition and Subtraction.* The sum (or difference) of two matrices is a matrix in which each term is the sum (or difference) of the corresponding terms in the two matrices. Thus if

$$[a] + [b] = [c],$$

then

$$c_{11} = a_{11} + b_{11}, c_{12} = a_{12} + b_{12}, \text{ etc.}$$

3. *Matrix Multiplication.* The product of [a] and [b] is only meaningful when the number of columns of [a] is equal to the number of rows of [b]. Then

$$[c] = [a] \times [b]$$

and

$$c_{ij} = \sum_{k=1}^{k=n} a_{ik} b_{kj}.$$

Two examples follow:

$$\begin{bmatrix} x_{11} & x_{12} \\ x_{21} & x_{22} \end{bmatrix} \begin{bmatrix} y_{11} & y_{12} \\ y_{21} & y_{22} \end{bmatrix} = \begin{bmatrix} (x_{11}y_{11} + x_{12}y_{21}) & (x_{11}y_{12} + x_{12}y_{22}) \\ (x_{21}y_{11} + x_{22}y_{21}) & (x_{21}y_{12} + x_{22}y_{22}) \end{bmatrix}$$

and

$$\begin{bmatrix} y_{11} & y_{12} \\ y_{21} & y_{22} \end{bmatrix} \begin{bmatrix} v_1 \\ v_2 \end{bmatrix} = \begin{bmatrix} (y_{11}v_1 + y_{12}v_2) \\ (y_{21}v_1 + y_{22}v_2) \end{bmatrix}$$

The commutative law does not generally hold

$$[a][b] \neq [b][a].$$

But distributive and associative laws are valid in matrix multiplication.

$$([a] + [b]) \times [c] = [a] \times [c] + [b] \times [c],$$

$$[a] \times [b] \times [c] = ([a] \times [b]) \times [c] = [a] \times ([b] \times [c]).$$

When multiplying a matrix by a constant K, each element of the matrix is multiplied by K. Thus

$$K[a] = [a'],$$

with $a_{11}' = Ka_{11}$, $a_{22}' = Ka_{22}$, etc.

4. *Matrix Inversion.*   It is not possible to divide by a matrix. However, to accomplish this result, matrix inversion is used. To find $[i]$ from the matrix equation

$$[v] = [z][i],$$

we multiply through by $[z]^{-1}$

$$[z]^{-1}[v] = [z]^{-1}[z][i] = [i].$$

$[i]$, therefore, is the product of $[z]^{-1}$ and $[v]$, because $[z]^{-1}[z] = [1] = \begin{bmatrix} 1 & 0 \\ 0 & 1 \end{bmatrix}$.

The inverse of a matrix is symbolized by $[a]^{-1}$. The elements of the inverse matrix are obtained from

$$[a_{ij}]^{-1} = [\Delta_{ij}]^t / D^a.$$

D^a is the determinant of $[a]$ and Δ_{ij} is the *cofactor* of the ith *column*, jth *row*. $[\Delta_{ij}]^t$ represents the cofactor matrix, transposed. Transposition is the interchanging of rows with columns. Thus

$$[a]^{-1} = \begin{bmatrix} a_{11} & a_{12} \\ a_{21} & a_{22} \end{bmatrix}^{-1} = \frac{1}{D^a} \begin{bmatrix} a_{22} & -a_{12} \\ -a_{21} & a_{11} \end{bmatrix}$$

B. Properties of the Terminated Four-Terminal Network

To Find	Given					
	z	y	h	g	a	b
Z_i	$\dfrac{\Delta^z + z_{11}Z_L}{z_{22} + Z_L}$	$\dfrac{1 + y_{22}Z_L}{y_{11} + \Delta^y Z_L}$	$\dfrac{h_{11} + \Delta^h Z_L}{1 + h_{22}Z_L}$	$\dfrac{g_{22} + Z_L}{\Delta^g + g_{11}Z_L}$	$\dfrac{a_{12} + a_{21}Z_L}{a_{22} + a_{21}Z_L}$	$\dfrac{b_{12} + b_{22}Z_L}{b_{11} + b_{21}Z_L}$
Z_o	$\dfrac{\Delta^z + z_{22}Z_G}{z_{11} + Z_G}$	$\dfrac{1 + y_{11}Z_G}{y_{22} + \Delta^y Z_G}$	$\dfrac{h_{11} + Z_G}{\Delta^h + h_{22}Z_G}$	$\dfrac{g_{22} + \Delta^g Z_G}{1 + g_{11}Z_G}$	$\dfrac{a_{12} + a_{22}Z_G}{a_{11} + a_{21}Z_G}$	$\dfrac{b_{12} + b_{11}Z_G}{b_{22} + b_{21}Z_G}$
A_v	$\dfrac{z_{21}Z_L}{\Delta^z + z_{11}Z_L}$	$\dfrac{-y_{21}Z_L}{1 + y_{22}Z_L}$	$\dfrac{-h_{21}Z_L}{h_{11} + \Delta^h Z_L}$	$\dfrac{g_{21}Z_L}{g_{22} + Z_L}$	$\dfrac{Z_L}{a_{12} + a_{11}Z_L}$	$\dfrac{\Delta^b Z_L}{b_{12} + b_{22}Z_L}$
A_i	$\dfrac{-z_{21}}{z_{22} + Z_L}$	$\dfrac{y_{21}}{y_{11} + \Delta^y Z_L}$	$\dfrac{h_{21}}{1 + h_{22}Z_L}$	$\dfrac{-g_{21}}{\Delta^g + g_{11}Z_L}$	$\dfrac{-1}{a_{22} + a_{21}Z_L}$	$\dfrac{-\Delta^b}{b_{11} + b_{12}Z_L}$

Δ is the parameter determinant. For example, if x parameters were to be defined, $\Delta^x = x_{11}x_{22} - x_{12}x_{21}$.

C. Matrix Conversions

To Find	Given					
	z	y	h	g	a	b
$[z]$	—	$\begin{matrix} \dfrac{y_{22}}{\Delta^y} & \dfrac{-y_{12}}{\Delta^y} \\[2mm] \dfrac{-y_{21}}{\Delta^y} & \dfrac{y_{11}}{\Delta^y} \end{matrix}$	$\begin{matrix} \dfrac{\Delta^h}{h_{22}} & \dfrac{h_{12}}{h_{22}} \\[2mm] \dfrac{-h_{21}}{h_{22}} & \dfrac{1}{h_{22}} \end{matrix}$	$\begin{matrix} \dfrac{1}{g_{11}} & \dfrac{-g_{12}}{g_{11}} \\[2mm] \dfrac{g_{21}}{g_{11}} & \dfrac{\Delta^g}{g_{11}} \end{matrix}$	$\begin{matrix} \dfrac{a_{11}}{a_{21}} & \dfrac{\Delta^a}{a_{21}} \\[2mm] \dfrac{1}{a_{21}} & \dfrac{a_{22}}{a_{21}} \end{matrix}$	$\begin{matrix} \dfrac{b_{22}}{b_{21}} & \dfrac{1}{b_{21}} \\[2mm] \dfrac{\Delta^b}{b_{21}} & \dfrac{b_{11}}{b_{21}} \end{matrix}$
$[y]$	$\begin{matrix} \dfrac{z_{22}}{\Delta^z} & \dfrac{-z_{12}}{\Delta^z} \\[2mm] \dfrac{-z_{21}}{\Delta^z} & \dfrac{z_{11}}{\Delta^z} \end{matrix}$	—	$\begin{matrix} \dfrac{1}{h_{11}} & \dfrac{-h_{12}}{h_{11}} \\[2mm] \dfrac{h_{21}}{h_{11}} & \dfrac{\Delta^h}{h_{11}} \end{matrix}$	$\begin{matrix} \dfrac{\Delta^g}{g_{22}} & \dfrac{g_{12}}{g_{22}} \\[2mm] \dfrac{-g_{21}}{g_{22}} & \dfrac{1}{g_{22}} \end{matrix}$	$\begin{matrix} \dfrac{a_{22}}{a_{12}} & \dfrac{-\Delta^a}{a_{12}} \\[2mm] \dfrac{-1}{a_{12}} & \dfrac{a_{11}}{a_{12}} \end{matrix}$	$\begin{matrix} \dfrac{b_{11}}{b_{12}} & \dfrac{-1}{b_{12}} \\[2mm] \dfrac{-\Delta^b}{b_{12}} & \dfrac{b_{22}}{b_{12}} \end{matrix}$
$[h]$	$\begin{matrix} \dfrac{\Delta^z}{z_{22}} & \dfrac{z_{12}}{z_{22}} \\[2mm] \dfrac{-z_{21}}{z_{22}} & \dfrac{1}{z_{22}} \end{matrix}$	$\begin{matrix} \dfrac{1}{y_{11}} & \dfrac{-y_{12}}{y_{11}} \\[2mm] \dfrac{y_{21}}{y_{11}} & \dfrac{\Delta^y}{y_{11}} \end{matrix}$	—	$\begin{matrix} \dfrac{g_{22}}{\Delta^g} & \dfrac{-g_{12}}{\Delta^g} \\[2mm] \dfrac{-g_{21}}{\Delta^g} & \dfrac{g_{11}}{\Delta^g} \end{matrix}$	$\begin{matrix} \dfrac{a_{12}}{a_{22}} & \dfrac{\Delta^a}{a_{22}} \\[2mm] \dfrac{-1}{a_{22}} & \dfrac{a_{21}}{a_{22}} \end{matrix}$	$\begin{matrix} \dfrac{b_{12}}{b_{11}} & \dfrac{1}{b_{11}} \\[2mm] \dfrac{-\Delta^b}{b_{11}} & \dfrac{b_{21}}{b_{11}} \end{matrix}$
$[g]$	$\begin{matrix} \dfrac{1}{z_{11}} & \dfrac{-z_{12}}{z_{11}} \\[2mm] \dfrac{z_{21}}{z_{11}} & \dfrac{\Delta^z}{z_{11}} \end{matrix}$	$\begin{matrix} \dfrac{\Delta^y}{y_{22}} & \dfrac{y_{12}}{y_{22}} \\[2mm] \dfrac{-y_{21}}{y_{22}} & \dfrac{1}{y_{22}} \end{matrix}$	$\begin{matrix} \dfrac{h_{22}}{\Delta^h} & \dfrac{-h_{12}}{\Delta^h} \\[2mm] \dfrac{-h_{21}}{\Delta^h} & \dfrac{h_{11}}{\Delta^h} \end{matrix}$	—	$\begin{matrix} \dfrac{a_{21}}{a_{11}} & \dfrac{-\Delta^a}{a_{11}} \\[2mm] \dfrac{1}{a_{11}} & \dfrac{a_{12}}{a_{11}} \end{matrix}$	$\begin{matrix} \dfrac{b_{21}}{b_{22}} & \dfrac{-1}{b_{22}} \\[2mm] \dfrac{\Delta^b}{b_{22}} & \dfrac{b_{12}}{b_{22}} \end{matrix}$
$[a]$	$\begin{matrix} \dfrac{z_{11}}{z_{21}} & \dfrac{\Delta^z}{z_{21}} \\[2mm] \dfrac{1}{z_{21}} & \dfrac{z_{22}}{z_{21}} \end{matrix}$	$\begin{matrix} \dfrac{-y_{22}}{y_{21}} & \dfrac{-1}{y_{21}} \\[2mm] \dfrac{-\Delta^y}{y_{21}} & \dfrac{-y_{11}}{y_{21}} \end{matrix}$	$\begin{matrix} \dfrac{-\Delta^h}{h_{21}} & \dfrac{-h_{11}}{h_{21}} \\[2mm] \dfrac{-h_{22}}{h_{21}} & \dfrac{-1}{h_{21}} \end{matrix}$	$\begin{matrix} \dfrac{1}{g_{21}} & \dfrac{g_{22}}{g_{21}} \\[2mm] \dfrac{g_{11}}{g_{21}} & \dfrac{\Delta^g}{g_{21}} \end{matrix}$	—	$\begin{matrix} \dfrac{b_{22}}{\Delta^b} & \dfrac{b_{12}}{\Delta^b} \\[2mm] \dfrac{b_{21}}{\Delta^b} & \dfrac{b_{11}}{\Delta^b} \end{matrix}$
$[b]$	$\begin{matrix} \dfrac{z_{22}}{z_{12}} & \dfrac{\Delta^z}{z_{12}} \\[2mm] \dfrac{1}{z_{12}} & \dfrac{z_{11}}{z_{12}} \end{matrix}$	$\begin{matrix} \dfrac{-y_{11}}{y_{12}} & \dfrac{-1}{y_{12}} \\[2mm] \dfrac{-\Delta^y}{y_{12}} & \dfrac{-y_{22}}{y_{12}} \end{matrix}$	$\begin{matrix} \dfrac{1}{h_{12}} & \dfrac{h_{11}}{h_{12}} \\[2mm] \dfrac{h_{22}}{h_{12}} & \dfrac{\Delta^h}{h_{12}} \end{matrix}$	$\begin{matrix} \dfrac{-\Delta^g}{g_{12}} & \dfrac{-g_{22}}{g_{12}} \\[2mm] \dfrac{-g_{11}}{g_{12}} & \dfrac{-1}{g_{12}} \end{matrix}$	$\begin{matrix} \dfrac{a_{22}}{\Delta^a} & \dfrac{a_{12}}{\Delta^a} \\[2mm] \dfrac{a_{21}}{\Delta^a} & \dfrac{a_{11}}{\Delta^a} \end{matrix}$	—

Answers to Selected Problems

1–2. $R = 100 \ \Omega \quad I = 10$ mA
1–9. 199, 200
1–13. 40, 100, 2
1–16. 1004.95 μA, 4.95 μA, 0.99, 505 μA
2–2. 38.6 V
2–6. 1.12×10^{13} pairs
2–7. 0.52 Ωcm, 33 Ω, 0.204 Ω
2–9. 3.65×10^6 A/m^2
3–14. -0.55 mA, $+0.81$ mA
3–15. 28.9 kΩ
3–22. 4.5 MΩ, 20 kΩ
3–27. $212 + 0.038R_B$, $42.3 + 0.004R_B$
3–28. $V_{C2} = 5.09$, $V_{C1} = V_{E2} = 0.04$, $V_{B2} = 0.32$, $V_{E1} = -2$, $V_{B1} = -1.72$
4–4. $h_{11} = 2000$, $h_{12}, = 2 \times 10^{-3}$, $h_{21} = 30$, $h_{22} = 20 \times 10^{-6}$
4–11. $h_{ie} = 528$, $h_{re} = 7.67 \times 10^{-4}$, $h_{fe} = 29.6$, $h_{oe} = 69.4 \times 10^{-6}$
4–12. $f_{\alpha e} = 150$ kc, $h_{feo} = 65.7$, $f_T = 9.85$ Mc, h_{fe} (1 Mc) $= 9.74$
4–16. $g_m = 0.06$, $r_{b'e} = 3333$, $r_{bb'} = 667$, $r_{ce} = 2.5 \times 10^6$, $r_{b'c} =$
3.33×10^6, $C_{b'e} = 191$ pF, $C_{b'c} = 1$ pF
5–11. $R_i = 41.2$, $R_o = 143$ kΩ, $A_v = 1110$
5–15. $A_v = 542$, $A_i = 152$, $G = 82{,}300$
5–24. 747 pF, 1.42 Mc
5–25. 800, 2200 pF
6–2. 0.53 μF
6–6. 19.5 μF
6–9. $R_e = [h_{fb}R_L/(1 + R_Lh_{ob}] - h_{ib}$
6–11. For $R_L > 500$, the transistor stage is superior.
7–4. 83.3 mW, 111 mW
7–9. 18:4; 12 V, 0.67A; 8 W; 1.33 A
7–14. 6.95 W
7–15. 8 in^2 $\frac{3}{16}$-in. vertical copper
8–4. 722, 1105
8–9. 1600, 3200, 900
8–13. $h_f = h_{f1} + h_{f2}(1 + h_{f1})$
$h_i = h_{i1} + h_{i2}(1 + h_{f1})$
8–14. (a) -2.2, 3.2 mA, 0.0016, -11.2; (b) 3.22 kΩ; (c) 5.15 mV; (d) 174
9–6. 40, 0.33, 126, 10.8 and 11.3
9–9. (a) 0.7, 0.6, 1.25, 1.95; (b) 2460; (c) about 2500; (d) 1.15
10–1. 13.04, $\pm 1.1\%$
10–4. $Z_{if} = Z_i/(1 - BA)$, $Z_{of} = Z_o(1 - BA)$
10–7. 48.5, 38.9, 13.9, 1.87, 0.19

10–13. 10^7, 500
11–1. 143 μV
11–11. 30.8 dB
11–12. (a) 2.73, (b) 1.14 Mc, (c) 1.29 dB, (d) 5220 Ω
12–11. (a) 252,000 cps, (b) 3,170, (c) 253,000 cps, (d) about 0.4%
12–16. $m_a{}^2/2 \times 100\%$, 225 W
12–18. $m_a = 0.4$
13–1. 65.3 mA
13–2. (a) 0.22 mW, (b) 22 mW, (c) 8.45 mW
13–15. $T_2 = T_4 = 0.0018$ sec

INDEX

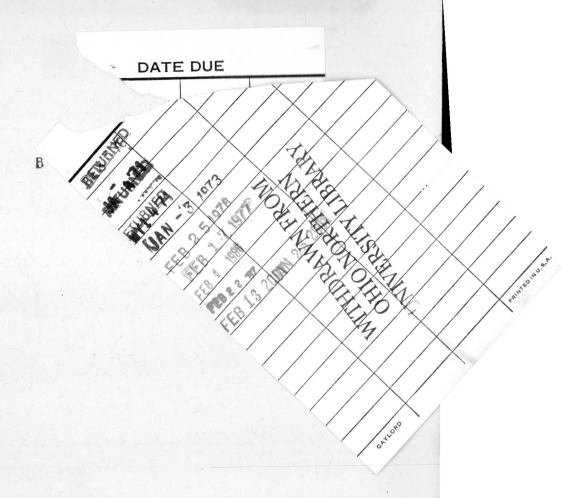